THERMODYNAMICS FOR CHEMISTS AND BIOLOGISTS

TERRELL L. HILL
University of California, Santa Cruz

THERMODYNAMICS FOR CHEMISTS AND BIOLOGISTS

ADDISON-WESLEY PUBLISHING COMPANY
Reading, Massachusetts · Menlo Park, California · London · Don Mills, Ontario

This book is in the

Addison-Wesley Series in the Principles of Chemistry

Francis T. Bonner, *Consulting Editor*

PRINTED IN THE UNITED STATES OF AMERICA. PUBLISHED SIMULTANEOUSLY IN CANADA. LIBRARY OF CONGRESS CATALOG CARD NO. 68-25925.

This book is for Tammy

PREFACE

Elementary thermodynamics is now being taught in freshman chemistry, and the treatment of thermodynamics in junior-senior physical chemistry courses is becoming more and more thorough. Physical chemistry courses even include, routinely now, a significant introduction to statistical mechanics.

Despite these developments, the usual graduate chemical thermodynamics course continues to exist much as it did 30 or 40 years ago. It tends to repeat the material presented in undergraduate physical chemistry, though naturally more details are covered at the graduate level.

The author feels that this repetition is wasteful and unnecessary. Some alternatives are: (a) omit graduate chemical thermodynamics from the curriculum, except for a sophisticated version aimed at physical chemists, especially theoreticians; (b) give a graduate course which combines thermodynamics and statistical mechanics; and (c) provide a graduate chemical thermodynamics course, at a level suitable for all chemists and many biologists, but one which is based on special topics *not* included in undergraduate physical chemistry.

The present book is designed as a text for alternative (c). The author has made this choice, and selected the special topics, having in mind another clear trend in physical chemistry, especially in research: the overlapping of physical chemistry with biochemistry and molecular biology.

Alternative (a) was rejected because thermodynamics, including nonequilibrium thermodynamics, remains a basic and powerful discipline for all chemists and many biologists. Additional competence in thermodynamics is undoubtedly desirable.

Alternative (b) seems doubly repetitious: introductions to both thermodynamics and statistical mechanics appear in the physical chemistry course. Attempts to combine these two subjects for pedagogical reasons, if made at all, should undoubtedly be made in an undergraduate course. A more advanced graduate offering in statistical mechanics for physical chemists, especially theoreticians, is, however, a necessity.

Thus this book is concerned with certain selected special topics in thermodynamics, chosen for their interest or potential interest to chemists and biologists. The treatment is brief, introductory, and *not* at an advanced level. The later chapters do tend, though, to be somewhat more lengthy and demanding than the earlier ones. The reader is assumed to have had some prior acquaintance with thermodynamics and statistical mechanics. Though this book is primarily thermodynamic in character, we have not hesitated to introduce examples at the molecular level (especially in Chapters 6 and 7). In this sense, it is a mixture of thermodynamics and statistical mechanics.

Although the author's earlier book, "Matter and Equilibrium" (W. A. Benjamin, New York, 1966), was written especially for the honor student at the freshman-sophomore level, it provides a large part of the necessary prerequisite material. If used, it should be supplemented for present purposes, however, with a modern physical chemistry textbook.

The material given here, except for Chapters 4 and 6 (Chapter 4 was included in the prior quarter on "standard" chemical thermodynamics), was employed in a one-quarter graduate course at the University of Oregon. The entire book could be covered in one semester. Chapter 6 is the most specialized topic, and would appear to be the obvious one to drop if insufficient time is available.

I am indebted to Professor Frank Andrews, Mr. Edward Paul, and Mr. Tieh-sheng Lee for reading the manuscript.

Santa Cruz
September 1967

T. L. H.

CONTENTS

CHAPTER 1

THERMODYNAMICS OF SURFACES

1.1 ONE-COMPONENT SYSTEM WITH PLANE INTERFACE

In this section, we consider the thermodynamics of a one-component system with a plane interface. More complicated systems (several components, spherical surfaces) are discussed in the two following sections.

The system of interest here is shown in Fig. 1.1. This is a two-phase, one-component system at equilibrium. The shaded region indicates the interface between the two phases. The important case is $\alpha =$ liquid, $\beta =$ gas, but we shall keep the notation general for comparison with Sections 1.2 and 1.3. In ordinary thermodynamics, surface effects, which are associated with the presence of the interface, are negligible compared to bulk contributions. But here the interface is the main object of our study. This seems to pose a dilemma, but we avoid it by using a method, due to Gibbs, in which we subtract out bulk contributions, leaving only surface terms to consider.

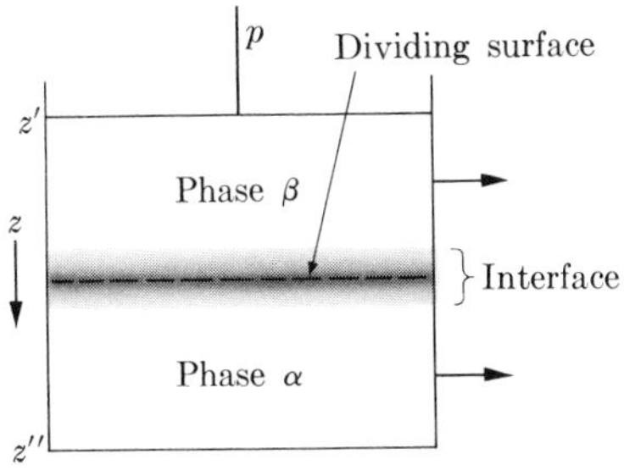

Fig. 1.1. Equilibrium two-phase system with interface.

Ordinarily, the thermodynamic properties of the system $(\alpha + \beta)$ in Fig. 1.1 would be functions of three variables only, for example: S, V, and N (number of molecules); p, T, and N; or μ (chemical potential), T, and V; etc. Using the first set, for instance, we have the familiar fundamental relation

$$dE = T\,dS - p\,dV + \mu\,dN. \tag{1.1}$$

However, since we want to include surface effects, the area of the interface, or some other variable characteristic of the surface, must be added to the list of independent variables. Thus the energy of the system $\alpha + \beta$, including the interface, is a function of S, V, N, *and* $\mathcal{A}$, though the dependence on $\mathcal{A}$ is relatively "weak."

Let us introduce the symbol γ (called the surface tension) to represent the derivative $(\partial E/\partial \mathcal{A})_{S,V,N}$. Then the extension of Eq. (1.1) is

$$dE = T\,dS - p\,dV + \gamma\,d\mathcal{A} + \mu\,dN. \tag{1.2}$$

By virtue of its definition, γ is an intensive property. Because the bulk phases are stable, γ is positive.

If the area $\mathcal{A}$ is increased without absorption of heat, and if N and V are held constant (the container is closed; its shape is altered), then $dE = \gamma\,d\mathcal{A}$ = the reversible work done on the system to create an additional surface area $d\mathcal{A}$. The dominant effect is associated with the potential energy: molecules taken from bulk liquid to form new surface lose some attractive interactions with neighbors.

We can integrate Eq. (1.2) from $E = 0$ to E, $S = 0$ to S, etc., if we imagine that the final system, as shown in the figure, has been produced by moving the right-hand wall in the direction indicated, starting with the right-hand and left-hand walls coinciding ($V = 0$). In this process, all intensive variables (for example, T, p, γ, and μ) remain constant, while extensive variables (for example, E, S, V, $\mathcal{A}$, and N) all increase in constant proportion. The result of the integration is

$$E = TS - pV + \gamma\mathcal{A} + \mu N. \tag{1.3}$$

In mathematical language, E is a linear homogeneous function of S, V, $\mathcal{A}$, and N. All terms in this equation, except $\gamma\mathcal{A}$, are of order NkT; $\gamma\mathcal{A}$ is of order $N^{2/3}kT$. Thus in Eq. (1.3), as it stands, the surface term is negligible—just as we should expect.

This one-component, two-phase system has one degree of freedom. That is, there is only one independent intensive variable. The temperature is usually the most convenient choice for this variable. Hence γ, the surface tension, may be considered a function of temperature only, $\gamma(T)$. We shall presently derive an equation for $d\gamma/dT$. Of course, p and μ are also functions of T only, with dp/dT and $d\mu/dT$ determined by the Clausius-Clapeyron equation:

$$\frac{dp}{dT} = \frac{\mathrm{s}^\beta - \mathrm{s}^\alpha}{\mathrm{v}^\beta - \mathrm{v}^\alpha} \tag{1.4}$$

and

$$d\mu = d\mu_\alpha = d\mu_\beta = -\mathrm{s}^\alpha \, dT + \mathrm{v}^\alpha \, dp,$$
$$\frac{d\mu}{dT} = -\mathrm{s}^\alpha + \mathrm{v}^\alpha \left(\frac{\mathrm{s}^\beta - \mathrm{s}^\alpha}{\mathrm{v}^\beta - \mathrm{v}^\alpha}\right) = \frac{\mathrm{s}^\beta \mathrm{v}^\alpha - \mathrm{s}^\alpha \mathrm{v}^\beta}{\mathrm{v}^\beta - \mathrm{v}^\alpha}. \tag{1.5}$$

Throughout the book a small capital letter is used to denote an extensive property per molecule: $\mathrm{s} = S/N$, etc.

Equations (1.2) and (1.3) can be put in a more useful form by subtracting out bulk terms, as follows. We introduce a mathematical dividing surface at some definite but, for the moment, arbitrary position in the interfacial region, as indicated by the dashed line in Fig. 1.1. Consider the hypothetical phase which would result if phase α maintained its isotropic bulk properties right up to the mathematical dividing surface. For such a phase, the following basic equations would apply:

$$dE^\alpha = T \, dS^\alpha - p \, dV^\alpha + \mu \, dN^\alpha, \tag{1.6}$$

$$E^\alpha = TS^\alpha - pV^\alpha + \mu N^\alpha. \tag{1.7}$$

Similarly, for phase β extended hypothetically to the dividing surface, we have

$$dE^\beta = T \, dS^\beta - p \, dV^\beta + \mu \, dN^\beta, \tag{1.8}$$

$$E^\beta = TS^\beta - pV^\beta + \mu N^\beta. \tag{1.9}$$

Of course, $V^\alpha + V^\beta = V$, the total volume of the container.

We now define the "surface excess" value X^s of any bulk extensive property X by

$$X^s = X - X^\alpha - X^\beta, \tag{1.10}$$

where X is the actual value in the system of Fig. 1.1, including the interface, while X^α and X^β refer to hypothetical phases without an interface, as in Eqs. (1.6) through (1.9).

The value of V^s is zero. The meaning of the quantity N^s is shown in Fig. 1.2. The solid curve represents a plot of the mean number density, $\rho = N/V$, as a function of position z normal to the interface (see also Fig. 1.1). The value of ρ makes a transition from ρ^β to ρ^α, over a distance of several molecular diameters. The area under the solid curve in Fig. 1.2, multiplied by $\mathcal{A}$, gives the actual number of molecules, N, in the system. Similarly, the area under the dashed curve leads to $N^\alpha + N^\beta$, for the particular choice of dividing surface indicated. Then N^s is the algebraic sum of the positive area, marked $+$, and the negative area, marked $-$, multiplied by $\mathcal{A}$. In this example, N^s is negative.

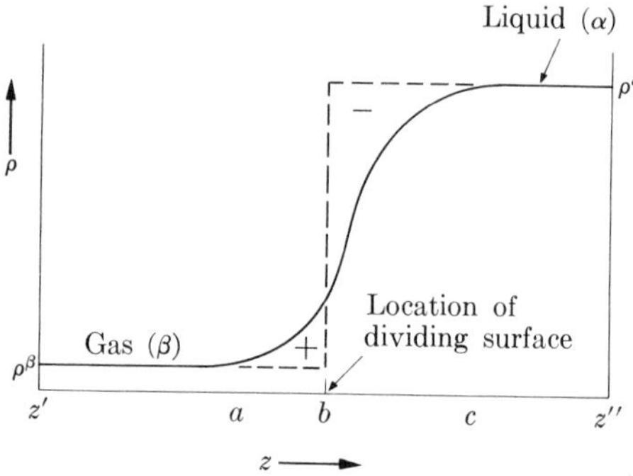

Fig. 1.2. Variation in mean number density at the interface; location of dividing surface.

It is clear that by proper location of the dividing surface, so that *area* + = *area* −, we could have $N^s = 0$. This is a dividing surface of particular interest.

If we subtract Eqs. (1.6) and (1.8) from Eq. (1.2), we obtain

$$dE^s = T\,dS^s + \gamma\,d\mathcal{A} + \mu\,dN^s. \tag{1.11}$$

Similarly, from Eqs. (1.3), (1.7), and (1.9),

$$E^s = TS^s + \gamma\mathcal{A} + \mu N^s. \tag{1.12}$$

Every term in Eq. (1.12) is now of order $N^{2/3}kT$; pure bulk contributions have been subtracted out as desired.

In Eq. (1.12), values of the quantities E^s, S^s, and N^s depend on the arbitrary location of the mathematical dividing surface. On the other hand, the quantities T, γ, $\mathcal{A}$, and μ are invariant to the location of the dividing surface.

From Eqs. (1.11) and (1.12), we find that

$$d(\gamma\mathcal{A}) = -S^s\,dT + \gamma\,d\mathcal{A} - N^s\,d\mu \tag{1.13}$$

and

$$d\gamma = -\,(S^s/\mathcal{A})\,dT - (N^s/\mathcal{A})\,d\mu. \tag{1.14}$$

But μ is a function of T, so we can replace $d\mu$ here by $(d\mu/dT)\,dT$, where $d\mu/dT$ is given by Eq. (1.5). In the common case where $\mathrm{v}^\beta \gg \mathrm{v}^\alpha$, we have $d\mu/dT \cong -\mathrm{s}^\alpha$. Then

$$\frac{d\gamma}{dT} \cong -\left(\frac{S^s}{\mathcal{A}}\right) + \left(\frac{N^s}{\mathcal{A}}\right)\mathrm{s}^\alpha. \tag{1.15}$$

The complete expression for $d\gamma/dT$, from Eq. (1.14), must not change its value when the dividing surface is moved, because $d\gamma/dT$ is itself invariant to the location of the dividing surface. Explicit verification of this statement is left to the reader (see Problem 1.1).

Equations (1.13) through (1.15) refer to an arbitrary dividing surface. These equations become much simpler if we choose the particular surface such that $N^s = 0$. We denote this choice by an asterisk: $N^* = 0$. For this surface, the basic relations become

$$dE^* = T\,dS^* + \gamma\,d\alpha, \tag{1.16}$$

$$E^* = TS^* + \gamma\alpha, \tag{1.17}$$

$$\gamma = (E^*/\alpha) - T\,(S^*/\alpha), \tag{1.18}$$

$$d(\gamma\alpha) = -S^*\,dT + \gamma\,d\alpha, \tag{1.19}$$

$$\frac{d\gamma}{dT} = -\frac{S^*}{\alpha}. \tag{1.20}$$

We can also easily derive

$$\gamma - T\frac{d\gamma}{dT} = \frac{d(\gamma/T)}{d(1/T)} = \frac{E^*}{\alpha}. \tag{1.21}$$

Equation (1.18) shows that γ is a type of Helmholtz free energy per unit area; it has an energy and an entropy contribution. Since γ and T are experimental quantities, experimental values of E^*/α and S^*/α may be deduced from the above equations.

For example, for liquid argon, from the experimental values $\gamma = 11.91$ ergs cm^{-2} at 90.0°K and $\gamma = 12.68$ ergs cm^{-2} at 87.0°K, we find for the mean temperature $T = 88.5$°K that $E^*/\alpha = 35.0$ ergs cm^{-2} and $TS^*/\alpha = 22.7$ ergs cm^{-2}. We expect E^* to be positive because of the potential energy effect already mentioned above: E^α includes attractive intermolecular interactions that are missing in E (because of the existence of the interface). Also, we should expect S^* to be positive. This follows because, in passing from the step function in Fig. 1.2 (with the dividing surface moved to the right so that $N^s = 0$) to the actual density curve, the molecules originally in the interval $b < z < c$ all experience a reduction in number density and hence an increase in entropy (the relatively small number of molecules in $a < z < b$ have a decrease in entropy). Thus $S > S^\alpha + S^\beta$ and $S^* > 0$.

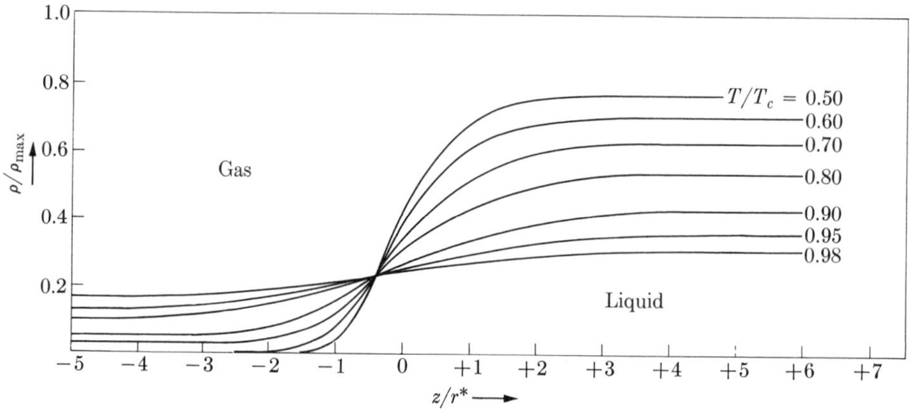

Fig. 1.3. Variation in mean number density at the interface, as a function of temperature, according to an approximate model. The diameter of the molecules is r^*. The location of $z = 0$ is arbitrary.

An accurate empirical expression for the temperature dependence of γ in simple liquids such as argon is

$$\gamma = \gamma_0\left(1 - \frac{T}{T_c}\right)^{11/9}, \tag{1.22}$$

where γ_0 is a constant and T_c is the critical temperature. The temperature range is $T/T_c = 0.45$ to 1.00. For argon, $\gamma_0 = 36.31$ ergs cm^{-2} and $T_c = 150.7$°K. Since the interface disappears ($\rho^\alpha = \rho^\beta$) at $T = T_c$, γ and all the surface excess functions (for example, E^* and S^*) have the value zero at $T = T_c$ (see Problem 1.2).

Figure 1.3 shows the effect of temperature (near $T = T_c$) on number density curves in the interfacial region, for simple spherical molecules, as calculated from an *approximate* theory.† These curves are presumably realistic, at least qualitatively.

An exact statistical mechanical expression for the surface tension of simple liquids, in terms of the intermolecular forces, has been derived by Kirkwood and Buff. However, this is too complicated to discuss here.‡ A simpler approximate equation, due to Fowler, can be obtained from the following considerations. Imagine that a sample of bulk liquid is divided into two semi-infinite parts by a mathematical plane of area $\mathfrak{a}$ and that the two parts or slabs are then separated reversibly by gradually increasing

---

† T. L. Hill, *J. Chem. Phys.* **20**, 141 (1952).

‡ See T. L. Hill, *Introduction to Statistical Thermodynamics*, Section 17.5. Reading, Mass.: Addison-Wesley, 1960.

the distance between them. We assume that each liquid slab remains isotropic right up to its edge plane of area $\mathcal{A}$ and that there is a vacuum (vapor of negligible density) between the two slabs. The potential energy of a pair of molecules a distance r apart is given as $u(r)$. Using the corresponding force, $-du/dr$, we can calculate the reversible work that has to be done to pull the two liquid slabs apart against the intermolecular forces tending to hold them together. This work is $2\gamma\mathcal{A}$ (since each slab has an area $\mathcal{A}$). The result found in this way for γ is

$$\gamma = \frac{\pi\rho^2}{8} \int_0^\infty r^4 \frac{du(r)}{dr} g(r, \rho, T)\, dr, \tag{1.23}$$

where $g(r)$ is the radial distribution function in the bulk liquid at the temperature T and density $\rho(T)$. Using the experimental $g(r)$ from x-ray diffraction measurements on liquid argon, $u(r)$ as deduced from second virial coefficient measurements (see Chapter 4), and Eq. (1.23) at 90°K, Kirkwood and Buff calculated that $\gamma = 14.9$ ergs cm^{-2} and $E^*/\mathcal{A} = 27$ ergs cm^{-2}. The agreement with experimental results (see above) is perhaps better than should be expected.

It is interesting to note the similarity between Eq. (1.23) and the exact statistical-mechanical expression for the pressure in a simple fluid:

$$p = \rho kT - \frac{2\pi\rho^2}{3} \int_0^\infty r^3 \frac{du(r)}{dr} g(r, \rho, T)\, dr. \tag{1.24}$$

1.2 TWO-COMPONENT SYSTEM WITH PLANE INTERFACE

We shall not pursue this subject very far. Our object is merely to show the sort of generalization necessary when more than one component is present.

Figure 1.1 still represents the system, but there are two components, 1 and 2, present in both phases. We might have α = liquid, β = gas or α = liquid, β = liquid (two immiscible binary solutions).

By defining excess quantities in the same manner as in the preceding section [Eq. (1.10)], we arrive at

$$dE^s = T\, dS^s + \gamma\, d\mathcal{A} + \mu_1\, dN_1^s + \mu_2\, dN_2^s \tag{1.25}$$

and

$$E^s = TS^s + \gamma\mathcal{A} + \mu_1 N_1^s + \mu_2 N_2^s \tag{1.26}$$

as the generalization of Eqs. (1.11) and (1.12). Also,

$$\mathcal{A}\, d\gamma = -S^s\, dT - N_1^s\, d\mu_1 - N_2^s\, d\mu_2. \tag{1.27}$$

These equations are for an arbitrary dividing surface. The right-hand side of Eq. (1.27) must be invariant to a shift in the dividing surface.

According to the Gibbs phase rule, this system has two degrees of freedom. For example, we might choose as independent intensive variables T and x_2^α (mole fraction of component 2 in phase α). In this case, in Eq. (1.27), we regard μ_1 and μ_2 as functions of T and x_2^α. The expression of $d\mu_1$ and $d\mu_2$ explicitly in terms of dT and dx_2^α is a routine problem in ordinary solution thermodynamics which we shall not work out here (see Problem 1.3).

Various special dividing surfaces may be chosen. For example, we can locate the surface so that $N_1^s = 0$. Let us use the superscript^{*1} to indicate this surface. Thus, in general, $N_2^{*1} \neq 0$. Equation (1.27) then becomes

$$\mathcal{A}\, d\gamma = -S^{*1}dT - N_2^{*1}d\mu_2. \tag{1.28}$$

This equation, with $T =$ const, is a form of the so-called *Gibbs adsorption isotherm*. It is of particular interest when there is an unusual concentration or depletion of component 2 at the interface.

1.3 SPHERICAL INTERFACE

We give an introductory treatment here of a spherical interface (drop or bubble) with any number of components. We begin by imagining the system in Fig. 1.1 (with additional components) distorted into a spherical cone of solid angle ω, as shown in Fig. 1.4. The system, with numbers of molecules $N_1, N_2, \ldots, N_c$, lies between the surfaces $r = R_\alpha$ and $r = R_\beta$. The temperature is T. We assume that contours of equal density, etc., lie on spherical surfaces with their centers at $r = 0$. All the thermo-

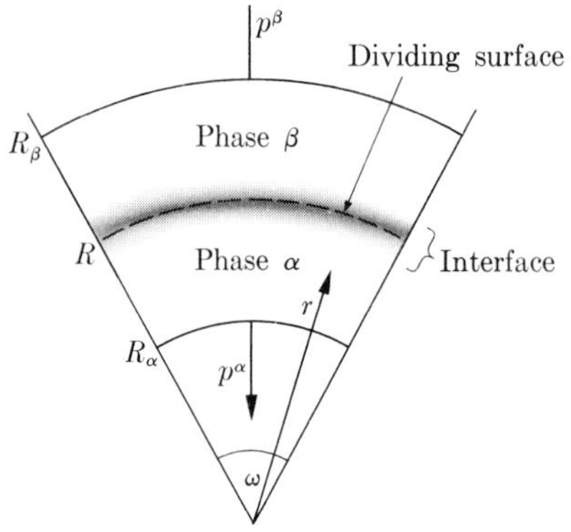

Fig. 1.4. Two-phase system with spherical interface.

dynamic properties of this equilibrium system are completely determined by the variables T, R_α, R_β, ω, N_1, N_2, . . . , N_c, or, alternatively, by S, R_α, R_β, ω, N_1, N_2, . . . , N_c (this is the analogue of the set S, V, N for a bulk one-component system). We are interested only in such values of these quantities as lead to a two-phase (α and β) system. The pressures in the bulk phases, far from the interface, are p^α and p^β. As we shall see, $p^\alpha \neq p^\beta$.

The generalization of Eq. (1.2), applicable to this system, is

$$dE = T\,dS - p^\beta \omega R_\beta^2\,dR_\beta + p^\alpha \omega R_\alpha^2\,dR_\alpha + \sigma\,d\omega + \sum_i \mu_i\,dN_i. \tag{1.29}$$

The terms in dR_β, dR_α, and $d\omega$ are the work terms. The areas at R_β and R_α are ωR_β^2 and ωR_α^2. The coefficient σ is *defined* by this equation as

$$\sigma = \left(\frac{\partial E}{\partial \omega}\right)_{S,R_\alpha,R_\beta,N_i}. \tag{1.30}$$

Integration of Eq. (1.29) at constant T, p^β, R_β, p^α, R_α, σ, and μ_i, from $\omega = 0$ to ω, leads to

$$E = TS + \sigma\omega + \sum_i \mu_i N_i \tag{1.31}$$

or

$$\sigma\omega = A - \sum_i \mu_i N_i, \tag{1.32}$$

where

$$A = E - TS. \tag{1.33}$$

We have not mentioned a dividing surface yet and none of the above variables or equations depends on this concept. But to proceed further we now consider that some criterion or condition be adopted for choosing a particular mathematical dividing surface at $r = R$ in the interfacial region. Unlike the plane surface case, the surface area $\mathcal{A}$ here depends on the location of the dividing surface: $\mathcal{A} = \omega R^2$.

With a choice of R, the total volume V can be divided into V^α and V^β:

$$V^\alpha = (\omega/3)(R^3 - R_\alpha^3), \tag{1.34}$$

$$V^\beta = (\omega/3)(R_\beta^3 - R^3). \tag{1.35}$$

If we take differentials, we can express $d\mathcal{A}$ in terms of $d\omega$ and dR, dV^α in terms of $d\omega$, dR, and dR_α, and dV^β in terms of $d\omega$, dR_β, and dR. By dR here, we mean a variation in R resulting from a variation in the equilibrium state of the system, the dividing surface criterion or condition being held fixed. Next, we solve the differential relations just referred to for dR_α, dR_β, and $d\omega$ in terms of dV^α, dV^β, and $d\mathcal{A}$, and substitute into Eq. (1.29). The algebraic details are left to the reader. The result, with the new independent variables, is

$$dE = T\,dS - p^\alpha\,dV^\alpha - p^\beta\,dV^\beta + \gamma\,d\mathcal{A} + C\,dR + \sum_i \mu_i\,dN_i, \tag{1.36}$$

where the symbols γ and C are used to represent the expressions

$$\gamma = \frac{1}{\mathcal{A}}\left[p^\alpha V^\alpha + p^\beta V^\beta - \left(\sum_i \mu_i N_i - A\right)\right], \tag{1.37}$$

$$C = \omega R^2(p^\alpha - p^\beta) - 2\omega\gamma R. \tag{1.38}$$

These equations refer to some particular but arbitrary dividing surface condition. The quantities appearing here which depend on the location of the dividing surface are V^α, V^β, γ, $\mathcal{A}$, C, and R. Note that integration of Eq. (1.36) from $\omega = 0$ to ω, holding R_α, R_β, and intensive properties constant, gives Eq. (1.37) again (which is a self-consistency check).

As was pointed out in the first paragraph of this section, the number of independent variables is $c + 4$. On the other hand, Eq. (1.36) shows $c + 5$ "independent" variables. This suggests [compare Eqs. (1.11) and (1.16)] adopting a dividing surface condition which eliminates one term from Eq. (1.36). The obvious choice, made by Gibbs, is to use $C = 0$ as the dividing surface condition. The dividing surface, so located, was called by Gibbs the "surface of tension," because of the mechanical significance of Eq. (1.40) below.

With this choice of dividing surface condition, the basic thermodynamic equation becomes

$$dE = T\,dS - p^\alpha\,dV^\alpha - p^\beta\,dV^\beta + \gamma\,d\mathcal{A} + \sum_i \mu_i\,dN_i, \qquad C = 0. \tag{1.39}$$

From Eq. (1.37) it is clear that the value of γ depends on the location of the dividing surface through $\mathcal{A}$, V^α, and V^β. From Eq. (1.38), the condition for the surface of tension is

$$2\gamma/R = p^\alpha - p^\beta, \qquad C = 0. \tag{1.40}$$

For given values of T, R_α, R_β, ω, $N_1, \ldots, N_c$, the quantity $p^\alpha - p^\beta$ in Eq. (1.40) is independent of the location of the dividing surface, while both γ and R depend on its location. The surface of tension may therefore be found by choosing that particular surface which gives the quantity $2\gamma/R$ the same value as the invariant quantity $p^\alpha - p^\beta$.

The surface tension γ depends on curvature (that is, on the value of R at the surface of tension), but not strongly. As R approaches infinity, γ approaches its value for a plane surface and $p^\alpha - p^\beta \to 0$.

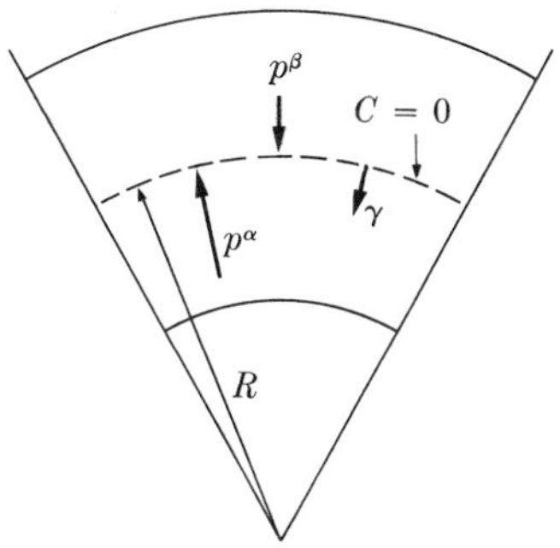

Fig. 1.5. Balance of forces at the surface of tension.

The surface of tension may be regarded as a surface in mechanical equilibrium, as indicated schematically in Fig. 1.5: p^α is balanced by p^β and γ. More precisely, if mechanical equilibrium exists, no work δW is required for an infinitesimal variation δR in the location of the surface:

$$\begin{aligned}\delta W &= 0 = p^\beta\,\delta(\omega R^3/3) + \gamma\,\delta(\omega R^2) - p^\alpha\,\delta(\omega R^3/3)\\ &= p^\beta\omega R^2\,\delta R + 2\gamma\omega R\,\delta R - p^\alpha\omega R^2\,\delta R.\end{aligned}$$

This result is the same as Eq. (1.40).

Surface excesses may be introduced as in the case of a plane interface. We imagine V^α to be filled with bulk phase α right up to the dividing surface, and similarly for V^β. Then, for these two hypothetical bulk phases, we have

$$\begin{aligned}dE^\alpha &= T\,dS^\alpha - p^\alpha\,dV^\alpha + \sum_i \mu_i\,dN_i^\alpha,\\ dE^\beta &= T\,dS^\beta - p^\beta\,dV^\beta + \sum_i \mu_i\,dN_i^\beta.\end{aligned}$$

We subtract these relations from Eq. (1.39) (we consider just the surface of tension) and obtain

$$dE^s = T\,dS^s + \gamma\,d\mathcal{a} + \sum_i \mu_i\,dN_i^s, \qquad C = 0. \tag{1.41}$$

On integrating, we have

$$E^s = TS^s + \gamma\mathcal{a} + \sum_i \mu_i N_i^s, \qquad C = 0. \tag{1.42}$$

Then

$$d(\gamma \alpha) = -S^s\, dT + \gamma\, d\alpha - \sum_i N_i^s\, d\mu_i, \qquad C = 0 \tag{1.43}$$

and

$$\alpha\, d\gamma = -S^s\, dT - \sum_i N_i^s\, d\mu_i, \qquad C = 0. \tag{1.44}$$

Comparing this last result with Eq. (1.28), for example, we note that this system has one more degree of freedom than it would if the interface were plane. This is because $p^\alpha \neq p^\beta$. Equation (1.44) with $T =$ const is the Gibbs adsorption isotherm for a spherical interface.

PROBLEMS

1.1 Move the dividing surface a distance δ in the direction $\alpha \to \beta$ and prove that the value of the right-hand side of Eq. (1.14) is unaffected.

1.2 Use Eq. (1.22) to derive similar equations for E^*/α and TS^*/α. Show that $E^*/TS^* \to 1$ as $T \to T_c$. Use the values of γ_0 and T_c given for argon to calculate S^*/α at 100°K.

1.3 For a two-phase (α and β), two-component (1 and 2) equilibrium, derive equations for $d\mu_1$ and $d\mu_2$ in terms of dT and dx_2^α (that is, T and x_2^α are chosen as independent intensive variables).

1.4 Use Eq. (1.21) and the values of γ for argon at 87.0°K and 90.0°K to verify the value given in the text for E^*/α.

SUPPLEMENTARY READING

HILL, T. L., *An Introduction to Statistical Thermodynamics*, Section 17.5. Reading, Mass.: Addison-Wesley, 1960.

HILL, T. L., *J. Phys. Chem.* **56,** 526 (1952).

KIRKWOOD, J. G., and I. OPPENHEIM, *Chemical Thermodynamics.* New York: McGraw-Hill, 1961.

ONO, S., and S. KONDO, *Handbuch der Physik,* Vol. 10. Berlin: Springer, 1960.

CHAPTER 2

THERMODYNAMICS OF GAS ADSORPTION

2.1 INTRODUCTION

When gas molecules are in the presence of a nonvolatile solid surface, they often accumulate on the surface as a result of attractive forces between the solid and the gas molecules. These forces may be chemical or physical (van der Waals, etc.), or intermediate (e.g., hydrogen bonds). For simplicity, we restrict ourselves in this chapter to a special case, though the generalization to more complicated systems presents no fundamental problems. We consider a one-component gas adsorbed on a solid surface by forces sufficiently weak so as not to perturb appreciably the structure of the solid itself. Some examples are argon on a sodium chloride crystal, nitrogen on graphite, etc. In this case, the solid, in effect, merely presents an external potential field for the gas molecules.

Adsorption (or binding) of solute molecules from a solution is obviously a closely related problem (e.g., see Chapters 3 and 4).

The gas molecules are involved in a phase equilibrium: the gas is one phase, while the adsorbed molecules form a second phase. Our approach is, first, to write the basic thermodynamic equations for a one-component adsorbed phase, and, second, to introduce the phase equilibrium (with gas) explicitly.

When the gas pressure is extremely low, the equilibrium amount of adsorption is slight and Henry's law is observed (the amount of adsorption is proportional to the gas pressure). Each adsorbed molecule behaves independently of the others (as in a very dilute gas). An adsorbed molecule may move quite freely ("mobile" adsorption) over the surface if the temperature is high enough (the adsorbed phase is then a two-dimensional ideal gas). On the other hand, at low temperatures an adsorbed molecule is localized or confined to a "site," and it undergoes vibrational motion about that site (a "site" is merely a position, on the surface, of minimum potential energy for an adsorbed molecule). Of course, a localized molecule occasionally jumps from one site to another (surface diffusion). At intermediate temperatures, the behavior of an adsorbed molecule is neither "localized" nor "mobile," but something in between.

As the gas pressure is increased, the surface concentration of adsorbed molecules also increases, though at first the adsorption is still confined to a monolayer. However, within the monolayer, intermolecular forces between adsorbed molecules may become important. In fact, a two-dimensional phase transition may occur between a dilute adsorbed monolayer and a more dense monolayer (whether the adsorption is localized or mobile).

At still higher gas pressures, if the temperature is below the critical temperature of the gas, multilayer adsorption takes place. As the gas pressure approaches the vapor pressure for the given temperature, the number of layers increases rapidly and goes to infinity at the vapor pressure (i.e., bulk liquid is condensed on the surface).

Let us now turn to the thermodynamic treatment of the sort of system we have been describing.

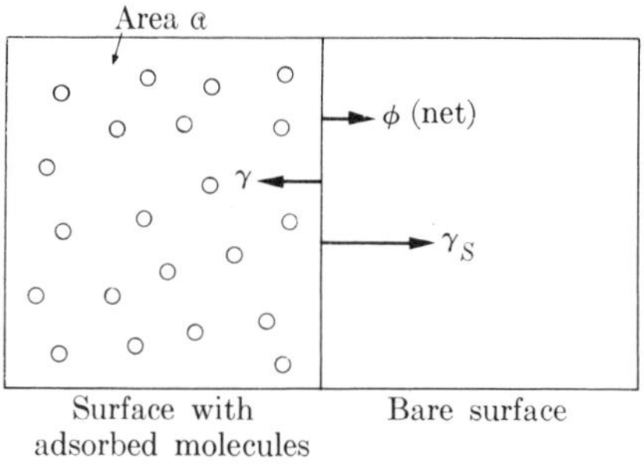

Fig. 2.1. Adsorbed molecules on a surface, with spreading pressure ϕ.

2.2 THERMODYNAMICS OF ADSORPTION

Let γ_S be the surface tension of the bare solid, and let γ be the surface tension of the solid (of area $\mathcal{A}$) with adsorbed molecules on it (Fig. 2.1). As indicated in the figure, the surface tension γ tends to decrease $\mathcal{A}$, while γ_S tends to increase $\mathcal{A}$. On the other hand, from the molecular point of view, the molecules in $\mathcal{A}$ will certainly spread over a larger area whenever possible. In other words, we must have $\gamma_S > \gamma$. We define the two-dimensional or "spreading" pressure ϕ by $\phi = \gamma_S - \gamma$, so that $\phi > 0$, just as in the case of the conventional three-dimensional pressure p. The corresponding work term is

$$\gamma_S \, d\mathcal{A} - \gamma \, d\mathcal{A} = \phi \, d\mathcal{A}.$$

Thus for a one-component adsorbed phase of area $\mathcal{A}$, we have

$$dE = T\,dS - \phi\,d\mathcal{A} + \mu\,dN. \tag{2.1}$$

This is formally identical with the familiar corresponding three-dimensional equation (where $p\,dV$ is used in place of $\phi\,d\mathcal{A}$). Integration with intensive properties constant gives

$$E = TS - \phi\mathcal{A} + \mu N. \tag{2.2}$$

We define

$$H = E + \phi\mathcal{A}, \qquad A = E - TS, \tag{2.3}$$

$$G = \mu N = E - TS + \phi\mathcal{A}. \tag{2.4}$$

Then

$$dA = -S\,dT - \phi\,d\mathcal{A} + \mu\,dN, \tag{2.5}$$

$$dG = d(\mu N) = -S\,dT + \mathcal{A}\,d\phi + \mu\,dN, \tag{2.6}$$

$$d\mu = -(S/N)\,dT + (\mathcal{A}/N)\,d\phi, \tag{2.7}$$

$$= -\,\mathrm{s}\,dT + (1/\Gamma)\,d\phi, \tag{2.8}$$

where

$$\mathrm{s} = S/N, \qquad \Gamma = N/\mathcal{A},$$

and Γ is the surface concentration. All of these equations are analogues of well-known three-dimensional relations.

Now let us turn to the phase equilibrium with gas. We have

$$\mu = \mu_G, \qquad d\mu = d\mu_G, \tag{2.9}$$

where G = gas. The proof of Eq. (2.9) is the subject of Problem 2.1. From Eqs. (2.3), (2.4), and (2.9),

$$\mathrm{H} - T\mathrm{s} = \mathrm{H}_G - T\mathrm{s}_G$$

or

$$\mathrm{H}_G - \mathrm{H} = T(\mathrm{s}_G - \mathrm{s}). \tag{2.10}$$

All of these quantities are, of course, to be evaluated *at* equilibrium. For example, $\mathrm{s}_G(p, T)$ is the entropy per molecule at the equilibrium gas pressure, and $\mathrm{s}(\Gamma, T)$ is the entropy per molecule at the equilibrium surface concentration.

From Eqs. (2.8) and (2.9),

$$-\,\mathrm{s}\,dT + (1/\Gamma)\,d\phi = -\,\mathrm{s}_G\,dT + \mathrm{v}_G\,dp \tag{2.11}$$

$$= -\,\mathrm{s}_G\,dT + kT\,d\ln p, \tag{2.12}$$

where Eq. (2.12) assumes that the gas phase is dilute enough to be treated as ideal. For simplicity, we shall make this assumption from this point on. The system (adsorbed phase plus gas) clearly has two degrees of freedom. Thermodynamically, it is analogous to a binary condensed phase (solution), with only one volatile component, which is in equilibrium with the one-component gas.

Equation (2.12) leads to two important results. The first is

$$d\phi = kT\Gamma\, d \ln p \qquad (T \text{ constant}) \tag{2.13}$$

$$\phi(p) = kT \int_0^p \frac{\Gamma(p', T)}{p'}\, dp' \qquad (T \text{ constant}). \tag{2.14}$$

Equation (2.13) is another "Gibbs adsorption isotherm" [see Eqs. (1.28) and (1.44)]. In Eq. (2.14), we have made use of the fact that $\gamma = \gamma_S$ and hence $\phi = 0$ at $p = 0$. The function $\Gamma(p, T)$, with T constant, is the *adsorption isotherm*, the amount of gas adsorbed per unit area as a function of the equilibrium gas pressure. This function usually represents the basic experimental information available. When applied to experimental data, the integrand in Eq. (2.14) has to be extrapolated to zero pressure. Equation (2.14) allows us to obtain the function $\phi(p)$, or, since $\Gamma(p)$ is known as well, we can also get $\phi(\Gamma)$, the equation of state. Applications of Eq. (2.14) will be included in the next section.

The second important consequence of Eq. (2.12) is

$$\left(\frac{\partial \ln p}{\partial T}\right)_\phi = \frac{\text{s}_G - \text{s}}{kT} = \frac{\text{H}_G - \text{H}}{kT^2}. \tag{2.15}$$

Using this equation, we can calculate the entropy and enthalpy of adsorbed molecules (relative to the gas phase), after ϕ has been found from Eq. (2.14) (see Section 2.3 for an example).

A variation on Eq. (2.15) follows if, in Eq. (2.12), we write

$$d\mu = -\text{s}\, dT + (1/\Gamma)\,[T\, d(\phi/T) + (\phi/T)\, dT]. \tag{2.16}$$

Then we find

$$\left(\frac{\partial \ln p}{\partial T}\right)_{\phi/T} = \frac{[\text{s}_G - \text{s} + (\phi/\Gamma T)]}{kT} = \frac{\text{H}_G - \text{E}}{kT^2}. \tag{2.17}$$

Since $\text{H}_G = \text{E}_G + kT$ (dilute gas), Eq. (2.17) provides a method to obtain the energy of the adsorbed molecules relative to gas. Another way is to use $\text{H}_G - \text{H}$ from Eq. (2.15), and ϕ: $\text{E} = \text{H} - (\phi/\Gamma)$.

A less fundamental Clausius-Clapeyron equation than (2.15), but one that is easier to apply because ϕ does not have to be calculated, can be derived by changing variables in $\mu(\phi, T)$ to $\mu(\Gamma, T)$. Thus, instead of Eq. (2.12), we write

$$\left(\frac{\partial \mu}{\partial T}\right)_\Gamma dT + \left(\frac{\partial \mu}{\partial \Gamma}\right)_T d\Gamma = -\text{s}_G\, dT + kT\, d \ln p. \tag{2.18}$$

However, from Eq. (2.5), we have

$$\frac{\partial^2 A}{\partial N\,\partial T} = \left(\frac{\partial \mu}{\partial T}\right)_\Gamma = -\left(\frac{\partial S}{\partial N}\right)_{\mathcal{A},T}. \tag{2.19}$$

On combining this with Eq. (2.18), we get

$$\left(\frac{\partial \ln p}{\partial T}\right)_\Gamma = \frac{\mathrm{s}_G - (\partial S/\partial N)_{\mathcal{A},T}}{kT}. \tag{2.20}$$

This equation gives the *differential* entropy, $\partial S/\partial N$, rather than the entropy per molecule, S/N, as in Eq. (2.15). Since

$$\mu = \left(\frac{\partial A}{\partial N}\right)_{\mathcal{A},T} = \left(\frac{\partial E}{\partial N}\right)_{\mathcal{A},T} - T\left(\frac{\partial S}{\partial N}\right)_{\mathcal{A},T} = \mu_G = \mathrm{H}_G - T\mathrm{s}_G, \tag{2.21}$$

another form of Eq. (2.20) is

$$\left(\frac{\partial \ln p}{\partial T}\right)_\Gamma = \frac{\mathrm{H}_G - (\partial E/\partial N)_{\mathcal{A},T}}{kT^2}. \tag{2.22}$$

This is, perhaps, a sufficient sample of general thermodynamic equations for an adsorption system. We turn to examples, experimental and theoretical, in the next two sections.

2.3 APPLICATIONS

Let us begin with Henry's law, which is obeyed at low gas pressures (unless the gas molecules dissociate on the surface; see Problem 2.2). This is an experimental result, independent of the nature of the adsorbed molecules, the surface, or how the molecules behave on the surface (these molecules are, of course, very dilute and therefore independent of each other). As $p \to 0$, the adsorption isotherm becomes linear:

$$\Gamma = a(T)p \qquad \text{(Henry's law)}. \tag{2.23}$$

The right-hand side of this equation may be viewed as the first term of a power series in p. From Eq. (2.14), we deduce

$$\phi = kTap = kT\Gamma, \qquad \phi\mathcal{A} = NkT. \tag{2.24}$$

Thus we find an ideal gas law for the equation of state of the dilute adsorbed phase, *regardless* of the nature of the adsorption (e.g., the molecules need not be mobile). This is a thermodynamic result, analogous to the ideal osmotic pressure equation [see Eq. (4.35)]. From Eq. (2.5) and the fact that E is independent of $\mathcal{A}$ for any very dilute adsorbed phase, we have

$$\phi = -\left(\frac{\partial A}{\partial \mathcal{A}}\right)_{N,T} = T\left(\frac{\partial S}{\partial \mathcal{A}}\right)_{N,T} = \frac{NkT}{\mathcal{A}}, \tag{2.25}$$

and hence, on integrating the last equation,

$$S = Nk \ln \mathcal{A} + f(N, T). \tag{2.26}$$

This kind of dependence of S on $\mathcal{A}$ (or V, etc.), in systems of independent molecules, is well known in statistical mechanics. From the molecular point of view, we may consider Eqs. (2.23) and (2.24) to be consequences of Eq. (2.26).

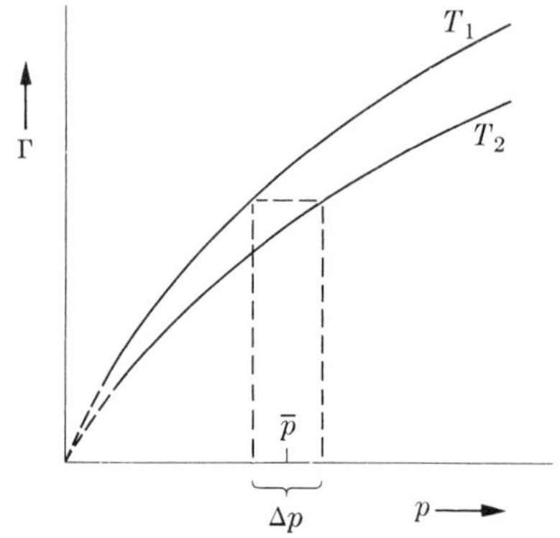

Fig. 2.2. Use of adsorption isotherms, with extrapolation, to calculate spreading pressure.

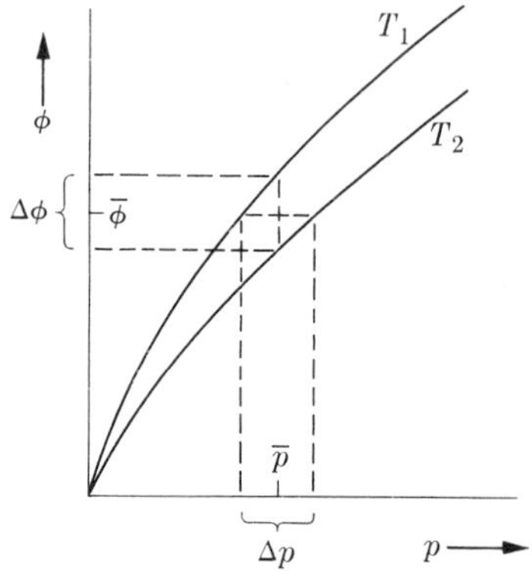

Fig. 2.3. Construction for calculation of entropy of adsorption.

Experimental isotherms. Next, we discuss the manipulation of adsorption isotherm data for the purpose of calculating thermodynamic properties of the adsorbed molecules. Figure 2.2 shows a plot of Γ against p for two neighboring temperatures. An extrapolation to $p = 0$ is necessary if ϕ is to be calculated. With the extrapolation, Eq. (2.14) may be applied to each $\Gamma(p)$ curve to find a $\phi(p)$ curve, as shown in Fig. 2.3. This latter figure then allows the computation of

$$\frac{1}{\bar{p}}\left(\frac{\Delta p}{\Delta T}\right)_\phi \cong \left(\frac{\partial \ln p}{\partial T}\right)_\phi,$$

where $\Delta T = T_2 - T_1 > 0$, for use in Eq. (2.15). Similarly, Fig. 2.2 gives $(1/\bar{p})(\Delta p/\Delta T)_\Gamma$ to be inserted in Eq. (2.20).

Figures 2.4 and 2.5, for nitrogen adsorbed on graphon (a carbon black) at 84°K, have been found in this way.* For convenience, the entropy and energy of the adsorbed molecules are shown in these figures relative to the bulk *liquid* state at the same temperature (and at the liquid vapor pressure, p_0). The abscissa is the amount of adsorption, in numbers of monolayers, θ.

*T. L. Hill, P. H. Emmett, and L. G. Joyner, *J. Am. Chem. Soc.* **73**, 5102 (1951).

The minimum in s occurs at about one monolayer (there is reason to expect this on theoretical grounds). At this concentration, the adsorbed molecules are seen to have less entropy (their motion is more restricted) than in the bulk liquid. Of course, both curves in this figure must approach zero as $\theta \rightarrow \infty$. The crossing of the two curves in Fig. 2.4, at the minimum in the $s - s_L$ curve, is the subject of Problem 2.3.

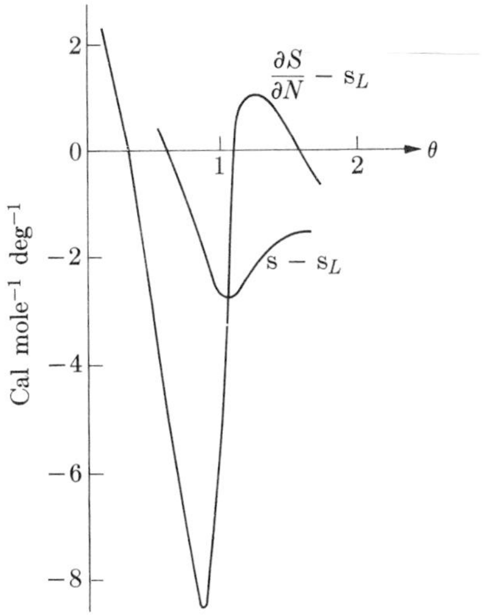

Fig. 2.4. Entropy of nitrogen molecules adsorbed on graphon at 84°K.

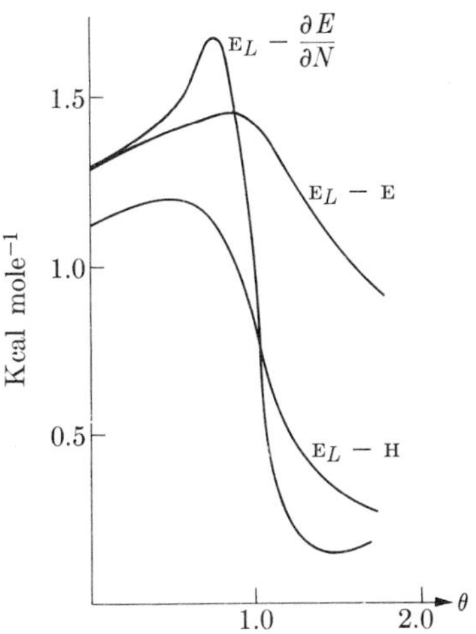

Fig. 2.5. Energy of nitrogen molecules adsorbed on graphon at 84°K.

Figure 2.5 is a similar plot for the energy of the same system. The adsorbed molecules have lower energy than liquid molecules because of strong attraction to the solid surface. The initial rise in the $E_L - E$ curve is due to attractive forces between adsorbed nitrogen molecules. A drop in this quantity, after $\theta = 1$, occurs because second-layer molecules are farther from the surface. This drop is even more evident in the $E_L - (\partial E/\partial N)$ curve.

In summary, the standard procedure in calculating thermodynamic properties of adsorbed molecules is the following: from measurements of $\Gamma(p)$, we first calculate $\phi(p)$, and then s, H, and E (relative to bulk gas or liquid). Calorimetric measurements can, of course, also be made and are very useful, but we shall not discuss them here.

Surface tension measurements. An interesting reversal of the usual procedure, in a special case, might be mentioned. When benzene vapor (a number of other substances could also be used) is adsorbed on the surface of liquid mercury, the structure of the liquid is presumably not much perturbed because of the heaviness of the mercury atoms. Hence, as a good approximation at least, we can apply the equations of Section 2.2. But, since mercury is a liquid, direct measurements of γ_S and γ may be carried out, while conventional adsorption data are difficult to obtain because the surface area is so small (a solid can be powdered to produce a large area). Thus the primary information available in this case is $\gamma_S - \gamma = \phi(p)$, and not $\Gamma(p)$. Given $\phi(p)$, we can calculate $\Gamma(p)$ from Eq. (2.13):

$$\Gamma = \frac{1}{kT}\left(\frac{\partial\phi}{\partial \ln p}\right)_T = -\frac{1}{kT}\frac{(\partial\phi/\partial T)_p}{(\partial \ln p/\partial T)_\phi}. \tag{2.27}$$

Direct use of the slope $\partial\phi/\partial \ln p$ is not very accurate. The practical equation to be applied (see Fig. 2.3) is

$$\Gamma = -\frac{\overline{p}}{k\overline{T}}\frac{(\Delta\phi/\Delta T)_p}{(\Delta p/\Delta T)_\phi} = -\frac{\overline{p}}{k\overline{T}}\frac{(\Delta\phi)_p}{(\Delta p)_\phi}.$$

This gives the concentration of adsorbed molecules, Γ, associated with $\overline{p}$, $\overline{T}$, $\overline{\phi}$, and with H and S as found from Eq. (2.15).

2.4 THE LANGMUIR ADSORPTION MODEL

As a further example, we consider a simple theoretical model for adsorption, originally due to Langmuir. The surface of area $\mathfrak{a}$ contains M equivalent, distinguishable, and independent sites for the localized adsorption of gas molecules—at most one molecule per site. Suppose the energy levels (written as nondegenerate) of an adsorbed molecule at a site are $\epsilon_1, \epsilon_2, \ldots$. For a monatomic molecule, these would be the levels of a three-dimensional oscillator. The partition function for one molecule at a site is then $q(T) = \sum_i e^{-\epsilon_i/kT}$. If we had M molecules on M sites, the partition function for the entire system would be q^M. However, when there are N molecules on M sites, with $N < M$, q^N has to be multiplied by a configurational degeneracy factor, $M!/N!(M-N)!$, this being the number of ways to distribute N indistinguishable molecules on M distinguishable sites. Thus the complete partition function of the system is

$$Q(N, M, T) = \frac{M!q(T)^N}{N!(M-N)!}. \tag{2.28}$$

The connection with thermodynamics is made via

$$A = -kT \ln Q. \tag{2.29}$$

The variable M is essentially the area. Let α, a constant, be the area per site. Then $\mathcal{A} = \alpha M$. Instead of Eq. (2.5), we write

$$dA = -S\,dT - \Phi\,dM + \mu\,dN, \tag{2.30}$$

where

$$\Phi M = \phi \mathcal{A}, \qquad \mathcal{A} = \alpha M, \qquad \Phi = \alpha\phi.$$

Since N and M are very large numbers, we employ Stirling's approximation,

$$\ln x! = x \ln x - x,$$

where x is large. Then

$$-\frac{A}{kT} = \ln Q = M \ln M - N \ln N - (M - N) \ln (M - N) + N \ln q(T). \tag{2.31}$$

The chemical potential is

$$\frac{\mu}{kT} = \left(\frac{\partial A/kT}{\partial N}\right)_{M,T} = \ln \frac{\theta}{(1-\theta)q}, \tag{2.32}$$

where θ is the fraction of sites occupied, N/M. To get the adsorption isotherm, we put $\mu = \mu_G$, where

$$\mu_G = \mu^0(T) + kT \ln p. \tag{2.33}$$

The explicit form of the function $\mu^0(T)$ is provided by statistical mechanics, and depends on the particular kind of molecule (just as q does). On combining Eqs. (2.32) and (2.33), we find

$$\theta(p, T) = \frac{\chi(T)p}{1 + \chi(T)p}, \tag{2.34}$$

where

$$\chi(T) = q(T)e^{\mu^0(T)/kT}.$$

Equation (2.34) is the well-known *Langmuir isotherm*. The form of the function $\theta(p)$ is shown in Fig. 2.6. The relation between Γ and θ is $\theta = \alpha\Gamma$.

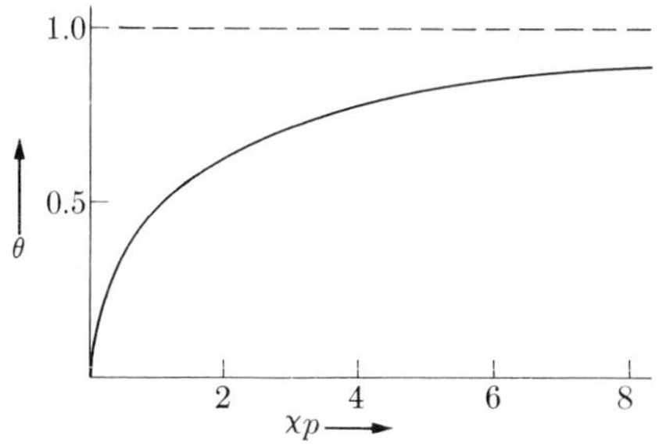

Fig. 2.6. Langmuir adsorption isotherm.

When $p \to 0$, $\theta \to \chi p$ and $\Gamma \to (\chi/\alpha)p$. Hence, in this model, the constant a in the Henry's law relation (2.23) is equal to χ/α.

The equation of state is simple:

$$\Phi/kT = -[\partial(A/kT)/\partial M]_{N,T} = -\ln(1-\theta) = \theta + \tfrac{1}{2}\theta^2 + \tfrac{1}{3}\theta^3 + \cdots \tag{2.35}$$

For small θ,

$$\Phi/kT = \theta, \qquad \Phi M = NkT, \tag{2.36}$$

as expected.

The entropy follows from $S = -(\partial A/\partial T)_{M,N}$. A more complicated way to find S is via Eq. (2.15), after expressing Φ as a function of p. These derivations are included in Problem 2.4.

Alternative forms of Eqs. (2.34) and (2.35) are

$$\theta = q\lambda/(1 + q\lambda) \tag{2.37}$$

and

$$\Phi/kT = \ln(1 + q\lambda), \tag{2.38}$$

where $\lambda = e^{\mu/kT}$. Since θ is the probability that any site may be occupied, it is clear that if we assign the weight unity to an empty site, then an occupied site must have the weight $q\lambda$.

Equation (2.37) is also the equation of a simple acid titration curve, if we take λ to be proportional to the concentration of hydrogen ions in solution. In this case, each acid anion provides one site for the binding of a hydrogen ion. Although the sites move around in the solvent, this has no effect on the titration curve so long as the acid concentration is low [see Eq. (4.61)].

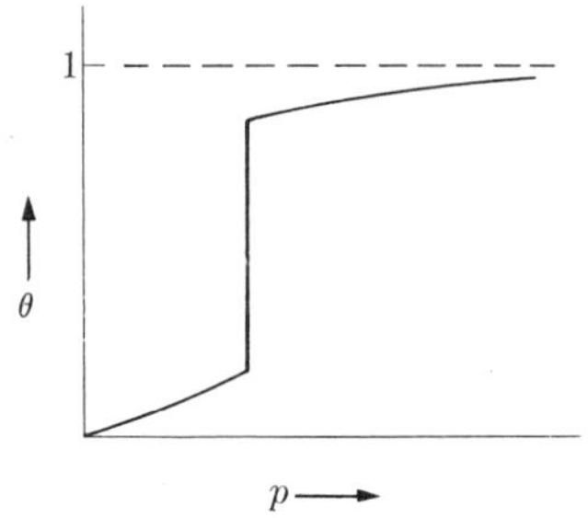

Fig. 2.7. Schematic adsorption isotherm showing a phase transition.

If attractive interactions between adsorbed molecules are included in a model of the Langmuir type, a phase transition and critical behavior arise (both theoretically and experimentally). Figure 2.7 shows a typical isotherm with such a transition. At the transition, the system (gas plus two adsorbed phases) has only one degree of freedom. From the appropriate generalization of Eq. (2.12), it is easy to derive expressions for $d\phi/dT$ and $d \ln p/dT$.

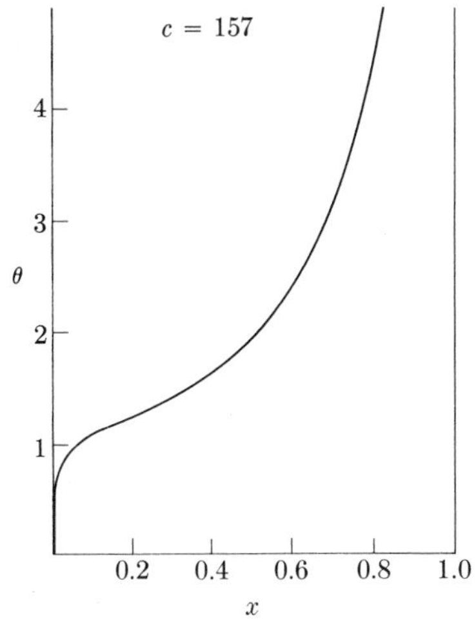

Fig. 2.8. BET multilayer adsorption isotherm for $c = 157$.

Multilayer adsorption. The Brunauer-Emmett-Teller (BET) adsorption model is a well-known simple extension of the Langmuir model which includes multilayer adsorption. The adsorption isotherm, which we shall not derive here, is

$$\theta = \frac{cx}{(1-x)(1-x+cx)}, \tag{2.39}$$

where $x = p/p_0$ and p_0 is the vapor pressure. A typical curve is shown in Fig. 2.8. Note that $\theta \to \infty$ as $x \to 1$ $(p \to p_0)$, as expected. When c is large (strong binding of gas molecules to the surface) and x is small,

$$\theta \to cx/(1+cx).$$

This is "Langmuir" first-layer adsorption. The connection with Eq. (2.34) is clearly $c/p_0 = \chi$.

PROBLEMS

2.1 Prove that the condition for equilibrium between the adsorbed phase and the gas phase is $\mu = \mu_G$.

2.2 When H_2 molecules are adsorbed on a certain surface they dissociate into H atoms. Suppose the adsorbed H atoms follow a Langmuir adsorption model (M sites and at most one atom per site). What is the adsorption isotherm? That is, find θ (fraction of sites occupied by H atoms) as a function of the pressure p of H_2 gas.

2.3 Prove that if $s = S/N$ and $(\partial S/\partial N)_{\alpha,T}$ are both plotted against Γ (T constant), then wherever the s versus Γ curve has a maximum or minimum, it is crossed by the $\partial S/\partial N$ versus Γ curve.

2.4 Derive equations for the entropy of a Langmuir adsorbed phase from (a) $S = -(\partial A/\partial T)_{M,N}$ and (b) from Eq. (2.15). Show that the two expressions are equivalent and that S has two parts: $S = S$ (configuration) $+ S$ (vibration).

2.5 Derive the spreading pressure $\Phi(x)$ from the BET $\theta(x)$. Show that the limit of Φ as $x \to 1$ does not correspond to reality.

2.6 The *virial expansion* (see Chapter 4) of ϕ is

$$\phi/kT = \Gamma + B_2(T)\Gamma^2 + B_3(T)\Gamma^3 + \cdots \tag{2.40}$$

Find B_2 for (a) the Langmuir model and (b) the BET model.

2.7 In both Figs. 2.2 and 2.3, the T_2 curve is lower than the T_1 curve ($T_2 > T_1$). What is the physical significance of this?

2.8 Discuss the Langmuir model for a *heterogeneous* surface (the sites are independent and distinguishable but not all equivalent).

SUPPLEMENTARY READING

Hill, T. L., in *Advances in Catalysis*, Vol. 4. New York: Academic Press, 1952.

Hill, T. L., *Introduction to Statistical Thermodynamics*, Chapter 7. Reading, Mass.: Addison-Wesley, 1960.

Young, D. M., and A. D. Crowell, *Physical Adsorption of Gases*. Washington: Butterworths, 1962.

CHAPTER 3

THERMODYNAMICS OF ELASTIC SYSTEMS

3.1 INTRODUCTION

In this chapter we consider the thermodynamics of elastic systems which are incompressible (to a sufficient approximation). Thus the volume will not appear as a thermodynamic variable, but in its place will be the length of the system L. Correspondingly, the pressure is replaced by the (pulling) force f. The system is shown schematically in Fig. 3.1.

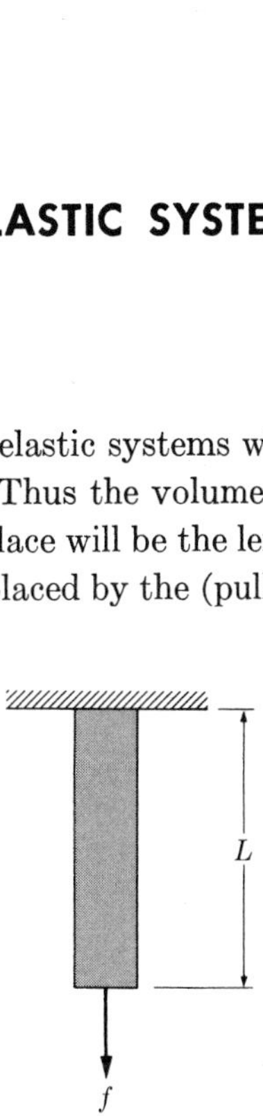

Fig. 3.1. Elastic system.

Rubber is a good example. Rubber consists of a network of long cross-linked polymer chains. Each chain wanders around within the sample in a more or less random way, but the chains are "condensed," as in a liquid (the system resembles, somewhat, a can of cross-linked worms).

Another example is a single long polymer chain, such as a synthetic polypeptide, which can vary its length by virtue of the units of the chain switching from a short form (α or *helix*) to a long form (β or *coil*).

We shall derive some general thermodynamic relations in Sections 3.2 and 3.5 (where adsorption or binding on the elastic material is included), and consider special cases or examples in Sections 3.3, 3.4, and 3.6.

3.2 THERMODYNAMICS OF ELASTICITY

The basic equation for the system in Fig. 2.1 is

$$dE = T\,dS + f\,dL + \mu\,dN. \tag{3.1}$$

That is, $-p\,dV$ is replaced by $+f\,dL$. The sign is reversed because the external pressure p compresses, but the external force f extends. The symbol N represents the number of chains, units, or monomers, etc., according to what is convenient (the definition of μ is affected, of course, by the definition of N). We shall take L to be an extensive variable (see Problem 3.1). Thus if we increase the length of the system holding T, f, and μ constant, then E, S, and N increase in proportion to L. Integration of Eq. (3.1) therefore leads to

$$E = TS + fL + \mu N. \tag{3.2}$$

We define, as usual,

$$A = E - TS, \qquad H = E - fL, \qquad G = E - TS - fL = \mu N. \tag{3.3}$$

Although N may be varied by choosing samples of different lengths, the system is not ordinarily "dynamically open." Hence, for practical purposes, we are primarily concerned with the thermodynamics of closed systems (N = const). We shall therefore omit N as a variable in the remainder of this section and in the following section.

The rest length $L_0(T)$ is defined as the value of L when $f = 0$.

Some basic calorimetric relations are the following:

$$DQ = T\,dS = dE \qquad (L \text{ constant}) \tag{3.4}$$

$$= dH \qquad (f \text{ constant}), \tag{3.5}$$

$$C_L = \left(\frac{\partial E}{\partial T}\right)_L = T\left(\frac{\partial S}{\partial T}\right)_L, \tag{3.6}$$

$$C_f = \left(\frac{\partial H}{\partial T}\right)_f = T\left(\frac{\partial S}{\partial T}\right)_f, \tag{3.7}$$

where DQ is the heat absorbed by the system, and C_L and C_f are heat capacities. A relation between C_f and C_L may be derived which is analogous to the C_p, C_V relation well known in ordinary thermodynamics.

From

$$dA = -S\,dT + f\,dL, \tag{3.8}$$

we have

$$f = \left(\frac{\partial A}{\partial L}\right)_T = \left(\frac{\partial E}{\partial L}\right)_T - T\left(\frac{\partial S}{\partial L}\right)_T. \tag{3.9}$$

Thus the force may be considered to have an energy contribution and an entropy contribution. The entropy term can be written in another way:

$$\frac{\partial^2 A}{\partial T\,\partial L} = -\left(\frac{\partial S}{\partial L}\right)_T = \left(\frac{\partial f}{\partial T}\right)_L, \tag{3.10}$$

so that

$$f = \left(\frac{\partial E}{\partial L}\right)_T + T\left(\frac{\partial f}{\partial T}\right)_L. \tag{3.11}$$

Similar equations follow from

$$dG = -S\,dT - L\,df. \tag{3.12}$$

Thus

$$-L = \left(\frac{\partial G}{\partial f}\right)_T = \left(\frac{\partial H}{\partial f}\right)_T - T\left(\frac{\partial S}{\partial f}\right)_T, \tag{3.13}$$

$$-\frac{\partial^2 G}{\partial T\,\partial f} = \left(\frac{\partial S}{\partial f}\right)_T = \left(\frac{\partial L}{\partial T}\right)_f, \tag{3.14}$$

$$L = -\left(\frac{\partial H}{\partial f}\right)_T + T\left(\frac{\partial L}{\partial T}\right)_f. \tag{3.15}$$

We apply some of these equations in the next section.

3.3 IDEAL RUBBER

If, for a typical rubber, the function $f(L)$ is measured at two neighboring temperatures (Fig. 3.2) for extensions between, say, $L = L_0$ and $L = 3L_0$, it is found, to a very good approximation, that $(\partial f/\partial T)_L \cong f/T$. Significant deviations from this relation occur at higher extensions. We *define* an ideal rubber to be one for which $(\partial f/\partial T)_L$ is exactly equal to f/T. With this definition, let us deduce other properties of an ideal rubber, keeping in mind that a typical real rubber is practically ideal through moderate extensions.

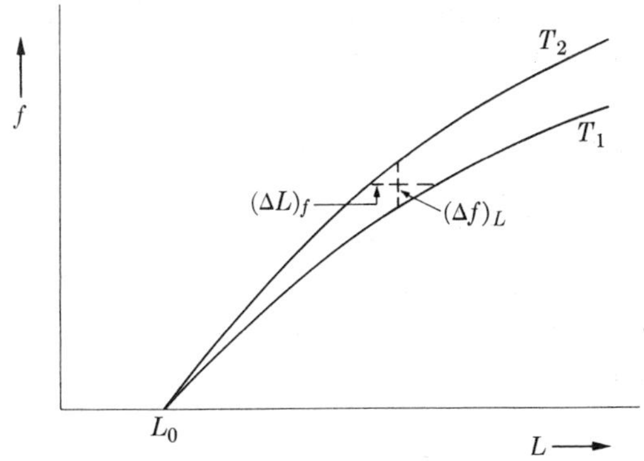

Fig. 3.2. Force-length curves for an ideal rubber.

The most important point is seen immediately: from Eq. (3.11), we have that $(\partial E/\partial L)_T = 0$. That is, E is a function of T only, and is independent of L. This is reminiscent of an ideal gas, for which $(\partial E/\partial V)_T = 0$. The explanation of the latter property is that an ideal gas has kinetic energy but no intermolecular potential energy (which would vary with V if it existed). In the case of the ideal rubber, the situation is a little different. The rubber is a condensed system (like a liquid) with constant volume. Its intermolecular potential energy is certainly not zero. However, when an ideal rubber is stretched, the significant occurrence at the molecular level is the partial straightening or extension of the chains, *without* a change in volume or in the potential energy of the "liquid." In brief, the potential energy is not zero, but it is *constant.*

According to Eq. (3.9), $f = -T(\partial S/\partial L)_T$. Thus, the force-length relation (Fig. 3.2) is entirely an entropy effect. The same is true, of course, of the pressure-volume relation in an ideal gas: $p = T(\partial S/\partial V)_T$.

If we integrate the defining equation of an ideal rubber, $df/f = dT/T$, we obtain $f = T\psi(L)$, where $\psi(L)$ is a function of L only. This resembles the ideal gas equation of state: $p = T \times$ function of V only.

For the entropy of an ideal rubber, we have

$$\left(\frac{\partial S}{\partial L}\right)_T = -\frac{f}{T} = -\psi(L) \tag{3.16}$$

and hence

$$S = \text{function of } T \text{ only} + \text{function of } L \text{ only.} \tag{3.17}$$

The latter function is the chain configuration entropy; it determines the force-length relation.

The term $(\partial E/\partial L)_T$ in Eq. (3.11) is equal to zero for an ideal rubber. One might then expect that the corresponding term $(\partial H/\partial f)_T$ in Eq. (3.15) would also vanish [recall that, for an ideal gas, $(\partial H/\partial p)_T = 0$]. This, however, is not the case, as will be shown below in a special example.

The reader may have noticed that, in Fig 3.2, L_0 is independent of T. This property of an ideal rubber follows from

$$\left(\frac{\partial f}{\partial T}\right)_L = \frac{f}{T} = -\frac{(\partial L/\partial T)_f}{(\partial L/\partial f)_T}. \tag{3.18}$$

When $f \to 0$, we must also have $(\partial L/\partial T)_f \to 0$.

Let us conclude with a few remarks on the adiabatic extension of an ideal rubber. We start with

$$dE = DQ + f\,dL. \tag{3.19}$$

Since E is a function of T only, and $DQ = 0$ (adiabatic process), we have

$$dE = (\partial E/\partial T)_L\,dT = C_L\,dT = f\,dL. \tag{3.20}$$

Now $f > 0$, $C_L > 0$, and $dL > 0$ (extension). Therefore, $dT > 0$. Thus if a piece of rubber is suddenly (hence, adiabatically) stretched, its temperature will rise (as can be verified with a rubber band). The work put into the stretching of the rubber appears as additional kinetic energy.

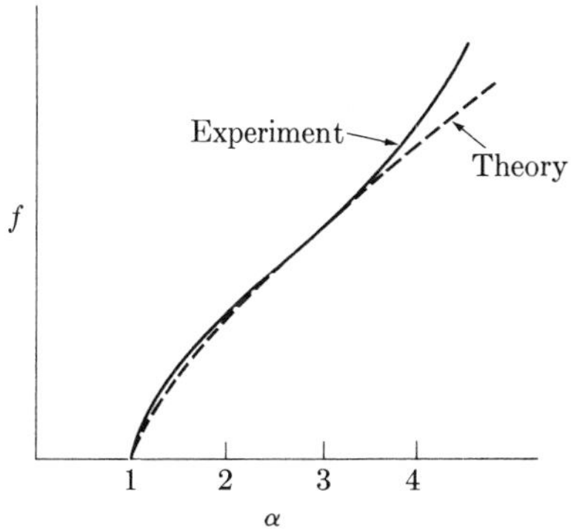

Fig. 3.3. Comparison of experimental and theoretical force-length relations for rubber in a typical case. The vertical scale has been adjusted to give best fit.

Wall's model of an ideal rubber. F. T. Wall considered each chain in an unstretched sample of rubber to be represented by a "random walk," and a chain in a stretched sample to be represented by an appropriately biased walk (with lower entropy). From this starting point he was able to derive the following specific force-length relation for an ideal rubber:

$$f = \frac{NkT}{L_0}\left(\alpha - \frac{1}{\alpha^2}\right), \tag{3.21}$$

where N is the number of chains in the network and $\alpha = L/L_0$. Figure 3.3 compares this function with a typical experimental curve. In this model,

$$\psi(L) = \frac{f}{T} = \frac{Nk}{L_0}\left(\alpha - \frac{1}{\alpha^2}\right) \tag{3.22}$$

and hence, from Eq. (3.16),

$$S = \text{function of } T \text{ only} - Nk\left(\frac{\alpha^2}{2} + \frac{1}{\alpha}\right) \tag{3.23}$$

or

$$S(\alpha) - S(1) = -Nk\left(\frac{\alpha^2}{2} + \frac{1}{\alpha} - \frac{3}{2}\right). \tag{3.24}$$

Let us verify that $(\partial H/\partial f)_T \neq 0$ in this model. For this purpose, we combine Eqs. (3.15) and (3.18) to obtain

$$\left(\frac{\partial H}{\partial f}\right)_T = -L - T\,\frac{(\partial f/\partial T)_L}{(\partial f/\partial L)_T}. \tag{3.25}$$

On introducing Eq. (3.21) for f, we find

$$\left(\frac{\partial H}{\partial f}\right)_T = -\,\frac{L_0\alpha(1 + 2\alpha^3)}{2 + \alpha^3} \neq 0. \tag{3.26}$$

3.4 ELASTICITY OF A LINEAR POLYMER CHAIN

As another specific example, we consider here a single linear incompressible polymer chain composed of units each of which can be in a short state α of length l_α or a long state β of length l_β ($l_\beta > l\alpha$). The lengths l_α and l_β are assumed to be constants. The units are interconvertible, as in an isomeric chemical reaction ($\alpha \rightleftarrows \beta$). In this simple model, neighboring units do not interact: the units are independent of each other. A more complicated case with interactions is mentioned in Section 3.6.

If a pulling force f is applied to the chain, some α units will be converted into longer β units and the chain will lengthen. This model is crudely representative of some real systems: the α–β transition in fibrous proteins; the helix–random coil transition in solutions of proteins, polypeptides, nucleic acids, and polynucleotides ($f = 0$); and possibly the elasticity of muscle (see Section 3.6) and some textiles.

Let N be the total number of units, with N_α and N_β units of the two types. The basic thermodynamic equation is (3.1), with

$$L = l_\alpha N_\alpha + l_\beta N_\beta. \tag{3.27}$$

It is convenient to replace L and N as independent variables in Eq. (3.1) by N_α and N. To accomplish this, we substitute Eq. (3.27), with $N_\beta = N - N_\alpha$, into Eq. (3.1) and find

$$dE = T\,dS - f(l_\beta - l_\alpha)\,dN_\alpha + (\mu + fl_\beta)\,dN \tag{3.28}$$

or

$$dA = -S\,dT - f(l_\beta - l_\alpha)\,dN_\alpha + (\mu + fl_\beta)\,dN. \tag{3.29}$$

We let $j_\alpha(T)$ and $j_\beta(T)$ represent the partition functions of one α and one β unit, respectively. The explicit forms used for j_α and j_β would depend

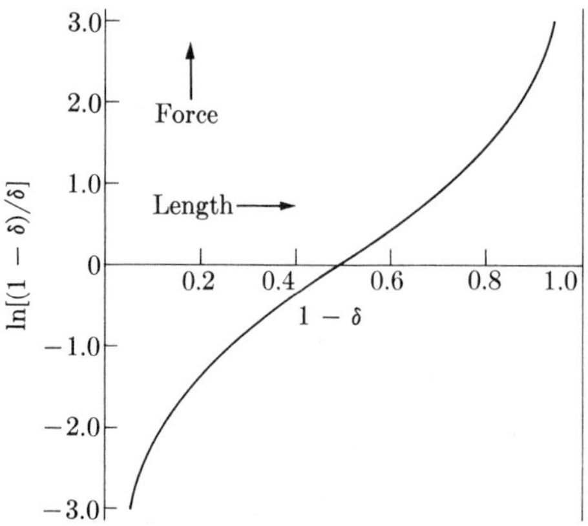

Fig. 3.4. Force-length relation for linear polymer chain of α and β units.

on the particular system of interest. The ratio of j_α to j_β reflects the relative intrinsic stability (i.e., unbiased by a force; $f = 0$) of the two kinds of units.

The canonical ensemble partition function is

$$Q(N_\alpha, N, T) = \frac{N! j_\alpha(T)^{N_\alpha} j_\beta(T)^{N-N_\alpha}}{N_\alpha!(N - N_\alpha)!}. \tag{3.30}$$

The very close resemblance to Eq. (2.28) for Langmuir adsorption should be noted. These two problems are practically identical.

With Eq. (3.30) available, it is easy to deduce the thermodynamic properties of the model. For example,

$$\begin{aligned}\frac{f(l_\beta - l_\alpha)}{kT} &= -\frac{1}{kT}\left(\frac{\partial A}{\partial N_\alpha}\right)_{N,T} = \left(\frac{\partial \ln Q}{\partial N_\alpha}\right)_{N,T} \\ &= \ln\left[\frac{1-\delta}{\delta}\cdot\frac{j_\alpha(T)}{j_\beta(T)}\right],\end{aligned} \tag{3.31}$$

where $\delta = N_\alpha/N$, the fraction of α units. Of course, $1 - \delta$ is the fraction of β units. Equation (3.31) is essentially the force-length relation (Fig. 3.4), since L and δ are related linearly, from Eq. (3.27), by

$$1 - \delta = \frac{L - Nl_\alpha}{N(l_\beta - l_\alpha)}. \tag{3.32}$$

At zero force, $f = 0$, and

$$\frac{\delta}{1-\delta} = \frac{N_\alpha}{N_\beta} = \frac{j_\alpha(T)}{j_\beta(T)} = K(T). \tag{3.33}$$

This is the intrinsic stability ratio (or equilibrium constant K) between α and β units, referred to above. Note that the "rest length" in Fig. 3.4 is at $1 - \delta_0 > 0.5$ if $K < 1$ and at $1 - \delta_0 < 0.5$ if $K > 1$ (short, or α, units are more stable). When the force is not zero,

$$\frac{\delta}{1-\delta} = \frac{N_\alpha}{N_\beta} = K(T)e^{-f(l_\beta - l_\alpha)/kT}. \tag{3.34}$$

When $f \to \infty$, $\delta \to 0$, and $L \to Nl_\beta$ (all long units).

The similarity between Eqs. (2.32) and (3.31) will be obvious. The chemical potential of the adsorbed molecules (determined by the gas pressure) and the force on a polymer chain play similar roles in altering the equilibrium ratio of the two possible states in each case (empty and occupied sites; α and β units).

It is clear from Eq. (3.31) that f/T is not a function of L only in this model (unless j_α and j_β are constants). Hence this system is not an "ideal rubber." Problem 3.2 concerns the derivation of an expression for $(\partial E/\partial L)_T$.

3.5 THERMODYNAMICS OF AN ELASTIC ADSORBENT

In this section we combine the treatments in Sections 2.2 and 3.2. The system consists of N_1 chains, units, or monomers, etc., of an elastic material with N_2 molecules of a second species adsorbed or bound thereto. The most obvious examples are polymeric systems, including biopolymers, in equilibrium with a solution which is dilute in component 2. The reservoir of component 2 molecules could be a gas, as in Section 2.2, but we shall use a notation appropriate to a solution.

In the systems of most interest, there is no well-defined surface area, but rather there are binding sites distributed along or within the elastic material. Therefore, we treat the elastic system, including bound molecules, as an incompressible binary solution. The variable N_1 replaces $\mathcal{A}$ of Section 2.2.

The basic thermodynamic equation [compare Eq. (3.1)] is

$$dE = T\,dS + f\,dL + \mu_1\,dN_1 + \mu_2\,dN_2. \tag{3.35}$$

We take L to be an extensive variable, as before. The size of the system is varied, in principle, by keeping L proportional to N_1, with T, f, μ_1, and μ_2 held constant. Thus, integration of Eq. (3.35) gives

$$E = TS + fL + \mu_1 N_1 + \mu_2 N_2. \tag{3.36}$$

We define

$$A = E - TS, \qquad H = E - fL,$$
$$G = E - TS - fL = \mu_1 N_1 + \mu_2 N_2. \tag{3.37}$$

Equation (3.35) cannot be compared directly with Eq. (2.1), for the latter equation refers to a *one*-component system of adsorbed molecules. We have to subtract out the pure adsorbent (elastic material) before such a comparison can be made. We shall carry out this procedure below [Eq. (3.48)].

When the system is in equilibrium with the surrounding solution, $\mu_2 = \mu_{2S}$ ($S =$ solution). For simplicity, we take the solution to be very dilute in component 2, and incompressible, so that

$$\mu_{2S} = \text{function of } T + kT \ln \rho_2$$
$$d\mu_{2S} = -\bar{s}_{2S}\,dT + kT\,d\ln \rho_2, \tag{3.38}$$

where $\bar{s}_{2S}$ is the partial molecular entropy of component 2 and ρ_2 is the concentration, N_{2S}/V_S, of component 2 in the solution.

In order to see the lines along which it is profitable to develop the thermodynamics, let us digress to indicate typical sorts of graphs that might be used to exhibit experimental results and from which thermodynamic calculations might be made. It will be left to the reader to draw schematic curves. First, adsorption isotherms may be plotted in four obvious ways: $\Gamma = N_2/N_1$ against ρ_2, with T constant, for several fixed values of L or f; or Γ against ρ_2, with L or f constant, for several fixed values of T. Second, force-length curves may be plotted, with ρ_2 constant, for several fixed values of T; or force against length, with T constant, for several fixed values of ρ_2. A third set of curves of some interest (there are examples in the next section) is obtained by plotting L against ρ_2, with T constant, for several fixed values of f; or L against ρ_2, with f constant, for several fixed values of T.

For the same system, the above curves are of course not all independent of each other, nor is the list exhaustive.

Let us return now to Eqs. (3.35) through (3.38) and derive a small sample of possible thermodynamic relations. From

$$dA = -S\,dT + f\,dL + \mu_1\,dN_1 + \mu_2\,dN_2, \tag{3.39}$$

we have

$$\left(\frac{\partial f}{\partial N_2}\right)_{T,L,N_1} = \left(\frac{\partial \mu_2}{\partial L}\right)_{T,N_1,N_2}. \tag{3.40}$$

This can be rewritten as

$$\left(\frac{\partial f}{\partial \Gamma}\right)_{T,l} = kT\left(\frac{\partial \ln \rho_2}{\partial l}\right)_{T,\Gamma}, \tag{3.41}$$

where $l = L/N_1$. Similarly, from

$$dG = -S\,dT - L\,df + \mu_1\,dN_1 + \mu_2\,dN_2, \tag{3.42}$$

we find

$$-\left(\frac{\partial l}{\partial \Gamma}\right)_{T,f} = kT\left(\frac{\partial \ln \rho_2}{\partial f}\right)_{T,\Gamma}. \tag{3.43}$$

The Gibbs-Duhem equation for this system is, from Eq. (3.42),

$$N_1\,d\mu_1 + N_2\,d\mu_2 + S\,dT + L\,df = 0. \tag{3.44}$$

With T and f constant, we find the Gibbs adsorption isotherm [compare Eq. (2.13)]:

$$-d\mu_1 = \Gamma\,d\mu_2 = kT\Gamma\,d\ln\rho_2 \qquad (T, f \text{ constant}) \tag{3.45}$$

and

$$\Phi(\rho_2) = \mu_1(0) - \mu_1(\rho_2) = kT\int_0^{\rho_2} \Gamma(\rho_2')\,d\ln\rho_2' \qquad (T, f \text{ constant}). \tag{3.46}$$

This equation defines Φ, an analogue of the spreading pressure ϕ in Chapter 2 (recall that, here, N_1 replaces $\mathfrak{A}$).

Equation (3.44) applies to the elastic material at f, T, and an arbitrary value of ρ_2. Let us consider the same system (same N_1, f, T), but with $\rho_2 = 0$ so that $N_2 = 0$ also (pure adsorbent). We write Eq. (3.44), in this case, as

$$N_1\, d\mu_1(0) + S(0)\, dT + L(0)\, df = 0. \tag{3.47}$$

On subtracting Eq. (3.47) from Eq. (3.44), we obtain

$$-N_1\, d\Phi + N_2\, d\mu_2 + S'\, dT + L'\, df = 0, \tag{3.48}$$

where $S' = S(\rho_2) - S(0)$ and $L' = L(\rho_2) - L(0)$. Then

$$d\mu_2 = -(S'/N_2)\, dT + (1/\Gamma)\, d\Phi - (L'/N_2)\, df. \tag{3.49}$$

Having "subtracted out" the pure elastic material, Eq. (3.49) is a pseudo one-component equation, the analogue of Eq. (2.8). To obtain the Clausius-Clapeyron equation corresponding to Eq. (2.15), we put $d\mu_2 = d\mu_{2S}$ and find

$$\left(\frac{\partial \ln \rho_2}{\partial T}\right)_{\Phi,f} = \frac{\bar{s}_{2S} - (S'/N_2)}{kT}, \tag{3.50}$$

where Φ is to be found from Eq. (3.46).

A second useful expression for $d\mu_2$ follows if we regard the elastic system as a binary solution rather than take the one-component approach implicit in Eq. (3.49). From Eq. (3.42), we have

$$\left(\frac{\partial \mu_2}{\partial T}\right)_{f,\Gamma} = -\left(\frac{\partial S}{\partial N_2}\right)_{T,f,N_1} = -\bar{s}_2, \tag{3.51}$$

$$\left(\frac{\partial \mu_2}{\partial f}\right)_{T,\Gamma} = -\left(\frac{\partial L}{\partial N_2}\right)_{T,f,N_1} = -\bar{L}_2, \tag{3.52}$$

where $\bar{s}_2$ and $\bar{L}_2$ are partial molecular quantities for the binary system. Then it follows that

$$d\mu_2 = -\bar{s}_2\, dT - \bar{L}_2\, df + \left(\frac{\partial \mu_2}{\partial \Gamma}\right)_{T,f} d\Gamma. \tag{3.53}$$

We again equate $d\mu_2$ and $d\mu_{2S}$, but this time we obtain

$$\left(\frac{\partial \ln \rho_2}{\partial T}\right)_{\Gamma,f} = \frac{\bar{s}_{2S} - \bar{s}_2}{kT}. \tag{3.54}$$

This is the analogue of Eq. (2.20).

Another whole series of equations may be derived in which the intensive variable f is replaced by l, but we shall not go into this (see Problem 3.3).

The next section is concerned with a specific example of an elastic system with adsorption.

3.6 LANGMUIR ADSORPTION ON A LINEAR POLYMER CHAIN

Suppose, in the model of Section 3.4, that each unit (component 1) contains one site for the binding of a molecule of component 2 (see Section 2.4). Let $q_\alpha(T)$ be the partition function for a component 2 molecule bound on an α unit and let $q_\beta(T)$ be the partition function for a molecule bound on a β unit. In general, of course, $q_\alpha \neq q_\beta$ and hence the binding of component 2 will bias and alter the length-tension behavior of the polymer. Conversely, stretching the polymer will affect the amount of binding. For example, if $q_\alpha > q_\beta$, an increase in ρ_2 at constant f will cause some β units to go over into α units, thus shortening the chain. It is conceivable that an effect of this kind could be involved in muscle contraction (see below).

The statistical mechanical derivation of the properties of this system requires an appropriate combination of Sections 2.4 and 3.4. We leave this to the interested reader (Problem 3.4). We shall merely state the main results here. The first is a generalization of Eq. (3.31) which we can also "deduce" by using the following simple intuitive argument. In connection with Eq. (2.37), it was pointed out that, in Langmuir adsorption at chemical potential μ, if an empty site is assigned the weight unity, then an occupied site has the weight $q\lambda$, where $\lambda = e^{\mu/kT}$. Now the partition function j_α in Eq. (3.31) refers to an empty unit, with no binding possible. If we allow binding, as in the present model, we should then expect to replace j_α by $j_\alpha(1 + q_\alpha\lambda_2)$, where $\lambda_2 = e^{\mu_2/kT}$. Also, j_β would become $j_\beta(1 + q_\beta\lambda_2)$. Of course λ_2 is proportional to the concentration ρ_2 in solution. Thus, the force-length relation turns out to be

$$\frac{f(l_\beta - l_\alpha)}{kT} = \ln\left\{\frac{1-\delta}{\delta}\cdot\frac{j_\alpha(T)[1 + q_\alpha(T)\lambda_2]}{j_\beta(T)[1 + q_\beta(T)\lambda_2]}\right\}, \tag{3.55}$$

where $\delta = N_{\alpha 1}/N_1$, the fraction of α units. If $q_\alpha > q_\beta$, we see that the force f must be greater to achieve the same length (or δ) when $\lambda_2 > 0$ than when $\lambda_2 = 0$. This is because the presence of bound molecules favors short units in this case. Figure 3.5 illustrates an equivalent effect: the shortening of the chain with increase in λ_2 at constant f when $q_\alpha > q_\beta$.

As we should anticipate from Eq. (2.37), θ_α (fraction of α sites occupied) and θ_β are given by

$$\theta_\alpha = \frac{q_\alpha\lambda_2}{1 + q_\alpha\lambda_2}, \qquad \theta_\beta = \frac{q_\beta\lambda_2}{1 + q_\beta\lambda_2}. \tag{3.56}$$

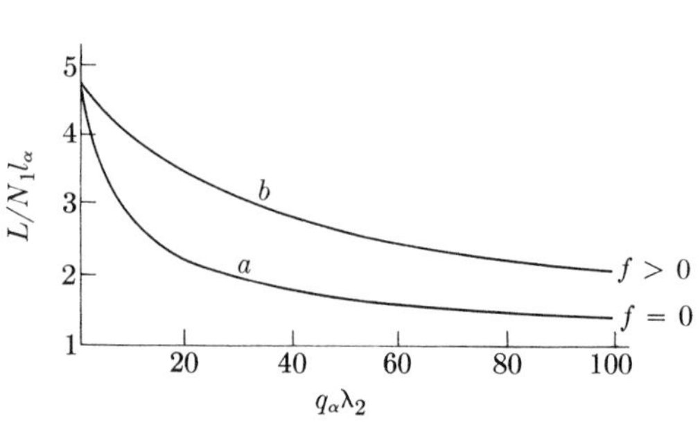

Fig. 3.5. Shortening of chain with increasing adsorbate concentration at constant f in the arbitrary special case $l_\beta/l_\alpha = 5$, $j_\alpha/j_\beta = \frac{1}{10}$ (β units longer and more stable than α), and $q_\beta = 0$ (no adsorption on β units). Curve a: $f = 0$ (rest length as function of λ_2). Curve b:

$$\exp\,[f(l_\beta - l_\alpha)/kT] = 3.5.$$

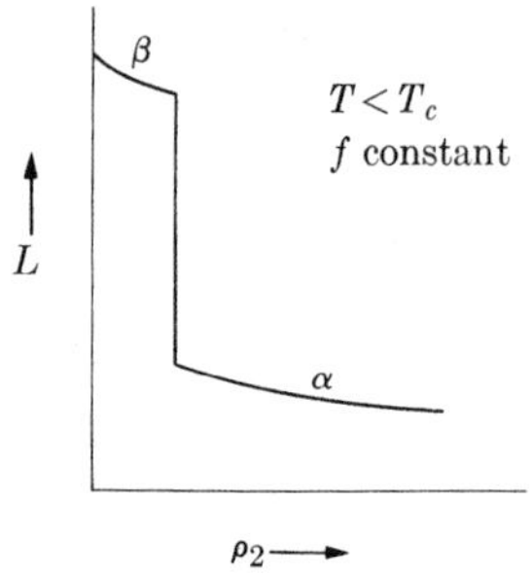

Fig. 3.6. Sudden change in length at constant force owing to a phase transition.

Then

$$\Gamma = N_2/N_1 = \theta_\alpha \delta + \theta_\beta (1 - \delta). \tag{3.57}$$

A much more dramatic effect can be obtained if there are interactions between units. Suppose, for example, we have a sheet of parallel polypeptide chains with hydrogen bonds (i.e., interactions) between nearest neighbor α units (one unit might be, say, several amino-acid residues) in the *same* chain or hydrogen bonds between nearest neighbor β units in *adjacent* chains. This leads to a cooperative effect. When f is small, the system (sheet) tends to be almost all α units; when f is large enough, there will be (below a critical temperature) a sudden cooperative switch or phase transition to almost all β units. If there is binding of a second component, a change in ρ_2 (at constant f) can be the trigger for the phase transition instead of a change in f. This is illustrated schematically in Fig. 3.6 where binding is assumed to be stronger on α units and hence there is a sudden shortening following a very small change in concentration, ρ_2, near a critical value of ρ_2. The use of a phase transition, of some sort, in muscle contraction seems to be a likely possibility* (component 2 = Ca^{++} or ATP?) because of the "amplification" provided in this way.

In current nomenclature, Fig. 3.6 illustrates an "allosteric effect." Binding of a subtrate alters the configuration of a macromolecular system from one state (β) to another (α).

* T. L. Hill, *J. Chem. Phys.* **20,** 1259 (1952); *Faraday Soc. Disc.* **13,** 132 (1953); *Proc. Nat. Acad. Sci.*, in press (March, 1968).

PROBLEMS

3.1 One can choose L as intensive and f as extensive for some systems. Explain. Show how Eqs. (3.1) and (3.2) are modified.

3.2 The linear polymer chain of Section 3.4 is not an "ideal rubber." Show that

$$\left(\frac{\partial E}{\partial L}\right)_T = -\frac{kT^2}{l_\beta - l_\alpha}\cdot\frac{d\ln K}{dT}. \tag{3.58}$$

3.3 Change independent variables in Eq. (3.39) from T, L, N_1, N_2 to T, l, N_1, N_2 by the substitution $L = N_1 l$. Define $\mu_1^* = \mu_1 + fl$. Obtain a new Gibbs-Duhem equation, in place of (3.44), with independent variables μ_1^*, μ_2, T, and l. Hence, prove that

$$\Phi^*(\rho_2) = \mu_1^*(0) - \mu_1^*(\rho_2) = kT\int_0^{\rho_2} \Gamma(\rho_2')\, d\ln\rho_2' \qquad (T, l \text{ constant}). \tag{3.59}$$

3.4 Provide a proper statistical mechanical derivation of Eqs. (3.55) and (3.56).

3.5 Using the approach of Problem 3.3, derive an expression for

$$(\partial \ln \rho_2/\partial T)_{\Phi^*, l},$$

similar to Eq. (3.50).

3.6 Derive Eq. (3.15) starting with the differentiation with respect to f (T constant) of both sides of the equation $H = E - fL$.

3.7 By a suitable modification of Eq. (3.39), prove that

$$-\left(\frac{\partial \Gamma}{\partial l}\right)_{T,\mu_2} = \left(\frac{\partial f}{\partial \mu_2}\right)_{T,l}. \tag{3.60}$$

Apply this to Eq. (3.55) and interpret the result.

3.8 Apply Eq. (3.59) [i.e., calculate $\Phi^*(\lambda_2)$] to Eq. (3.57). Compare with Eq. (2.38).

SUPPLEMENTARY READING

HILL, T. L., *Introduction to Statistical Thermodynamics*, Chapters 7 and 13. Reading, Mass.: Addison-Wesley, 1960.

HILL, T. L., *J. Chem. Phys.* **18,** 791 (1950); **20,** 1259 (1952).

WALL, F.T., *Chemical Thermodynamics* (Second Edition). San Francisco: Freeman, 1965.

CHAPTER 4

IMPERFECT GASES AND SOLUTIONS, OSMOTIC PRESSURE AND THE DONNAN EQUILIBRIUM

The theme that runs through this chapter is the expression of deviations from ideal behavior by means of series expansions. We shall pay particular attention to first deviations from ideality (slightly imperfect gases, etc.). The first section is concerned with imperfect gases; the remainder of the chapter is devoted to solutions.

4.1 IMPERFECT GASES

This section is intended primarily as background for the treatment of solutions in the remainder of the chapter. We consider a one-component gas, for the most part. Gas mixtures receive some attention at the end of the section.

To establish notation, we begin with a very dilute gas. The equation of state, in the limit $p \to 0$ or $\rho \to 0$, is $p = \rho kT = kT/\mathrm{v}$, where $\rho = N/V = 1/\mathrm{v}$. Then, from the thermodynamic relation $d\mu = \mathrm{v}\, dp$ (T constant), we have

$$\mu(p, T) = \mu^0(T) + kT \ln p \qquad (p \to 0). \tag{4.1}$$

This can also be written

$$\mu(\rho, T) = \mu'(T) + kT \ln \rho \qquad (\rho \to 0), \tag{4.2}$$

where

$$\mu' = \mu^0 + \mu' kT \ln kT.$$

When the gas is *not* dilute, we *define* the fugacity f so that it bears the same relation to μ for *arbitrary* p that p does to μ when $p \to 0$. That is,

$$\mu(p, T) = \mu^0(T) + kT \ln f(p, T), \tag{4.3}$$

where $\mu^0(T)$ is the same function as in Eq. (4.1). Of course, f is a function of both p and T. It is in fact just a "substitute" chemical potential which has dimensions of pressure and which is especially convenient because it contains no arbitrary zeros of energy or entropy (these are included in μ^0). When $p \to 0, f \to p$.

Similarly, we define an activity z which is related to μ, at arbitrary ρ, just as ρ is related to μ when $\rho \to 0$. Thus,

$$\mu(\rho, T) = \mu'(T) + kT \ln z(\rho, T). \tag{4.4}$$

The activity is also a substitute chemical potential, similar to the fugacity. We have $z \to \rho$ when $\rho \to 0$. Clearly $f = zkT$ (this "preserves" the ideal gas law, in a formal way, to arbitrary densities). The activity coefficient γ is defined by $z = \rho\gamma$.

Let us suppose that p, ρ, T measurements are made on a gas and that the results are summarized in the empirical equation (the *virial expansion*)

$$p/kT = \rho + B_2(T)\rho^2 + B_3(T)\rho^3 + \cdots, \tag{4.5}$$

where B_n is called the nth virial coefficient. Tables of measured values of the first few virial coefficients are available for a number of gases. Figure 4.1 shows the experimental curve, $B_2(T)$, for three gases. It can be shown, in statistical mechanics, that B_2 depends on the nature of the interaction between a pair of gas molecules in the volume V (no other molecules present; $\rho \to 0$), that B_3 depends, in addition, on the interaction between a triplet of molecules in V, etc. In fact, the explicit theoretical formula for $B_2(T)$ for a monatomic or effectively spherical molecule (except at very

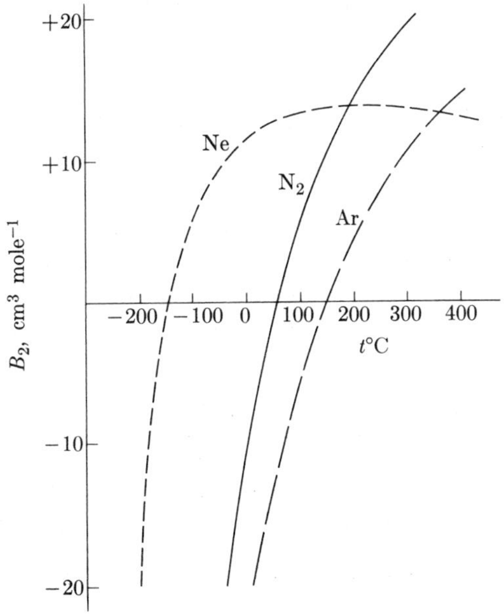

Fig. 4.1. Second virial coefficient as a function of temperature for Ne, N_2, and Ar.

low temperatures) is

$$B_2(T) = -\tfrac{1}{2}\int_0^\infty [e^{-u(r)/kT} - 1]4\pi r^2\,dr, \tag{4.6}$$

where $u(r)$ is the potential energy of a pair of molecules a distance r apart in a vacuum. Similar, but more complicated equations can be written for B_3, etc.

An integration by parts puts Eq. (4.6) in the form

$$B_2 = -\frac{1}{6kT}\int_0^\infty r\,\frac{du(r)}{dr}\,e^{-u(r)/kT}4\pi r^2\,dr. \tag{4.7}$$

Comparison with Eq. (1.24) then shows that an expansion of the radial distribution function $g(r, \rho, T)$ in powers of ρ has $e^{-u/kT}$ for the leading term.

It can be seen from either Eq. (4.6) or (4.7) that repulsion between the pair of molecules tends to make B_2 positive while attraction contributes negatively to B_2. The temperature enters through the Boltzmann factor, $e^{-u/kT}$. At high temperatures, repulsion dominates (see Fig. 4.1).

Equation (4.5) is an expansion in powers of ρ that can also be written, from a formal mathematical point of view, as

$$\frac{p}{\rho kT} = 1 + \left(\frac{\partial p/\rho kT}{\partial \rho}\right)_{T,\rho=0}\rho + \frac{1}{2!}\left(\frac{\partial^2 p/\rho kT}{\partial \rho^2}\right)_{T,\rho=0}\rho^2 + \cdots \tag{4.8}$$

Thus

$$B_2 = \left(\frac{\partial p/\rho kT}{\partial \rho}\right)_{T,\rho=0}, \qquad B_3 = \frac{1}{2!}\left(\frac{\partial^2 p/\rho kT}{\partial \rho^2}\right)_{T,\rho=0}, \quad \text{etc.} \tag{4.9}$$

That these derivatives are to be evaluated at $\rho = 0$ corresponds to the fact that the pair, triplet, etc., interactions which enter into B_2, B_3, etc., are those for a pair, triplet, etc., of molecules in a *vacuum*.

Given the experimental information about an imperfect gas contained in Eq. (4.5), what are μ, f, z, and γ? These are easily found by integrating $d\mu = \text{v}\,dp$ (T constant):

$$d\left(\frac{\mu}{kT}\right) = \frac{1}{\rho}\,d\left(\frac{p}{kT}\right) = \frac{1}{\rho}\left(\frac{\partial p/kT}{\partial \rho}\right)_T d\rho \qquad (T \text{ constant}). \tag{4.10}$$

We substitute Eq. (4.5) into Eq. (4.10), integrate term by term, and evaluate the integration constant at $\rho \to 0$ by use of Eq. (4.2). The result is

$$\mu(\rho, T) = \mu'(T) + kT\ln\rho + kT[\tfrac{2}{1}B_2(T)\rho + \tfrac{3}{2}B_3(T)\rho^2 + \cdots]. \tag{4.11}$$

Thus, from Eq. (4.4),

$$\ln z = \ln\rho + \tfrac{2}{1}B_2(T)\rho + \tfrac{3}{2}B_3(T)\rho^2 + \cdots \tag{4.12}$$

$$\ln\gamma = \tfrac{2}{1}B_2(T)\rho + \tfrac{3}{2}B_3(T)\rho^2 + \cdots \tag{4.13}$$

and we have

$$\ln f = \ln \rho kT + \tfrac{2}{1}B_2(T)\rho + \tfrac{3}{2}B_3(T)\rho^2 + \cdots \tag{4.14}$$

The power series $z(\rho)$, itself, is more complicated. From Eq. (4.12),

$$z = \rho + 2B_2\rho^2 + (\tfrac{3}{2}B_3 + 2B_2^2)\rho^3 + \cdots \tag{4.15}$$

This is also the series for f/kT.

An alternative virial expansion, often more convenient in practice but a less direct consequence of statistical mechanical theory, is

$$p\mathrm{v}/kT = 1 + B_2'(T)p + B_3'(T)p^2 + \cdots \tag{4.16}$$

The B_n' are of course related to the B_n (Problem 4.1). Integration of $d\mu = \mathrm{v}\,dp$ (T constant) in this case leads to

$$\mu(p, T) = \mu^0(T) + kT\ln p + kT[B_2'(T)p + \tfrac{1}{2}B_3'(T)p^2 + \cdots] \tag{4.17}$$

$$\ln f = \ln p + B_2'(T)p + \tfrac{1}{2}B_3'(T)p^2 + \cdots \tag{4.18}$$

For a slightly imperfect gas (retain B_2' terms only),

$$f = pe^{B_2'p+\cdots} = p(1 + B_2'p + \cdots) = \frac{p^2\mathrm{v}}{kT}. \tag{4.19}$$

This is a useful approximation for moderate pressures.

Binary gas mixture. By analogy with Eq. (4.5), experimental equation of state data for a binary gas (components 1 and 2) can be expressed as a series with p/kT expanded in powers of ρ_1 and ρ_2 (where $\rho_i = N_i/V$). We shall use the notation

$$p/kT = \rho_1 + \rho_2 + B_{11}(T)\rho_1^2 + 2B_{12}(T)\rho_1\rho_2 + B_{22}(T)\rho_2^2 + \cdots \tag{4.20}$$

We confine ourselves to linear and quadratic terms, as indicated. With the B_{ij} defined in this way, statistical mechanics shows that B_{12}, for monatomic or effectively spherical gases, is given by Eq. (4.6), where in this case $u(r)$ is the potential energy, $u_{12}(r)$, between two *unlike* molecules. Of course B_{11} and B_{22} are just the "pure" second virial coefficients for components 1 and 2, respectively, already discussed above.

The activities z_1 and z_2 are defined by

$$\mu_1(\rho_1, \rho_2, T) = \mu_1'(T) + kT\ln z_1(\rho_1, \rho_2, T), \tag{4.21}$$

$$\mu_2(\rho_1, \rho_2, T) = \mu_2'(T) + kT\ln z_2(\rho_1, \rho_2, T). \tag{4.22}$$

The extension of Eq. (4.15) to mixtures will clearly have the form (to quadratic terms)

$$\begin{aligned} z_1 &= \rho_1[1 + 2B_{11}\rho_1 + a\rho_2 + \cdots], \\ z_2 &= \rho_2[1 + 2B_{22}\rho_2 + b\rho_1 + \cdots], \end{aligned} \tag{4.23}$$

where a and b may be determined as follows. The inverses of Eqs. (4.23) are easily found to be

$$\begin{aligned} \rho_1 &= z_1 - 2B_{11}z_1^2 - az_1z_2 + \cdots, \\ \rho_2 &= z_2 - 2B_{22}z_2^2 - bz_1z_2 + \cdots \end{aligned} \tag{4.24}$$

Substitution of Eqs. (4.24) in Eq. (4.20) gives p/kT in powers of z_1 and z_2. Now this latter series can be manipulated thermodynamically in a useful way. We have

$$dp = \rho_1\, d\mu_1 + \rho_2\, d\mu_2 \qquad (T \text{ constant}) \tag{4.25}$$

and therefore

$$\rho_1 = z_1 \left(\frac{\partial p/kT}{\partial z_1}\right)_{z_2,T}, \qquad \rho_2 = z_2 \left(\frac{\partial p/kT}{\partial z_2}\right)_{z_1,T}. \tag{4.26}$$

If we perform the operations indicated in Eqs. (4.26) on the series $p(z_1, z_2)/kT$ mentioned above, we obtain ρ_1 and ρ_2 expressed in powers of z_1 and z_2. Comparison of these series with Eqs. (4.24) then shows that $a = b = 2B_{12}$. Hence Eqs. (4.23) become

$$\begin{aligned} z_1 &= \rho_1 + 2B_{11}\rho_1^2 + 2B_{12}\rho_1\rho_2 + \cdots, \\ z_2 &= \rho_2 + 2B_{22}\rho_2^2 + 2B_{12}\rho_1\rho_2 + \cdots, \end{aligned} \tag{4.27}$$

or

$$\begin{aligned} \gamma_1 &= z_1/\rho_1 = 1 + 2B_{11}\rho_1 + 2B_{12}\rho_2 + \cdots, \\ \gamma_2 &= z_2/\rho_2 = 1 + 2B_{22}\rho_2 + 2B_{12}\rho_1 + \cdots \end{aligned} \tag{4.28}$$

These equations make the generalization to any number of components obvious: for the jth component out of a total of ν components,

$$\gamma_j = z_j/\rho_j = 1 + 2\sum_{i=1}^{\nu} B_{ij}\rho_i + \cdots, \tag{4.29}$$

where $B_{ij} = B_{ji}$. We shall need this equation in the next section. For monatomic or spherical molecules, Eq. (4.6) applies to each B_{ij}, provided that $u_{ij}(r)$ is used in the integrand.

4.2 OSMOTIC PRESSURE

In Fig. 4.2, component 1 (the *solvent*) can pass through the membrane but component 2 (the *solute*) cannot. The whole system is in thermal equilibrium with a heat bath at a constant temperature T. Suppose we start at equilibrium with pure solvent on both sides of the membrane at pressure p_0. Next, some solute is added to the "in" side of the system, keeping p_0 and T constant. The chemical potential μ_1^{in} is lowered by the addition of *any* solute. Hence the system goes out of equilibrium, because now

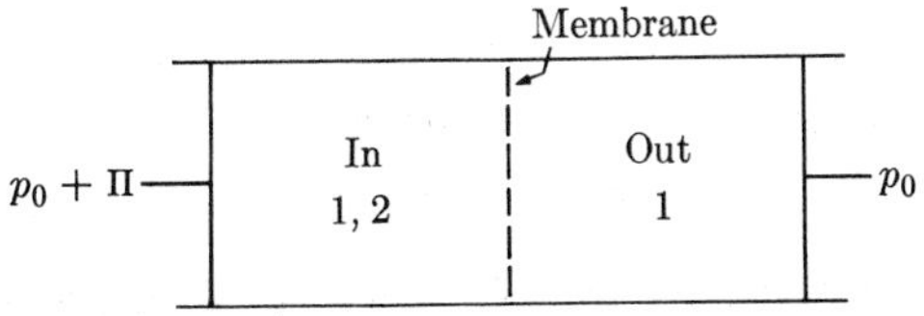

Fig. 4.2. Osmotic system.

$\mu_1^{\text{in}} < \mu_1^{\text{out}}$. Equilibrium may be reestablished by an increase in the inside pressure (holding the outside pressure p_0 constant) sufficient to bring μ_1^{in} back up to its initial value, μ_1^{out}.

The additional pressure on the inside, required to maintain $\mu_1^{\text{in}} = \mu_1^{\text{out}}$ when solute is added to the inside, is called the osmotic pressure Π.

The above argument may be expressed mathematically as follows. For the inside, which is a binary solution,

$$d\mu_1 = -\bar{s}_1\, dT + \bar{v}_1\, dp + \left(\frac{\partial \mu_1}{\partial x_2}\right)_{T,p} dx_2, \tag{4.30}$$

where $\bar{s}_1 = (\partial S/\partial N_1)_{p,T,N_2}$, etc., and x_2 is the mole fraction of solute. If desired, we could replace x_2 in Eq. (4.30) by any convenient function of N_2/N_1 (see, for example, Section 4.4). We vary p and x_2 (T constant) in such a way that μ_1 remains constant. Thus

$$d\mu_1 = 0 = \bar{v}_1\, dp + \left(\frac{\partial \mu_1}{\partial x_2}\right)_{T,p} dx_2. \tag{4.31}$$

Since T is constant, this may be regarded as a differential equation in p and x_2 (the coefficients of dp and dx_2 are functions of p and x_2). Integration from $p = p_0$, $x_2 = 0$ to $p_0 + \Pi$, x_2 gives $\Pi(x_2, p_0, T)$. Actually, another choice of independent variables is much more convenient and allows a treatment which is closely analogous to that given in the preceding section for imperfect gases. Because of this, we shall pursue Eq. (4.31) only far enough to derive the limiting ($x_2 \to 0$) law for Π.

We need at this point a brief digression on chemical potentials and fugacities in a binary solution. We define the fugacities in the solution by the equations

$$\begin{aligned} \mu_1(p, T, x_2) &= \mu_1^0(T) + kT \ln f_1(p, T, x_2), \\ \mu_2(p, T, x_2) &= \mu_2^0(T) + kT \ln f_2(p, T, x_2). \end{aligned} \tag{4.32}$$

The functions $\mu_i^0(T)$ are the same as in Eq. (4.1); each is a property of the dilute one-component *gas*. The fugacity f_i has dimensions of pressure, and is again just a convenient substitute for μ_i (in the solution). Furthermore, because of the use of μ_i^0 in its definition, f_i (solution) $= f_i$ (gas) in a phase equilibrium (just as for the chemical potential).

In a very dilute solution ($x_2 \to 0$), as is well known, Henry's law is observed by the solute and Raoult's law by the solvent:

$$f_2 = k_2(p, T)x_2, \qquad f_1 = f_1^{\triangle}(p, T)(1 - x_2), \tag{4.33}$$

where k_2 is the Henry's law constant for the solute and $f_1^{\triangle}$ is the fugacity of pure component 1. Equations (4.33) are consistent with the Gibbs-Duhem equation (i.e., one of the two equations is redundant).

We return now to Π, in the limit $x_2 \to 0$. From Eqs. (4.32) and (4.33),

$$\left(\frac{\partial \mu_1}{\partial x_2}\right)_{p,T} = -\frac{kT}{1 - x_2} \to -kT \qquad (x_2 \to 0). \tag{4.34}$$

This result is an entropy of mixing effect that has nothing to do with the nature of the solute or its interaction with the solvent. In the limit $x_2 \to 0$, $\bar{\text{v}}_1 \to V/N_1$ and $x_2 \to N_2/N_1$. Hence, Eq. (4.31) yields

$$\Pi V = N_2 kT \qquad \text{or} \qquad \Pi = \rho_2 kT \quad (\rho_2 \to 0) \tag{4.35}$$

as the limiting expression for Π.

Equation (4.31) is inconvenient to apply to nondilute solutions because two of the three (T, p, and x_2) independent variables actually vary. This suggests that we replace T and p by T and μ_1, both of which are held constant in the process under consideration. This, in turn, leads to a different choice of composition variable as we shall see.

We begin with

$$N_1\, d\mu_1 + N_2\, d\mu_2 = -S\, dT + V\, dp. \tag{4.36}$$

Since μ_1 and T are constant,

$$dp = \rho_2\, d\mu_2 = \rho_2 \left(\frac{\partial \mu_2}{\partial \rho_2}\right)_{T,\mu_1} d\rho_2 \qquad (T,\ \mu_1 \text{ constant}). \tag{4.37}$$

We shall use this equation instead of Eq. (4.31). It of course applies to the same system (Fig. 4.2), but the independent variables are T, μ_1, and ρ_2. The "outside" is characterized by T and μ_1 rather than by T and p_0 (i.e., we now regard p_0 as a function of T and μ_1).

An important advantage of the new approach is that it is essentially unaffected by the introduction of a multicomponent solvent (all components of which can pass through the membrane). In this case, *all* of the solvent μ's in Eq. (4.36) are held constant (because of the phase equilibrium) and Eq. (4.37) still follows. With a multicomponent solvent, the symbol μ_1 represents a *set* of solvent chemical potentials, not just one.

In experimental work, Π is measured as a function of ρ_2 (a plot of Π/ρ_2 against ρ_2 is often used). The results can be summarized by means of a virial expansion, just as in Eq. (4.5):

$$\Pi/kT = \rho_2 + B_2(T, \mu_1)\rho_2^2 + B_3(T, \mu_1)\rho_2^3 + \cdots \tag{4.38}$$

The leading term agrees with Eq. (4.35). The virial coefficients are functions of T and μ_1. For example, if component 2 is a protein and μ_1 represents both μ_{H_2O} and μ_{NaCl} in the outside solution, the virial coefficients will depend on the salt concentration in the outside solution (T and p_0 constant).

The analogue of Eq. (4.9) is

$$B_2 = \left(\frac{\partial \Pi/\rho_2 kT}{\partial \rho_2}\right)_{T,\mu_1,\rho_2=0}, \quad \text{etc.} \tag{4.39}$$

That is, B_2 is a property of the *outside* system ($\rho_2 = 0$). In fact, McMillan and Mayer proved that Eq. (4.6) holds for the osmotic second virial coefficient of spherical solute molecules provided $u(r)$ is now understood to represent the reversible work $w(r)$ necessary to bring two solute molecules together from $r = \infty$ to r, in the *outside* system [rather than in a vacuum, as in Eq. (4.6)]. This work, a function of T and μ_1 as well as of r, is called the potential of average force, where "average" refers to statistical mechanical averaging. In Eq. (4.6), for a gas, $u(r)$ is a purely quantum mechanical quantity, a function of r only.

Let us now obtain a series expansion for μ_2, analogous to Eq. (4.11). First, consider the limit $\rho_2 \to 0$. We have, in this limit,

$$\mu_2 = \mu_2^0(T) + kT \ln f_2,$$
$$f_2 = k_2(T, \mu_1)x_2 = k_2(T, \mu_1)\mathrm{v}_1(T, \mu_1)\rho_2,$$

where v_1 is the molecular volume of the solvent (outside). Then

$$\mu_2 = \mu_2'(T, \mu_1) + kT \ln \rho_2 \qquad (\rho_2 \to 0), \tag{4.40}$$

where

$$\mu_2' = \mu_2^0(T) + kT \ln k_2(T, \mu_1)\mathrm{v}_1(T, \mu_1). \tag{4.41}$$

Equation (4.40) is the analogue of Eq. (4.2) for a dilute gas.

We now want to combine Eqs. (4.37), (4.38), and (4.40) to give $\mu_2(\rho_2)$. First, we rewrite Eq. (4.37) in the form

$$d\left(\frac{\mu_2}{kT}\right) = \frac{1}{\rho_2}\left(\frac{\partial \Pi/kT}{\partial \rho_2}\right)_{T,\mu_1} d\rho_2 \qquad (T,\ \mu_1 \text{ constant}), \tag{4.42}$$

using $p = \Pi + p_0$ and $dp = d\Pi$. Then we find easily

$$\mu_2(\rho, T, \mu_1) = \mu_2'(T, \mu_1) + kT \ln \rho_2 + kT[\tfrac{2}{1}B_2(T, \mu_1)\rho_2 + \tfrac{3}{2}B_3(T, \mu_1)\rho_2^2 + \cdots]. \tag{4.43}$$

If we define the activity $z_2(\rho_2, T, \mu_1)$ by

$$\mu_2 = \mu_2' + kT \ln z_2, \tag{4.44}$$

then exact analogues of Eqs. (4.12), (4.13), and (4.15) hold.

We shall need below the generalization of some of these results to a multicomponent solute (we have already seen that the solvent may be multicomponent). We denote the solute species by 2, 3, . . . , ν. To quadratic terms [see Eqs. (4.20) and (4.29)], we have

$$\frac{\Pi}{kT} = \sum_{i=2}^{\nu} \rho_i + \sum_{i,j=2}^{\nu} B_{ij}(T, \mu_1)\rho_i\rho_j + \cdots \tag{4.45}$$

and

$$\gamma_j = z_j/\rho_j = 1 + 2\sum_{i=2}^{\nu} B_{ij}(T, \mu_1)\rho_i + \cdots \qquad (j = 2, \ldots, \nu). \tag{4.46}$$

In statistical mechanics, for spherical solute molecules, B_{ij} is given by Eq. (4.6) with $u(r)$ the potential of average force for one i-solute molecule and one j-solute molecule immersed in the outside system.

Binding on solute molecules. We now consider a special case which is important in biochemistry. Suppose, in an osmotic equilibrium, that there is only one solute component, say a protein, that the solvent is multicomponent, and that one of the solvent components (e.g., hydrogen ions) can bind on the solute. Let ρ be the concentration of solute molecules (we drop the subscript 2, used above), and let s be the maximum number of bound molecules (or ions) per solute molecule (the bound component will be designated by a, with absolute activity $\lambda_a = e^{\mu_a/kT}$). There will then be $s + 1$ different species of solute, depending on the number of bound molecules; these are denoted by subscripts 0, 1, . . . , s, and are called 0-solute, 1-solute, etc. Thus ρ_i is the concentration of solute molecules with i bound molecules, and

$$\sum_{i=0}^{s} \rho_i = \rho. \tag{4.47}$$

Because of the existence of different solute species 0, 1, . . . , s, the solute is, in a sense, multicomponent, and Eqs. (4.45) and (4.46) apply (we shall work here only to quadratic terms). But all these species are not independent (in fact, only one is); there are various binding equilibria to take into consideration. The corresponding equilibrium relations will of course modify Eqs. (4.45) and (4.46).

The fraction of solute molecules of species n is denoted by $p_n = \rho_n/\rho$. The average value of n is $\bar{n} = \sum_n np_n$, with $0 \le \bar{n} \le s$. We let p_n^0 represent the value of p_n in the limit $\rho \to 0$. Also, $\bar{n} \to \bar{n}^0$ when $\rho \to 0$. Since we shall make only first-order corrections in the concentration ρ, we will have

$$p_n = p_n^0 + O(\rho), \tag{4.48}$$

$$\bar{n} = \bar{n}^0 + O(\rho). \tag{4.49}$$

The explicit formulas will be found below. Equation (4.49) is of particular interest: the amount of binding depends on the solute concentration ρ.

From Eq. (4.45), the osmotic pressure is

$$\Pi/kT = \rho + \rho^2 \sum_{n,m=0}^{s} B_{nm}(T, \mu_{\text{out}}) p_n p_m + \cdots, \tag{4.50}$$

where μ_{out} represents the complete set of solvent chemical potentials and B_{nm} is the second virial coefficient of an n, m solute pair. In view of Eq. (4.48), this can be written

$$\Pi/kT = \rho + B(T, \mu_{\text{out}})\rho^2 + \cdots, \tag{4.51}$$

where

$$B = \sum_{n,m=0}^{s} B_{nm} p_n^0 p_m^0. \tag{4.52}$$

The form of Eq. (4.51) reminds us that if we were unaware of the binding on the solute, this would be considered an ordinary osmotic system with a one-component solute. $B(T, \mu_{\text{out}})$ is the quantity measured experimentally, whether we take the binding into account or not. The binding is introduced explicitly to help interpret the observed $B(T, \mu_{\text{out}})$. The discussion in this subsection is therefore somewhat extrathermodynamic.

Let us now derive equations for p_n, p_n^0, $\bar{n}$, and $\bar{n}^0$. Consider the equilibrium:

$$(0 - \text{solute}) + n(a) \leftrightarrows (n - \text{solute}).$$

The equilibrium condition is

$$\mu_0 + n\mu_a = \mu_n, \tag{4.53}$$

or

$$\mu_0' + kT \ln z_0 + n\mu_a = \mu_n' + kT \ln z_n,$$

or

$$\frac{z_n}{z_0 \lambda_a^n} = e^{(\mu_0' - \mu_n')/kT} = q_n(T, \mu_{\text{out}}). \tag{4.54}$$

The "equilibrium constant" q_n is defined in this particular way to establish a close analogy with the discussion of binding in Sections 2.4 and 3.6. When the solute is dilute, $z_n \to \rho_n$. When a is dilute, λ_a is proportional to ρ_a.

From Eq. (4.54),

$$z_n = z_0 q_n \lambda_a^n = q_n \lambda_a^n \textstyle\sum / \xi, \tag{4.55}$$

where we have eliminated z_0 by use of

$$\sum = \sum_{m=0}^{s} z_m \qquad \text{and} \qquad \xi = \sum_{m=0}^{s} q_m \lambda_a^m. \tag{4.56}$$

The sum ξ has the form of a grand partition function for binding on a single solute molecule [compare Eq. (2.37)]. In the limit $\rho \to 0$, Eq. (4.55) becomes

$$\rho_n = q_n \lambda_a^n \rho / \xi \qquad (\rho \to 0). \tag{4.57}$$

Therefore

$$p_n^0 = q_n \lambda_a^n / \xi \qquad \text{and} \qquad z_n = p_n^0 \sum. \tag{4.58}$$

Next, we make use of Eq. (4.46):

$$\begin{aligned} z_n &= \rho_n \left(1 + 2 \sum_{m=0}^{s} B_{nm} \rho_m + \cdots \right) \\ &= p_n^0 \sum = p_n^0 \left(\rho + 2 \sum_{k,m} B_{km} \rho_k \rho_m + \cdots \right), \end{aligned}$$

where we have applied the definition $\sum$ above. Then, solving for ρ_n in the first line of the above equation,

$$\rho_n = \frac{p_n^0(\rho + 2\rho^2 \sum_{k,m} B_{km} p_k p_m + \cdots)}{1 + 2\rho \sum_m B_{nm} p_m + \cdots}$$

and, finally, to linear terms in ρ,

$$p_n = \frac{\rho_n}{\rho} = p_n^0 \left[1 + 2\rho \left(B - \sum_m B_{nm} p_m^0\right) + \cdots \right]. \tag{4.59}$$

This shows the effect of ρ on p_n.

To find $\bar{n}$, we multiply Eq. (4.59) by n and sum over n:

$$\bar{n} = \bar{n}^0 + 2\rho \left(\bar{n}^0 B - \sum_{n,m} n B_{nm} p_n^0 p_m^0 \right) + \cdots, \tag{4.60}$$

where

$$\bar{n}^0 = \sum_n n p_n^0 = \frac{\sum_n n q_n \lambda_a^n}{\sum_n q_n \lambda_a^n}. \tag{4.61}$$

Although the notation is somewhat disguised, (4.61) is a well-known equation in protein binding work, etc. An alternative expression for $\bar{n}$, easily verified, is

$$\bar{n} = \bar{n}^0 - \rho \left(\frac{\partial B}{\partial \ln \lambda_a}\right)_{T,\mu_{\text{out}}} + \cdots \tag{4.62}$$

The derivative here is a formal one in which the μ_a included in μ_{out} is held constant. Incidentally, the next term in Eq. (4.62) can be shown to be $-(\frac{1}{2})\rho^2(\partial C/\partial \ln \lambda_a)$, where C is the third virial coefficient.

Binding affects intersolute interactions through Eq. (4.52) (see Problem 4.2) and, conversely, these interactions affect the amount of binding via Eq. (4.62). This latter equation can be understood qualitatively as follows. If, for example, binding a molecules on a pair of solute molecules increases the repulsion between the solute molecules (that is, $\partial B/\partial \ln \lambda_a > 0$), then, when two solute molecules are brought together from $r = \infty$, they will desorb some a molecules. This is essentially what happens when the concentration of solute is increased: pairs of solute molecules spend more time near each other, so $\bar{n}$ decreases, as in Eq. (4.62).

4.3 DONNAN EQUILIBRIUM

A Donnan equilibrium system is an osmotic system in which the solute is charged. The solvent, in this case, must include an electrolyte to achieve electrical neutrality on both sides of the semipermeable membrane.

Before pursuing this subject any further, we give a brief summary (without proof) of needed results from the Debye-Hückel theory of electrolytes.

Debye-Hückel theory. In this subsection we also consider an osmotic system (Fig. 4.2): the outside contains a nonionic solvent, say, water, with dielectric constant ϵ. The inside contains the solvent and also at least two kinds of ions, for neutrality (these ionic species are the solute; no ions can pass through the membrane). Let ρ_i be the concentration of ions of type i with charge $Z_i\mathbf{e}$, where $\mathbf{e}$ is the charge on a proton and Z_i is the charge number (for example, $Z_{\mathrm{Na}^+} = +1$). Neutrality requires that $\sum_i \rho_i Z_i = 0$.

A special case is a gaseous plasma (gas of ions) in which the "solvent" is a vacuum. When we speak of the osmotic pressure Π of the electrolyte solution described above, for the plasma we have simply the gas pressure p. If the plasma includes electrons, quantum statistics must be used in place of the Debye-Hückel classical approach (unless the temperature is high).

The potential of average force between an i ion and a j ion, a distance r apart in the outside solvent, is given by the well-known formula

$$w_{ij}(r) = \frac{Z_i Z_j \mathbf{e}^2}{\epsilon r}, \tag{4.63}$$

which treats the solvent as a continuum. This can also be written as

$$w_{ij}(r) = Z_i\mathbf{e}\psi_j(r) = Z_j\mathbf{e}\psi_i(r), \tag{4.64}$$

$$\psi_j(r) = \frac{Z_j\mathbf{e}}{\epsilon r}, \qquad \psi_i(r) = \frac{Z_i\mathbf{e}}{\epsilon r}, \tag{4.65}$$

where $\psi_j(r)$ is the electrostatic potential at a distance r from an isolated ion of type j in the outside solvent. The electrostatic potential at a point is defined as the work necessary to bring unit positive charge from infinity (where no other charges are present) to the point.

Off-hand, it would appear that since we have here an osmotic system with a multicomponent solute, the expansions (4.45) and (4.46) should apply. Experimental results show otherwise; a virial expansion of Π does not exist. For example, if the solute is a simple 1–1 electrolyte of concentration ρ, then it is found experimentally that $\Pi/kT = 2\rho + O(\rho^{3/2})$. The factor of 2 in the first term is, of course, expected because of dissociation, but the second term in a virial expansion would be $O(\rho^2)$.

The failure of an osmotic pressure virial expansion for an electrolyte solution can be confirmed theoretically by using Eq. (4.63), which is appropriate for this case, in place of $u(r)$ in Eq. (4.6). The resulting B_{ij} diverges. This can be seen by taking r large enough, say $r \geq r'$, so that $e^{-w_{ij}/kT} = 1 - (w_{ij}/kT)$. Then the integral $\int_{r'}^{\infty}$ is infinite (in fact, $w_{ij} \sim r^{-2}$ or r^{-3} also leads to a divergence). Physically, the explanation of this behavior is the following. The existence of a virial expansion depends on short-range forces: as the concentration increases from zero, pair interactions must first be taken into account (B_2), then triplet interactions (B_3), etc. But the potential w_{ij} in Eq. (4.63) has a very long range; no concentration exists for which only pair, triplet, etc., interactions are involved—the interactions are a "collective" phenomenon from the outset.

A new theoretical approach is required for this problem, the original and simplest version of which is the Debye-Hückel theory. The first correction to the ideal osmotic pressure equation is found to be

$$\Pi/kT = \sum_i \rho_i - (\kappa^3/24\pi), \tag{4.66}$$

where

$$\kappa^2 = \frac{4\pi e^2}{\epsilon kT} \sum_i \rho_i Z_i^2. \tag{4.67}$$

For a 1–1 electrolyte, Eq. (4.66) is a good approximation when

$$\rho < 10^{-2} \text{ mole liter}^{-1}$$

and an excellent one when $\rho < 10^{-3}$ mole liter^{-1}. For larger ρ, higher terms are needed.

To the same order as Eq. (4.66), the activity coefficient of species i is

$$\ln \gamma_i = -\frac{Z_i^2 e^2 \kappa}{2\epsilon kT}. \tag{4.68}$$

The potential of average force between two ions *in the electrolyte solution* (inside) is

$$w_{ij}(r) = \frac{Z_i Z_j \mathrm{e}^2 e^{-\kappa r}}{\epsilon r}, \tag{4.69}$$

and

$$\psi_j(r) = \frac{Z_j \mathrm{e} e^{-\kappa r}}{\epsilon r}. \tag{4.70}$$

The new factor $e^{-\kappa r}$ [compare Eq. (4.63)] arises because of the "screening" of the bare i and j ions by ion atmospheres with mean net charges of opposite sign. Note that $e^{-\kappa r}$ converts the potential $w_{ij}(r)$ into one of "short range."

The mean (local) concentration of i ions at a distance r from a specified j ion is

$$\rho_i(r) = \rho_i e^{-Z_i \mathrm{e} \psi_j(r)/kT} = \rho_i e^{-w_{ij}(r)/kT}, \tag{4.71}$$

where ρ_i is the bulk concentration and ψ_j and w_{ij} are given by Eqs. (4.69) and (4.70). That is, to this order, a simple Boltzmann factor enters into the concentration ratio. Similarly,

$$\rho_j(r) = \rho_j e^{-w_{ij}(r)/kT}. \tag{4.72}$$

The above are exact limiting expressions for a very dilute solution. We shall need below one other result, related to Eq. (4.69), but not exact. Suppose two large spherical molecules (say, protein molecules or colloidal particles) of diameter a and charge $Z\mathrm{e}$ are immersed in a dilute electrolyte solution of small ions (characterized by κ and ϵ). Then an approximation to the potential of average force between the two large molecules is

$$\begin{aligned} w(r) &= +\infty \qquad (r < a) \\ &= \frac{Z^2 \mathrm{e}^2 e^{-\kappa(r-a)}}{\epsilon r(1+\kappa a)} \qquad (r \geq a). \end{aligned} \tag{4.73}$$

Donnan equilibrium by the Donnan method. The system of interest is shown in Fig. 4.3. A nonionic solvent, say, water, is present in all three chambers. The electrolyte is present in the "in" and "out" chambers; ions of species i with charge $Z_i\mathrm{e}$ have a concentration ρ_i inside and a concentration ρ_i^0 outside. Finally, *on the inside only*, there are ions of charge $Z\mathrm{e}$ and concentration ρ (the solute). The dashed lines in the figure represent semipermeable membranes with appropriate properties. The concentrations ρ_i^0, ρ_i, and ρ are all small. Our object is to learn something about the second virial coefficient B_2 of the in-out osmotic pressure Π:

$$\Pi/kT = \rho + B_2\rho^2 + \cdots \tag{4.74}$$

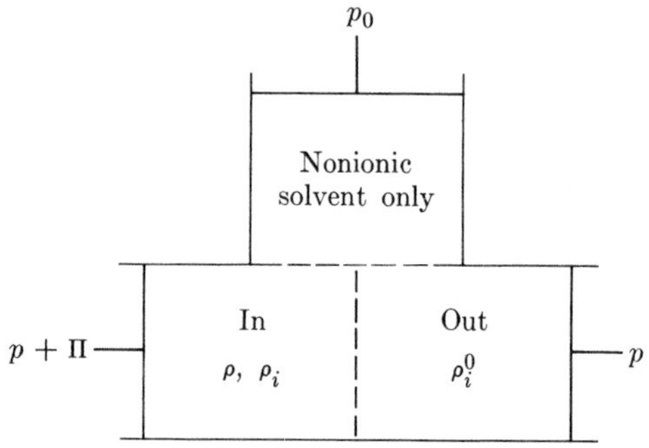

Fig. 4.3. Osmotic arrangement for Donnan equilibrium.

We expect a virial expansion in this case because pairs, triplets, etc., of solute ions, immersed in the outside solution, have short range interactions in consequence of Debye-Hückel screening.

We use first a method due to Donnan. As a second approach, we shall apply the statistical-mechanical equation, (4.6). Applied correctly, the two methods should agree.

If $\rho = 0$, then $\rho_i = \rho_i^0$ (inside and outside solutions become identical). But if $\rho > 0$, $\rho_i \neq \rho_i^0$. This is a necessary consequence of the requirement of electrical neutrality outside and in:

$$\sum_i \rho_i^0 Z_i = 0 \tag{4.75}$$

$$\rho Z + \sum_i \rho_i Z_i = 0. \tag{4.76}$$

For example, if $Z > 0$, then for positive ions $\rho_+ < \rho_+^0$ and for negative ions $\rho_- > \rho_-^0$. The fact that $\rho_i \neq \rho_i^0$ and yet that i ions are in equilibrium on the two sides of the membrane ($\mu_i^{\text{in}} = \mu_i^{\text{out}}$) requires the existence of a membrane potential. That is, the electrostatic potential on the inside, ψ_{in}, cannot equal ψ_{out}. The membrane potential ψ is defined by

$$\psi = \psi_{\text{in}} - \psi_{\text{out}}.$$

To see this, we have to introduce electrochemical potentials [or use an analogy with Eq. (4.71)]. Consider an electrolyte solution with electrostatic potential $\psi = 0$. Then, for species i,

$$\mu_i(\psi = 0) = \mu_i' + kT \ln \rho_i + kT \ln \gamma_i. \tag{4.77}$$

Now consider an identical solution, except at electrostatic potential ψ. Potentials of typical magnitude can be produced, for example, by the distribution of a practically infinitesimal amount of fixed charge of one sign on the surface of the containing vessel. In this latter solution,

$$\mu_i(\psi) = \mu_i' + kT \ln \rho_i + kT \ln \gamma_i + Z_i \mathrm{e}\psi. \tag{4.78}$$

The extra term is the reversible work required to transport a charge $Z_i\mathrm{e}$ from $\psi = 0$ to ψ. The quantity $\mu_i(\psi)$ is called an electrochemical potential. It is analogous, for example, to the chemical potential of a molecule in a gravitational field (the extra term, in this case, is mgh, where h = height).

Now we apply Eq. (4.78) to the equilibrium of i ions in our osmotic system (we neglect the activity coefficients at low concentrations):

$$\begin{aligned}\mu_i^{\mathrm{in}} &= \mu_i' + kT \ln \rho_i + Z_i \mathrm{e}\psi_{\mathrm{in}} \\ &= \mu_i^{\mathrm{out}} = \mu_i' + kT \ln \rho_i^0 + Z_i \mathrm{e}\psi_{\mathrm{out}}.\end{aligned}$$

Hence

$$\rho_i = \rho_i^0 e^{-Z_i \mathrm{e}(\psi_{\mathrm{in}} - \psi_{\mathrm{out}})/kT} = \rho_i^0 e^{-Z_i \mathrm{e}\psi/kT}. \tag{4.79}$$

This is very similar to Eq. (4.71).

The concentrations ρ_i and ρ_i^0, with $\rho_i \neq \rho_i^0$, have to be adjusted so that Eqs. (4.75), (4.76), and (4.79) are all satisfied. When $\rho \to 0$, $\rho_i \to \rho_i^0$ and $\psi \to 0$.

Since the concentrations are small, the osmotic pressure between the outside and the nonionic solvent is

$$(p - p_0)/kT = \sum_i \rho_i^0.$$

Similarly, the osmotic pressure between the inside and the nonionic solvent is

$$(p + \Pi - p_0)/kT = \rho + \sum_i \rho_i.$$

On subtraction we get

$$\Pi/kT = \rho + \left(\sum_i \rho_i - \sum_i \rho_i^0\right) \cdot \tag{4.80}$$

The term in parentheses is of order ρ^2, as we shall see.

Since ρ is small, ψ is small. Hence, we can expand Eq. (4.79):

$$\rho_i = \rho_i^0 \left[1 - \frac{Z_i \mathrm{e}\psi}{kT} + \frac{1}{2}\left(\frac{Z_i \mathrm{e}\psi}{kT}\right)^2 - \cdots\right]. \tag{4.81}$$

We sum this over i as it stands, and also after multiplying by Z_i. Using Eqs. (4.75) and (4.76), these operations yield

$$\sum_i \rho_i - \sum_i \rho_i^0 = \tfrac{1}{2}(\mathrm{e}\psi/kT)^2 \sum_i \rho_i^0 Z_i^2$$

and

$$\sum_i \rho_i Z_i = -\rho Z = -(\mathrm{e}\psi/kT) \sum_i \rho_i^0 Z_i^2.$$

In this way we find that the system has the following properties:

$$\frac{\mathsf{e}\psi}{kT} = \frac{\rho Z}{\sum_i \rho_i^0 Z_i^2}, \tag{4.82}$$

$$\rho_i = \rho_i^0 \left(1 - \frac{\rho Z_i Z}{\sum_i \rho_i^0 Z_i^2} + \cdots\right), \tag{4.83}$$

and

$$\frac{\Pi}{kT} = \rho + \frac{\rho^2 Z^2}{2\sum_i \rho_i^0 Z_i^2} + \cdots \tag{4.84}$$

Hence the second virial coefficient is

$$B_2 = \frac{Z^2}{2\sum_i \rho_i^0 Z_i^2} = \frac{2\pi \mathsf{e}^2 Z^2}{\epsilon kT \kappa_0^2}, \tag{4.85}$$

where κ_0 refers to the outside solution.

The membrane potential is proportional to ρ and has the sign of Z. The concentration $\rho_i < \rho_i^0$ if Z_i and Z have the same sign, while $\rho_i > \rho_i^0$ if Z_i and Z have opposite signs. The second virial coefficient is always positive, and diverges when $\kappa_0 \to 0$, as expected (the "screening" of solute ions disappears in this limit). From the statistical mechanical point of view, we expect B_2 to be positive because two solute ions with the same charge $Z\mathsf{e}$, immersed in the outside solution, repel each other (see below).

Donnan equilibrium by the McMillan-Mayer method. The virial expansion (4.74) for the in-out system of Fig. 4.3 is a special case of Eq. (4.38). As pointed out in connection with the latter equation, B_2 is given, in statistical mechanics, by Eq. (4.6) with $u(r)$ replaced by the potential of average force between two solute molecules immersed in the outside system. In the Donnan equilibrium, with a dilute electrolyte, the potential between two solute ions is [see Eq. (4.69)]

$$w(r) = \frac{Z^2 \mathsf{e}^2 e^{-\kappa_0 r}}{\epsilon r}, \tag{4.86}$$

where κ_0 refers to the outside solution:

$$\kappa_0^2 = \frac{4\pi \mathsf{e}^2}{\epsilon kT} \sum_i \rho_i^0 Z_i^2. \tag{4.87}$$

We now substitute Eq. (4.86) in Eq. (4.6) to calculate B_2. To get first-order effects, we introduce the expansion

$$e^{-w/kT} - 1 = -\frac{w}{kT} + \frac{1}{2}\left(\frac{w}{kT}\right)^2 - \cdots \tag{4.88}$$

The integrals are elementary. We find, from the respective terms in Eq. (4.88),

$$B_2 = \frac{Z^2}{2\sum_i \rho_i^0 Z_i^2} - \frac{Z^4 \alpha}{8\sum_i \rho_i^0 Z_i^2}, \tag{4.89}$$

where

$$\alpha = \mathsf{e}^2 \kappa_0 / \epsilon k T.$$

The parameter α is important in the Debye-Hückel theory. For that theory to be valid, we must have $\alpha \ll 1$. Equation (4.89) is the beginning of a power series in α.

The first term in Eq. (4.89) agrees with Eq. (4.85) from the Donnan method. The Donnan method takes into account electrical neutrality, while the McMillan-Mayer method uses the Debye-Hückel w. This contrast is not so odd as it seems, for one can show* that it is in fact only the *neutrality* property of the potential w that is required to produce the first term in Eq. (4.89) (i.e., the total charge in the ion atmosphere around a solute ion must be the negative of the solute charge).

If the Donnan method is repeated, in a self-consistent way, using Debye-Hückel activity coefficients and osmotic pressure expressions, one finds† to the linear term in α,

$$B_2 = \frac{Z^2}{2\sum_i \rho_i^0 Z_i^2} - \frac{\alpha}{8\sum_i \rho_i^0 Z_i^2}\left(Z^2 - Z\frac{\sum_i \rho_i^0 Z_i^3}{\sum_i \rho_i^0 Z_i^2}\right)^2. \tag{4.90}$$

This is the extension of Eq. (4.85) to the linear term in α. The discrepancy between Eqs. (4.89) and (4.90) is due to the fact that Eq. (4.86) for $w(r)$ is not quite adequate for this purpose. The next higher term in $w(r)$ is needed.

Note that, in the statistical mechanical calculation of Π, there is no mention of a membrane potential or of any details about the inside solution. All we need in order to find Π is knowledge of the interaction between pairs, triplets, etc., of solute ions immersed in the *outside* solution. From this knowledge, we can also derive, incidentally, the equivalent of Eq. (4.83) for ρ_i/ρ_i^0.

Finally, we give the formula for B_2 found from Eq. (4.73) (with $\kappa = \kappa_0$) for a Donnan system in which the solute consists of large spherical ions of charge $Z\mathsf{e}$ and diameter a, and the electrolyte is made up of small ions (with κ_0 outside). Again, the details* are complicated and are omitted.

* T. L. Hill, *Faraday Soc. Disc.* **21,** 31 (1956).
† T. L. Hill, *loc. cit.* The details are too complicated to include here.

We find

$$B_2 = \frac{2\pi a^3}{3} + \frac{Z^2}{2\sum_i \rho_i^0 Z_i^2} - \frac{Z^4 \alpha}{8(1+\kappa_0 a)^2 \sum_i \rho_i^0 Z_i^2}. \tag{4.91}$$

This is a generalization of Eq. (4.89). The first term is the same as the second virial coefficient of a gas of hard spheres of diameter a (Problem 4.3).

4.4 SINGLE-PHASE BINARY SOLUTION

To contrast with the emphasis placed on osmotic systems (Figs. 4.2 and 4.3) so far in this chapter, we consider in this section a one-phase binary solution with independent intensive variables p, T, and $m = N_2/N_1$. This is the same as the inside solution discussed at the beginning of Section 4.2. The composition variable m is essentially the molality of component 2 (molality = 1000 m/molecular weight of 1.) A very similar analysis can be given using x_2 (mole fraction) in place of m. Our interest will center on series expansion in powers of m of some of the important properties of the solution.

Dilute solution. We consider, first, the limit $m \to 0$ to provide the leading terms in the various series. Equations (4.32) and (4.33) furnish the starting point. For the solute (component 2), we have

$$\begin{aligned} \mu_2 &= \mu_2^0(T) + kT \ln k_2(p, T)m \\ &= \mu_2''(p, T) + kT \ln m \qquad (m \to 0), \end{aligned} \tag{4.92}$$

where

$$\mu_2'' = \mu_2^0 + kT \ln k_2. \tag{4.93}$$

For the solvent (component 1),

$$\begin{aligned} \mu_1 &= \mu_1^0(T) + kT \ln f_1^{\triangle}(p, T)(1-m) \\ &= \mu_1^{\triangle}(p, T) - kTm \qquad (m \to 0), \end{aligned} \tag{4.94}$$

where $\mu_1^{\triangle}$ is the chemical potential of the pure solvent at p and T:

$$\mu_1^{\triangle} = \mu_1^0 + kT \ln f_1^{\triangle}. \tag{4.95}$$

Since, from Eq. (4.30),

$$\bar{v}_i = \left(\frac{\partial \mu_i}{\partial p}\right)_{T,m}, \tag{4.96}$$

we have

$$\bar{v}_1^{\square}(p, T) = v_1(p, T) \qquad \text{and} \qquad \bar{v}_2^{\square}(p, T) = kT\left(\frac{\partial \ln k_2}{\partial p}\right)_T, \tag{4.97}$$

where the superscript $^{\square}$ means the limiting value as $m \to 0$, and v_1 is the molecular volume of pure solvent. Both k_2 and $\bar{v}_2^\square$ are properties of isolated ($m \to 0$) solute molecules in the solvent at p and T. Equation (4.97) shows how k_2 and $\bar{v}_2^\square$ are related.

To discuss $\bar{H}_i$ and $\bar{S}_i$ we need a digression on a very dilute gas. For such a gas, from (Eq. 4.1),

$$-S = \left(\frac{\partial \mu}{\partial T}\right)_p = \frac{d\mu^0}{dT} + k \ln p$$
$$= \frac{d\mu^0}{dT} + \frac{\mu - \mu^0}{T}.$$

We also have $\mu = H - TS$. Therefore

$$\frac{d\mu^0}{dT} = \frac{\mu^0(T) - H^*(T)}{T}. \tag{4.98}$$

It is convenient to use the symbol H^* to denote the limit of $H(p, T)$ for a gas, as $p \to 0$.

Returning now to the dilute binary solution, we use the general thermodynamic relation

$$\bar{H}_i = -T^2 \left(\frac{\partial \mu_i/T}{\partial T}\right)_{p,m} \tag{4.99}$$

to find

$$\bar{H}_1^\square(p, T) = H_1(p, T) \qquad \text{and} \qquad \frac{H_2^*(T) - \bar{H}_2^\square(p, T)}{kT^2} = \left(\frac{\partial \ln k_2}{\partial T}\right)_p. \tag{4.100}$$

The quantity $H_2^* - \bar{H}_2^\square$ is the heat of transferring a molecule of solute from the dilute solution to the dilute gas.

For the partial molecular entropies, we have, from $\mu_i = \bar{H}_i - T\bar{S}_i$,

$$\bar{S}_1^\square = S_1(p, T) \quad \text{and} \quad \bar{S}_2 = \frac{\bar{H}_2^\square - (\mu_2'' + kT \ln m)}{T} \qquad (m \to 0). \tag{4.101}$$

The quantity $\bar{S}_2$, like μ_2, does not have a finite limiting value in a dilute solution: $\bar{S}_2 \to +\infty$ and $\mu_2 \to -\infty$ as $m \to 0$.

Nondilute solution. As our experimental starting point (analogous to the virial expansion in earlier sections) for a nondilute solution, we use the chemical potential of the solvent in the solution relative to its value in the pure solvent. Information of this type can be obtained, for example, from solvent vapor pressure (or fugacity) measurements. The basic equation is

$$\frac{\mu_1(p, T, m) - \mu_1^\triangle(p, T)}{kT} = \ln \frac{f_1(p, T, m)}{f_1^\triangle(p, T)}. \tag{4.102}$$

Thus we assume that we have available the series

$$\ln \frac{f_1^{\triangle}}{f_1} = \frac{\mu_1^{\triangle} - \mu_1}{kT} = m + C_2(p, T)m^2 + C_3(p, T)m^3 + \cdots \tag{4.103}$$

The leading term here was established in Eq. (4.94). In statistical mechanics, C_2 is determined by the interaction between a pair of solute molecules in the pure solvent at p and T, etc. But the relationship is not the same* as for B_2 in the osmotic pressure expansion.

Given the series (4.103), we can deduce μ_2 by integrating the Gibbs-Duhem equation:

$$\left(\frac{\partial \mu_2/kT}{\partial m}\right)_{p,T} = -\frac{1}{m}\left(\frac{\partial \mu_1/kT}{\partial m}\right)_{p,T}. \tag{4.104}$$

With the aid of Eq. (4.92), we find

$$\mu_2 = \mu_2'' + kT \ln m + kT(\tfrac{2}{1}C_2 m + \tfrac{3}{2}C_3 m^2 + \cdots). \tag{4.105}$$

The quantity in parentheses is the logarithm of the appropriate activity coefficient.

The partial molecular volumes then follow from Eqs. (4.96), (4.103), and (4.105):

$$\bar{v}_1 = v_1 - kT\left[\left(\frac{\partial C_2}{\partial p}\right)_T m^2 + \left(\frac{\partial C_3}{\partial p}\right)_T m^3 + \cdots\right] \tag{4.106}$$

$$\bar{v}_2 = \bar{v}_2^{\square} + kT\left[\frac{2}{1}\left(\frac{\partial C_2}{\partial p}\right)_T m + \frac{3}{2}\left(\frac{\partial C_3}{\partial p}\right)_T m^2 + \cdots\right]. \tag{4.107}$$

Note that the first "correction" term in $\bar{v}_1$ is quadratic in m, while it is linear in m for $\bar{v}_2$. This is a property of solute-solvent pairs of those partial molecular quantities which do not show a divergence at $m = 0$, and is a consequence of the general equation

$$\left(\frac{\partial \bar{R}_1}{\partial m}\right)_{p,T} = -m\left(\frac{\partial \bar{R}_2}{\partial m}\right)_{p,T}, \tag{4.108}$$

where R is any extensive variable. Equation (4.104) is, of course, a special case of Eq. (4.108).

The partial molecular enthalpies are easily shown to be

$$\bar{H}_1 = H_1 + kT^2\left[\left(\frac{\partial C_2}{\partial T}\right)_p m^2 + \left(\frac{\partial C_3}{\partial T}\right)_p m^3 + \cdots\right] \tag{4.109}$$

---

* See T. L. Hill, *Introduction to Statistical Thermodynamics*, pp. 362–368. Reading, Mass.: Addison-Wesley, 1960.

and

$$\overline{\text{H}}_2 = \overline{\text{H}}_2^\square - kT^2\left[\frac{2}{1}\left(\frac{\partial C_2}{\partial T}\right)_p m + \frac{3}{2}\left(\frac{\partial C_3}{\partial T}\right)_p m^2 + \cdots\right]. \tag{4.110}$$

Finally, from $\mu_i = \overline{\text{H}}_i - T\overline{\text{s}}_i$,

$$\overline{\text{s}}_1 = \text{s}_1 + k\left[m + \left(C_2 + T\frac{\partial C_2}{\partial T}\right)m^2 + \left(C_3 + T\frac{\partial C_3}{\partial T}\right)m^3 + \cdots\right] \tag{4.111}$$

$$\overline{\text{s}}_2 = \frac{\overline{\text{H}}_2^\square - (\mu_2'' + kT\ln m)}{T} - k\left[\frac{2}{1}\left(C_2 + T\frac{\partial C_2}{\partial T}\right)m + \frac{3}{2}\left(C_3 + T\frac{\partial C_3}{\partial T}\right)m^2 + \cdots\right]. \tag{4.112}$$

Osmotic pressure. Suppose we have osmotic equilibrium between the solution at p, T, m and the pure solvent at $p - \Pi$, T:

$$\mu_1(p, T, m) = \mu_1(p - \Pi, T, 0).$$

But, for the pure solvent,

$$\mu_1(p, T, 0) - \mu_1(p - \Pi, T, 0) = \int_{p-\Pi}^{p} \text{v}_1(p', T)\, dp'.$$

Therefore, from Eq. (4.103),

$$\frac{1}{kT}\int_{p-\Pi}^{p} \text{v}_1(p', T)\, dp' = m + C_2(p, T)m^2 + C_3(p, T)m^3 + \cdots \tag{4.113}$$

This equation gives Π as a function of m, p, and T. Note that, in C_n, p is the pressure on the solution, not the pressure on the solvent [contrast this with Eq. (4.38)].

A simple example: Suppose that solvent and solution are incompressible; $\overline{\text{v}}_1 = \text{v}_1 = \text{const}$; and $\overline{\text{v}}_2 = \text{v}_2 = \text{const}$. Then the left-hand side of Eq. (4.113) becomes $\Pi\text{v}_1/kT$ and it is easy to show (Problem 4.4), for example, that

$$C_2 = (B_2 - \text{v}_2)/\text{v}_1. \tag{4.114}$$

PROBLEMS

4.1 Express B_2' and B_3' [Eq. (4.16)] in terms of B_2 and B_3.

4.2 In connection with Eqs. (4.6) and (4.52), given that w_{nm} is the potential of average force in B_{nm} and w is the potential in B (regarding the solute as a single component), express $w(r)$ in terms of the $w_{nm}(r)$.

4.3 Use Eq. (4.6) to show that $B_2 = 2\pi a^3/3$ for a gas of hard spheres of diameter a.

4.4 For a binary solution with $\bar{\text{v}}_1 = \text{v}_1 = \text{const}$ and $\bar{\text{v}}_2 = \text{v}_2 = \text{const}$, show that [see Eqs. (4.38) and (4.113)]

$$C_2 = (B_2 - \text{v}_2)/\text{v}_1.$$

4.5 For a van der Waals gas, $B_2 = b - (a/kT)$, where a and b are van der Waals constants. Look up the values of a and b for nitrogen, plot B_2 against temperature, and compare your result with the experimental nitrogen curve in Fig. 4.1.

4.6 Give a physical interpretation of Eq. (4.59).

4.7 Derive Eq. (4.7) from Eq. (4.6).

4.8 Use Eq. (4.108) to test the self-consistency of the series for $\bar{\text{v}}_i$, H_i, and $\bar{\text{s}}_i$.

4.9 Find $\bar{\text{v}}_1$ for the binary gas represented by Eq. (4.20).

4.10 Find series expansions in powers of p for $\text{s}(p, T)$ and $\text{H}(p, T)$, from Eq. (4.17).

4.11 a) Show that for an aqueous 1–1 electrolyte solution at 25°C ($\epsilon = 78.5$)

$$\frac{1}{\kappa} = \frac{3.04}{\rho^{1/2}} \qquad (\text{in Å}),$$

where ρ is the salt concentration in moles liter^{-1}.

b) In the osmotic pressure equation $\Pi/kT = 2\rho - (\kappa^3/24\pi)$, the correction term is what percentage of the leading term when $\rho = 0.01$ moles liter^{-1}?

4.12 In a Donnan system, suppose the diffusible electrolyte is 1–1 with concentration (outside) $\rho_+^0 = \rho_-^0 = 0.10$ mole liter^{-1}. That is, $Z_+ = +1$, $Z_- = -1$. Suppose the solute has $\rho = 0.02$ mole liter^{-1} and $Z = +1$.

a) Calculate ρ_+ and ρ_- (inside), and verify neutrality inside.

b) Calculate the osmotic second virial coefficient,

$$B_2 = \frac{Z^2}{2\sum_i \rho_i^0 Z_i^2}.$$

c) In the equation $\Pi/kT = \rho + B_2\rho^2 + \cdots$, $B_2\rho^2$ is what percentage of the leading term?

4.13 Extend the Donnan derivation of

$$\frac{\Pi}{kT} = \rho + \rho^2\left(\frac{Z^2}{2\sum_i \rho_i^0 Z_i^2}\right) + \cdots$$

to the case where there are *two* solutes with concentrations ρ_{I} and ρ_{II} and charge numbers Z_{I} and Z_{II}.

4.14 a) If, in a Donnan system, $e\psi/kT = 0.100$, calculate the membrane potential ψ in millivolts ($t = 25$°C).

b) For this same system, calculate the ratio ρ_+/ρ_+^0 for a singly charged positive ion.

SUPPLEMENTARY READING

Hill, T. L., *Introduction to Statistical Thermodynamics*, Chapters 15, 18, and 19. Reading, Mass.: Addison-Wesley, 1960. More specialized references may be found in these chapters.

Hill, T. L., *Faraday Soc. Disc.* **21,** 31 (1956).

CHAPTER 5

THERMODYNAMICS OF AN ELECTRIC FIELD

This chapter provides an introduction to the thermodynamics of a dielectric (nonelectrolyte) in an electric field. The first section introduces the basic thermodynamics; the remainder of the chapter is devoted to a few special topics.

There is a very close parallel between the thermodynamics of an electric field and that of a magnetic field. This analogy is discussed briefly in the final section.

5.1 BASIC THERMODYNAMICS OF AN ELECTRIC FIELD

A number of alternative and equivalent thermodynamic formulations can be devised for a dielectric fluid in an electric field. Koenig* has given a very full discussion of this subject. The corresponding treatment for magnetic systems is contained in papers by Guggenheim.† We confine ourselves in this section to the one particular formulation that is most convenient for dilute and imperfect gases. For condensed systems, there are some advantages to other choices (see Section 5.4, for example).

Consider the parallel plate condenser in Fig. 5.1. The plate surface-charge densities are $+\sigma$ and $-\sigma$ as indicated. The condenser is assumed to have a large enough plate area so that edge effects can be ignored. The volume V contains the dielectric fluid whose properties interest us. For simplicity, we take the fluid as one component with N molecules, but it could be multicomponent as well. One wall of the fluid container, parallel to the condenser plates, serves as a piston to vary the volume V. The equilibrium pressure on the piston is p. The regions between the fluid container and the condenser plates are evacuated. As a consequence of polarization of the dielectric in the field of the condenser plates, there are induced surface-charge densities $-\sigma'$ and $+\sigma'$ on the inside surfaces of the indicated walls (Fig. 5.1) of the fluid container, where $\sigma' < \sigma$.

---

* F. O. Koenig, *J. Phys. Chem.* **41,** 597 (1937).

† E. A. Guggenheim, *Proc. Roy. Soc.* **155A,** 49, 70 (1936).

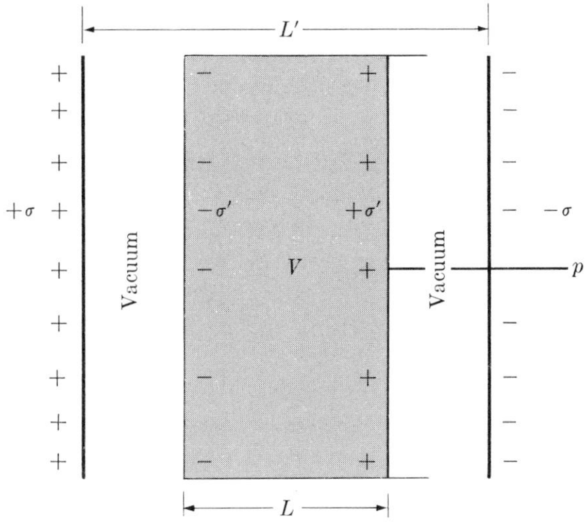

Fig. 5.1. Dielectric fluid in volume V between two condenser plates; V can be varied by a piston with pressure p.

Let us consider the electric field acting at any point in the fluid. The field due to the condenser surface charge $+\sigma$ is $2\pi\sigma$, as can easily be deduced from Coulomb's law (Problem 5.1). The field arising from the surface charge $-\sigma$ is also $2\pi\sigma$ (acting in the same direction). The total field from the charge on the condenser plates is therefore $4\pi\sigma$. This field is called the dielectric displacement D; $D = 4\pi\sigma$. We regard D as a variable intensive parameter on which the thermodynamic properties of the fluid depends. An external field D can be controlled from outside the thermodynamic system (fluid) itself. At a point in V, the field D has the same value whether or not a dielectric fills V; that is, it is determined solely by σ. In addition to the field D due to external charges acting at the point in V, there is, clearly, also a field $-4\pi\sigma'$ due to charges induced on the surfaces of the dielectric. An equivalent point of view is that this second field arises from molecular dipoles throughout V induced and oriented somewhat in the external field D. It is customary to use the symbol P (polarization) in place of σ'. Then the total electric field acting at a point in V is $D - 4\pi P$. This field is denoted by $\mathcal{E}$ (electric field strength):

$$\mathcal{E} = D - 4\pi P, \qquad D = \mathcal{E} + 4\pi P, \qquad D \geq \mathcal{E}, \tag{5.1}$$

where $\mathcal{E}$, D, and P all have the same sign. (If $+\sigma$ and $-\sigma$ are interchanged in Fig. 5.1, the signs are reversed.) The dielectric constant ϵ is then defined by $D = \epsilon\mathcal{E}$; necessarily, $\epsilon \geq 1$.

We now consider the thermodynamic functions of the fluid molecules. In these functions we include only contributions from the molecules themselves, and exclude contributions that would be associated with the space V and field D if no molecules were present in V. This is a natural choice if one is interested in the molecular interpretation of the thermodynamic equations. Thus the energy E includes the molecular kinetic energy, the potential energy of interaction of the molecules with the external field D, and the potential energy of interaction between the molecules themselves.

In the expression*

$$dE = DQ - DW + \mu\, dN, \tag{5.2}$$

there are two contributions to DW. One is the usual $p\,dV$ term associated with a volume change (N and D constant, $DQ = 0$), and the other is related to changes in D (N and V constant, $DQ = 0$). Consider the work that must be done on the entire system shown in Fig. 5.1 if σ is to be changed by $d\sigma$. Let $\mathcal{A}$ be the cross-sectional area of a condenser plate. Then we have to transport an amount of positive charge $\mathcal{A}\, d\sigma$ from the negative condenser plate to the positive plate. This charge has to be moved against a field $\mathcal{E}$ through the distance L (fluid) and against a field D through the distance $L' - L$ (vacuum). The total work done on the system is thus

$$\mathcal{E}L\mathcal{A}\, d\sigma + D(L' - L)\mathcal{A}\, d\sigma. \tag{5.3}$$

However, to get the quantity we want, the work done *on the fluid*, we have to subtract from (5.3) the work which would have to be done to increase σ by $d\sigma$ when the volume V is evacuated. This work is

$$DL'\mathcal{A}\, d\sigma. \tag{5.4}$$

On subtracting (5.4) from (5.3), we get

$$\mathcal{E}L\mathcal{A}\, d\sigma - DL\mathcal{A}\, d\sigma = -PV\, dD. \tag{5.5}$$

This is work done *on* the fluid. The desired contribution to DW is $+PV\, dD$, since DW is work done *by* the fluid.

We note that $PV = (\sigma'\mathcal{A})L$, which is just the total dipole moment (charge $\times$ separation distance) of the fluid in V. We call the total moment M and replace PV by M. Finally, then, Eq. (5.2) becomes

$$dE = T\, dS - p\, dV - M\, dD + \mu\, dN. \tag{5.6}$$

* The D's in this equation indicate inexact differentials; they are not to be confused with the dielectric displacement.

Koenig has shown that the pressure p in this equation has the operational significance implied by the particular kind of volume change indicated in Fig. 5.1. On integrating Eq. (5.6), holding intensive properties constant, we find

$$E = TS - pV + \mu N, \qquad G = \mu N = A + pV. \tag{5.7}$$

Alternative useful forms of Eq. (5.6) are

$$dA = -S\,dT - p\,dV - M\,dD + \mu\,dN, \tag{5.8}$$

$$d(pV) = S\,dT + p\,dV + M\,dD + N\,d\mu, \tag{5.9}$$

$$dG = -S\,dT + V\,dp - M\,dD + \mu\,dN, \tag{5.10}$$

$$d\mu = -\mathrm{s}\,dT + \mathrm{v}\,dp - \mathrm{M}\,dD, \tag{5.11}$$

where $\mathrm{M} = M/N$.

Since E, T, S, p, ϵ, etc., are independent of the direction of the field, they must be even functions of D. On the other hand, M, P, $\mathcal{E}$, etc., are odd functions of D. Unless D is extremely large, it usually suffices to consider only quadratic and linear terms in D in the respective cases.

Maxwell relations deduced from Eq. (5.8) show how S, p, and μ are influenced by the field D:

$$\left(\frac{\partial S}{\partial D}\right)_{T,V,N} = \left(\frac{\partial M}{\partial T}\right)_{D,V,N},$$

$$\left(\frac{\partial p}{\partial D}\right)_{T,V,N} = \left(\frac{\partial M}{\partial V}\right)_{T,D,N},$$

$$\left(\frac{\partial \mu}{\partial D}\right)_{T,V,N} = -\left(\frac{\partial M}{\partial N}\right)_{T,D,V}.$$

These can be rewritten as follows:

$$\left(\frac{\partial \mathrm{s}}{\partial D}\right)_{T,\rho} = \left(\frac{\partial \mathrm{M}}{\partial T}\right)_{D,\rho}, \tag{5.12}$$

$$\left(\frac{\partial p}{\partial D}\right)_{T,\rho} = \left(\frac{\partial \mathrm{M}}{\partial \mathrm{v}}\right)_{T,D} = -\rho^2\left(\frac{\partial \mathrm{M}}{\partial \rho}\right)_{T,D}, \tag{5.13}$$

$$\left(\frac{\partial \mu}{\partial D}\right)_{T,\rho} = -\left(\frac{\partial P}{\partial \rho}\right)_{T,D}, \tag{5.14}$$

where $P = M/V$.

The change in density with field strength (usually called *electrostriction*), at constant chemical potential, is also of interest. For example, imagine that part of a sample of gas is at $D = 0$ while another part, with which the first part is in equilibrium at the same μ and T, is in a field D. Which part has the greater density? From Eq. (5.9),

$$\left(\frac{\partial N}{\partial D}\right)_{T,\mu,V} = \left(\frac{\partial M}{\partial \mu}\right)_{T,D,V},$$

or

$$\left(\frac{\partial \rho}{\partial D}\right)_{T,\mu} = \left(\frac{\partial P}{\partial \mu}\right)_{T,D} = \left(\frac{\partial P}{\partial \rho}\right)_{T,D}\left(\frac{\partial \rho}{\partial \mu}\right)_{T,D}. \tag{5.15}$$

Another form of this equation, from Eq. (5.15), is

$$\left(\frac{\partial \rho}{\partial D}\right)_{T,\mu} = \rho\left(\frac{\partial P}{\partial p}\right)_{T,D} = \rho\left(\frac{\partial P}{\partial \rho}\right)_{T,D}\left(\frac{\partial \rho}{\partial p}\right)_{T,D}. \tag{5.16}$$

In the next section we shall apply these equations to a special case (and answer the question formulated above).

5.2 DILUTE GAS

We consider a one-component gas in the limit $\rho \to 0$. In the absence of a field, the equation of state is $p = \rho kT$, and $\mu(\rho, T)$ is given by Eq. (4.2). Since $\rho \to 0$, the molecules do not interact. Therefore $M = N\text{M}_0(T, D)$, where M_0 is the limit of M as $\rho \to 0$; M_0 is also the mean moment per (isolated) molecule.

If we apply Eq. (5.13) to this system, we conclude, since M is independent of ρ, that p is independent of D. Therefore the equation of state is $p = \rho kT$ at any D.

Since $P = \rho\text{M}_0(T, D)$,

$$\left(\frac{\partial \mu}{\partial D}\right)_{T,\rho} = -\text{M}_0(T, D).$$

Unless the field is very large, $\text{M}_0 = Df(T)$, where $f(T)$ is positive. Then integration yields

$$\mu(\rho, T, D) = \mu'(T) + kT \ln \rho - \tfrac{1}{2}D^2 f(T). \tag{5.17}$$

The chemical potential is lowered and the molecules are stabilized by the field.

Equation (5.15) gives for the electrostriction,

$$\left(\frac{\partial \rho}{\partial D}\right)_{T,\mu} = \frac{\rho D f(T)}{kT}.$$

We separate variables (ρ and D), integrate, and obtain

$$\rho(D) = \rho(0)e^{D^2 f(T)/2kT} \qquad (\mu \text{ and } T \text{ constant}). \tag{5.18}$$

Thus $\rho(D) > \rho(0)$. The effect is quite small here as we shall see below.

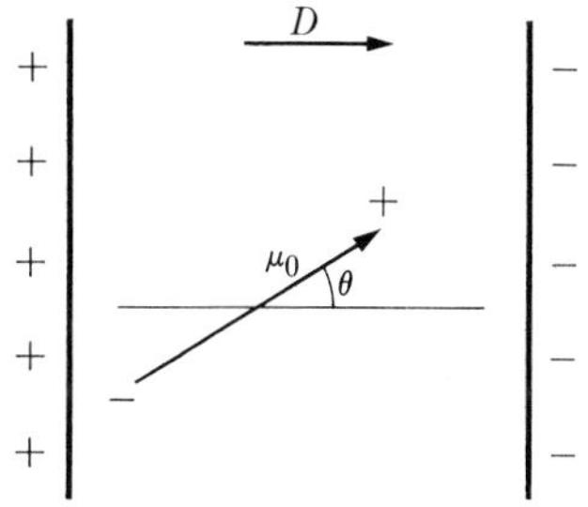

Fig. 5.2. Permanent moment μ_0 in external field D.

Equation (5.18) also follows directly from Eq. (5.17) and the equilibrium condition $\mu(\rho, T, D) = \mu(\rho(0), T, 0)$. Equation (5.18) represents a Boltzmann distribution between a region with $D = 0$ and one with $|D| > 0$. The general resemblance to Eq. (4.79) should be noted.

Dipolar model. Let us now turn to an explicit model. We suppose the molecule has a permanent dipole moment μ_0 (not to be confused with the chemical potential). Also, we assume that the field induces in the molecule a further additive moment αD (in the direction of the field), where α is the polarizability. The polarizability is a purely quantum mechanical quantity, independent of T. The work necessary to create this induced moment is [note $dE = -M\,dD$ in Eq. (5.6)]

$$w = -\int_0^D \alpha D'\,dD' = -\alpha D^2/2.$$

Let θ be the angle between the direction of the field and the axis of the permanent moment μ_0 (Fig. 5.2). In the presence of the field, the rotation of the molecule is not free, because of the dependence on θ of the potential energy u of the permanent dipole:

$$u = -\mu_0 D \cos\theta.$$

Let us now use this potential energy to calculate $\bar{\mu}_0$, the average component of μ_0 in the direction of the field:

$$\bar{\mu}_0 = \frac{\int_0^\pi \mu_0 \cos\theta e^{\mu_0 D\cos\theta/kT} \sin\theta\,d\theta}{\int_0^\pi e^{\mu_0 D\cos\theta/kT} \sin\theta\,d\theta}.$$

Integration over an azimuthal angle ϕ need not be included because both integrands depend only on θ. We need $\bar{\mu}_0$ only to the linear term in D. Hence we can put

$$e^{\mu_0 D\cos\theta/kT} = 1 + \frac{\mu_0 D\cos\theta}{kT}.$$

Elementary integrations then give

$$\bar{\mu}_0 = \mu_0^2 D/3kT. \tag{5.19}$$

If we define $y = \mu_0 D/kT$, then usually $y \ll 1$. For example, if $\mu_0 = 1$ Debye (that is, 1×10^{-18} esu · cm), $D = 1000$ v cm^{-1} and $T = 300°$K, then $y = O(10^{-4})$ (Problem 5.2). If the permanent moment μ_0 were completely oriented by the field ($D \to \infty$ or $T \to 0$), $\bar{\mu}_0$ would approach μ_0 itself. That is, $\bar{\mu}_0^{\max} = \mu_0$. It is clear that at ordinary field strengths and temperatures the rotation is almost free and the orientation of μ_0 in the field is very slight for

$$\bar{\mu}_0/\bar{\mu}_0^{\max} = \mu_0 D/3kT \ll 1.$$

In the limit $T \to \infty$ or $D \to 0$, $\bar{\mu}_0 \to 0$.

The total moment per molecule, M_0, for this model is then

$$\mathrm{M}_0 = \alpha D + \bar{\mu}_0 = Df(T) = D[\alpha + (\mu_0^2/3kT)]. \tag{5.20}$$

The terms α and $\mu_0^2/3kT$ have similar magnitudes. For example, for HCl gas at 300°K, the ratio $\alpha/(\mu_0^2/3kT)$ is about 0.3 (Problem 5.3).

If we put Eq. (5.20) into Eqs. (5.17) and (5.18), we obtain explicit formulas for μ and $\rho/\rho(0)$ (μ and T constant). Let us also find the entropy from Eq. (5.12):

$$\left(\frac{\partial \mathrm{s}}{\partial D}\right)_{T,\rho} = -\frac{D\mu_0^2}{3kT^2},$$

$$\mathrm{s}(T, \rho, D) = \mathrm{s}(T, \rho, 0) - \frac{k}{6}\left(\frac{D\mu_0}{kT}\right)^2 \qquad (\rho \text{ and } T \text{ constant}). \tag{5.21}$$

The entropy is reduced in the presence of a field because rotation is slightly hindered.

From $E = TS - pV + \mu N$, we have

$$\mathrm{E}(T, \rho, D) = \mathrm{E}(T, \rho, 0) - D^2\left(\frac{\alpha}{2} + \frac{1}{3}\frac{\mu_0^2}{kT}\right) \qquad (\rho \text{ and } T \text{ constant}). \tag{5.22}$$

The electric field term here is equal to $w + \bar{u} = w - \bar{\mu}_0 D$ (see u and w above).

As we have mentioned already, the presence of a field stabilizes the molecules [Eq. (5.17)]. We see here that this is an energy effect [Eq. (5.22)]; the entropy acts in the opposite direction [Eq. (5.21)].

The terms in D^2 in the above equations for μ, s, and E are very small, say of order 10^{-6} to 10^{-8} of the leading terms, in typical cases.

From Eq. (5.1),

$$D = \mathcal{E} + 4\pi P = (D/\epsilon) + (4\pi M/V)$$

or

$$(\epsilon - 1)/\epsilon = 4\pi M/DV. \tag{5.23}$$

In the limit $\rho \to 0$ and for this model, we then have the following equation for the dielectric constant ϵ of the gas:

$$\epsilon - 1 = 4\pi \mathrm{M}_0 N/DV = 4\pi\rho[\alpha + (\mu_0^2/3kT)]. \tag{5.24}$$

A plot of the experimental quantity $(\epsilon - 1)/4\pi\rho$ against $1/T$ will give α as the intercept and $\mu_0^2/3k$ as the slope. This well-known method of determining permanent dipole moments is treated in physical chemistry texts and will not be considered further here.

The electric field is given by

$$\mathcal{E} = \frac{D}{\epsilon} = D\left[1 - 4\pi\rho\left(\alpha + \frac{\mu_0^2}{3kT}\right)\right]. \tag{5.25}$$

Incidentally, the quantity $P/\mathcal{E}$ is called the electric susceptibility (χ_e). It is easy to see that χ_e is equal to $(\epsilon - 1)/4\pi$.

5.3 IMPERFECT GAS

The system which we shall investigate in this section is a one-component imperfect gas in the external field D (Fig. 5.1). The use of the external field D as an independent variable, rather than $\mathcal{E}$, is still convenient because the virial coefficients are properties of pairs, triplets, etc., of molecules at $\rho = 0$ [see Eq. (5.28)].

We use the equation of state as the experimental basis for our treatment. Measurements of p, ρ, and T have to be made at different external fields D. We have already seen that $p = \rho kT$ when $\rho \to 0$. At higher densities, the data can be put in the form

$$p/kT = \rho + B_2(T, D)\rho^2 + B_3(T, D)\rho^3 + \cdots \tag{5.26}$$

The virial coefficients are necessarily even functions of D. Thus

$$B_n(T, D) = B_n^{(0)}(T) + D^2 B_n^{(2)}(T) + \cdots, \tag{5.27}$$

where $B_n^{(0)}$ is the usual zero-field nth virial coefficient (Section 4.1). Higher terms in the series (5.27) are seldom needed. The coefficients $B_n^{(2)}$ have to do, obviously, with the effect of the field D on the intermolecular forces.*

---

* T. L. Hill, *Introduction to Statistical Thermodynamics*, pp. 281–283. Reading, Mass.: Addison-Wesley, 1960; and T. L. Hill, *J. Chem. Phys.* **28**, 61 (1958).

The virial coefficients have the following mathematical significance:

$$B_2 = \left(\frac{\partial p/\rho kT}{\partial \rho}\right)_{\substack{T,D,\\ \rho=0}}, \qquad B_3 = \frac{1}{2!}\left(\frac{\partial^2 p/\rho kT}{\partial \rho^2}\right)_{\substack{T,D,\\ \rho=0}}, \quad \text{etc.} \tag{5.28}$$

Let us now derive a few other properties of the gas in terms of the $B_n(T, D)$. We first find the expansion of M in powers of ρ. From Eq. (5.13),

$$\left(\frac{\partial \text{M}}{\partial \rho}\right)_{T,D} = -\frac{kT}{\rho^2}\left[\left(\frac{\partial B_2}{\partial D}\right)_T \rho^2 + \left(\frac{\partial B_3}{\partial D}\right)\rho^3 + \cdots\right].$$

Hence

$$\text{M} = \text{M}_0(T, D) - kT\left[\left(\frac{\partial B_2}{\partial D}\right)_T \rho + \frac{1}{2}\left(\frac{\partial B_3}{\partial D}\right)_T \rho^2 + \cdots\right] \tag{5.29}$$

$$= D\{f(T) - 2kT[B_2^{(2)}(T)\rho + \tfrac{1}{2}B_3^{(2)}(T)\rho^2 + \cdots]\}. \tag{5.30}$$

The ordinary virial coefficients $B_n^{(0)}$ do not contribute to M. Equations (5.29) and (5.30) are, essentially, also series for the polarization P, since $P = \text{M}\rho$.

The dielectric constant ϵ is an even function of D;

$$\epsilon = \epsilon^{(0)}(\rho, T) + D^2\epsilon^{(2)}(\rho, T) + \cdots, \tag{5.31}$$

where $\epsilon^{(0)}$ is the usual low-field dielectric constant. From Eq. (5.23),

$$P = \text{M}\rho = [(\epsilon - 1)/4\pi\epsilon]D. \tag{5.32}$$

If we put $\epsilon = \epsilon^{(0)}$ and substitute Eq. (5.30), this becomes

$$(\epsilon^{(0)} - 1)/4\pi\epsilon^{(0)} = f(T)\rho - 2kT[B_2^{(2)}\rho^2 + \tfrac{1}{2}B_3^{(2)}\rho^3 + \cdots]. \tag{5.33}$$

This is a generalization of Eq. (5.24).

The chemical potential follows from Eq. (5.11):

$$\left(\frac{\partial \mu}{\partial \rho}\right)_{T,D} = \frac{1}{\rho}\left(\frac{\partial p}{\partial \rho}\right)_{T,D}.$$

Integration gives

$$\mu(\rho, T, D) = \mu'(T) + kT \ln \rho - \tfrac{1}{2}D^2 f(T) + kT(\tfrac{2}{1}B_2\rho + \tfrac{3}{2}B_3\rho^2 + \cdots) \tag{5.34}$$

$$= \mu(\rho, T, 0) - D^2[\tfrac{1}{2}f(T) - kT(\tfrac{2}{1}B_2^{(2)}\rho + \tfrac{3}{2}B_3^{(2)}\rho^2 + \cdots)]. \tag{5.35}$$

Equation (5.35) can also be derived from Eq. (5.14) (Problem 5.4).

A series in ρ for the electrostriction derivative $(\partial\rho/\partial D)_{T,\mu}$ is easy to obtain, but this is left to the reader (Problem 5.5).

5.4 CONDENSED SYSTEMS

For condensed systems, the actual electric field $\mathcal{E}$ in the system is a more convenient and practical independent variable than the dielectric displacement, or external field, D. Furthermore, D and $\mathcal{E}$ may be quite different in magnitude ($D = \epsilon\mathcal{E}$), as for example in liquid water. But once we have decided to use $\mathcal{E}$, there are still several alternative ways to redefine thermodynamic variables.

Using one procedure, we begin with Eq. (5.6) (which we now extend to two components, to include binary solutions) and define

$$E' = E + 2\pi P^2 V,$$
$$p' = p - 2\pi P^2.$$

The physical significance of p' is discussed by Koenig.* We then find that

$$dE' = T\,dS - p'\,dV - M d\mathcal{E} + \mu_1\,dN_1 + \mu_2\,dN_2. \tag{5.36}$$

Comparison with Eq. (5.6) shows that the independent variables are the same except that $\mathcal{E}$ replaces D. Then

$$dA' = -S\,dT - p'\,dV - M d\mathcal{E} + \mu_1\,dN_1 + \mu_2\,dN_2, \tag{5.37}$$

$$dG = -S\,dT + V\,dp' - M\,d\mathcal{E} + \mu_1\,dN_1 + \mu_2\,dN_2, \tag{5.38}$$

$$d(p'V) = S\,dT + p'\,dV + M\,d\mathcal{E} + N_1\,d\mu_1 + N_2\,d\mu_2, \tag{5.39}$$

where

$$A' = E' - TS, \qquad G = A' + p'V = N_1\mu_1 + N_2\mu_2. \tag{5.40}$$

The Gibbs-Duhem equation is

$$N_1\,d\mu_1 + N_2\,d\mu_2 = -S\,dT + V\,dp' - M\,d\mathcal{E}. \tag{5.41}$$

For a one-component system, Eq. (5.37) gives

$$\left(\frac{\partial \mathrm{s}}{\partial \mathcal{E}}\right)_{T,\rho} = \left(\frac{\partial \mathrm{M}}{\partial T}\right)_{\mathcal{E},\rho} \tag{5.42}$$

$$\left(\frac{\partial \mu}{\partial \mathcal{E}}\right)_{T,\rho} = -\left(\frac{\partial P}{\partial \rho}\right)_{T,\mathcal{E}}. \tag{5.43}$$

Also, from Eq. (5.39),

$$\left(\frac{\partial \rho}{\partial \mathcal{E}}\right)_{T,\mu} = \left(\frac{\partial P}{\partial \mu}\right)_{T,\mathcal{E}} = \left(\frac{\partial P}{\partial \rho}\right)_{T,\mathcal{E}}\left(\frac{\partial \rho}{\partial \mu}\right)_{T,\mathcal{E}}. \tag{5.44}$$

These relations are all analogues of those in Section 5.1.

---

* *Loc. cit.*

For a binary solution, we have, for example,

$$\left(\frac{\partial \mu_2}{\partial \mathcal{E}}\right)_{T,\rho_1,\rho_2} = -\left(\frac{\partial P}{\partial \rho_2}\right)_{T,\mathcal{E},\rho_1} \tag{5.45}$$

and

$$\left(\frac{\partial \rho_2}{\partial \mathcal{E}}\right)_{T,\mu_1,\mu_2} = \left(\frac{\partial P}{\partial \mu_2}\right)_{T,\mathcal{E},\mu_1} = \left(\frac{\partial P}{\partial \rho_2}\right)_{T,\mathcal{E},\mu_1}\left(\frac{\partial \rho_2}{\partial \mu_2}\right)_{T,\mathcal{E},\mu_1}. \tag{5.46}$$

This is a generalized electrostriction equation. If the solution is very dilute in component 2 (Problem 5.6),

$$\left(\frac{\partial \rho_2}{\partial \mathcal{E}}\right)_{T,\mu_1,\mu_2} = \frac{\rho_2}{kT}\left(\frac{\partial P}{\partial \rho_2}\right)_{\substack{T,\mathcal{E},\mu_1\\ \rho_2=0}} \qquad (\rho_2 \to 0). \tag{5.47}$$

The derivative on the right-hand side is, roughly, the moment increment per (isolated) solute molecule in the presence of solvent. When this quantity is positive, for example, when the solute is much more polar than the solvent, solute molecules are attracted into the field $\mathcal{E}$: they are more concentrated at $\mathcal{E}$ than at $\mathcal{E} = 0$.

This general topic could obviously be pursued at some length, but we leave it at this point.

Effect of electric field on two-state equilibrium. This is a very simple application, closely related to Sections 2.4 and 3.4. To avoid use of unfamiliar partition functions, we use a purely thermodynamic approach.

Suppose we have a membrane or sheet of identical macromolecules (say, a protein) arranged in a two-dimensional lattice (actually, if the molecules were dispersed in a solvent, the discussion would be almost the same). Each molecule can be in one of two states or configurations, A or B, and we assume that the state of one molecule is independent of the state of the others. In the absence of a field, there will be an equilibrium between the two forms governed by $\mu_A = \mu_B$ and

$$\begin{aligned}\mu_A &= \mu_A''(T) + kT \ln x,\\ \mu_B &= \mu_B''(T) + kT \ln (1 - x),\end{aligned} \tag{5.48}$$

where x is the fraction of A units. This is, essentially, an ideal binary solution for which Raoult's law holds over the whole composition range; see Eq. (4.33). We are ignoring pressure effects. Then

$$N_A/N_B = x/(1 - x) = e^{(\mu_B'' - \mu_A'')/kT} = K(T), \tag{5.49}$$

where K is the equilibrium constant [compare Eq. (3.33)].

In the presence of a field $\mathcal{E}$, let $\mathcal{E}g_A(T)$ and $\mathcal{E}g_B(T)$ be the respective moments of molecules of types A and B. Though a correction is not difficult, in this simple treatment we ignore the interaction between the molecular moments themselves (this is more reasonable, in fact it is quite proper, if the molecules are dispersed at low concentration in a solvent). Thus

$$M = N_A \mathcal{E} g_A(T) + N_B \mathcal{E} g_B(T).$$

From Eq. (5.38),

$$\left(\frac{\partial \mu_A}{\partial \mathcal{E}}\right)_{T,x} = -\left(\frac{\partial M}{\partial N_A}\right)_{T,\mathcal{E},N_B} = -\mathcal{E} g_A(T).$$

Therefore

$$\mu_A = \mu_A'' + kT \ln x - \tfrac{1}{2}\mathcal{E}^2 g_A,$$
$$\mu_B = \mu_B'' + kT \ln (1 - x) - \tfrac{1}{2}\mathcal{E}^2 g_B. \tag{5.50}$$

At equilibrium, since $\mu_A = \mu_B$, we have

$$x/(1 - x) = K(T) e^{\mathcal{E}^2(g_A - g_B)/2kT}. \tag{5.51}$$

The equilibrium is clearly shifted by the electric field. For example, if A molecules are more polarizable than B molecules ($g_A > g_B$), the equilibrium is shifted to favor the A form (Problem 5.7). Equations (2.32) and (3.34) are formally very similar to the above result (an equilibrium is shifted by an absolute activity and a force, respectively).

Just as on pp. 22 and 36, if interactions (van der Waals, hydrogen bonds, etc.) between neighbor molecules in the lattice are taken into account, and if AA and BB nearest neighbor pairs are more stable than AB pairs, then a small change in $\mathcal{E}$ may lead to a phase transition (for example, predominantly $B \rightarrow$ predominantly A). If there is binding (at absolute activity λ) of another component on the A and B molecules, as in Eq. (3.55), variation in λ can also give rise to a transition.* Effects of this kind could conceivably be of importance in biological membranes.

Osmotic electric field. For variety, in the remainder of this section we discuss an electric-field analogue† of the osmotic pressure. This subject, too, requires a change of variables, but one different from that introduced at the beginning of this section.

First, let us consider the experimental situation in general terms,‡ restricting the discussion to the binary solution case. In Fig. 5.3, two large parallel condenser plates, C_1 and C_2, are placed in a container at a

* See J.-P. Changeux, J. Thiéry, Y. Tung, and C. Kittel, *Proc. Nat. Acad. Sci.* **57,** 335 (1967); T. L. Hill, *Proc. Nat. Acad. Sci.* **58,** 111 (1967).

† See T. L. Hill, *J. Chem. Phys.* **30,** 1161 (1959).

‡ Actual experiments of this type have not been carried out, so far as the author is aware.

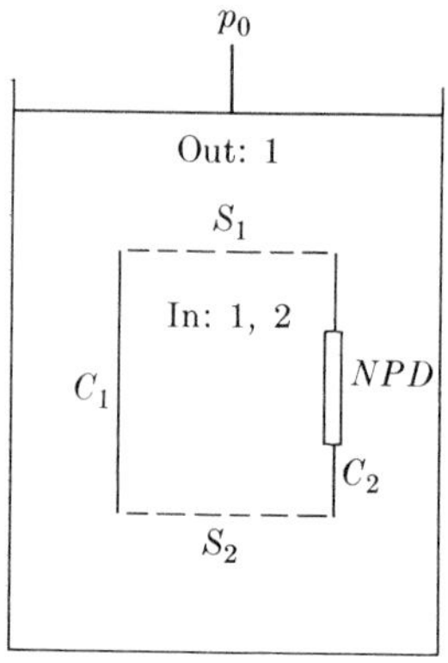

Fig. 5.3. Experimental arrangement for osmotic electric field.

fixed distance apart. At the ends of the condenser are semipermeable membranes S_1 and S_2—permeable to the solvent (species 1) but not to the solute (species 2). The abbreviation NPD represents a small conducting null pressure-differential detection device. As a crude and schematic example, NPD might be a nonrigid impermeable membrane which will bow in or out slightly if the pressure on the two sides is not balanced.

Suppose we start with solvent at p_0 and T, both inside and outside the condenser, and with the condenser uncharged. Thus NPD is balanced at its equilibrium position. In the conventional osmotic pressure situation, we add solute to the inside, keeping p_0 and T constant outside. Hence $d\mu_1^{\text{out}} = 0$. The addition of solute inside lowers μ_1^{in}. Because of the resulting gradient in μ_1, solvent will flow from the outside to the inside to increase the inside pressure sufficiently (pressure increase $= \Pi$, the osmotic pressure) to restore μ_1^{in} to its original value (net $d\mu_1^{\text{in}} = 0$). Of course, NPD will bow out in this situation.

Alternatively, suppose that we add solute inside (holding p_0 and T constant outside) and simultaneously charge up the condenser plates to an extent that is sufficient to maintain the balance of NPD at its equilibrium position. Then $d\mu_1^{\text{in}} = 0$ (assured by the flow of solvent through S_1 and S_2) and also $dp^\dagger = 0$, where $p^\dagger$ is the pressure exerted on NPD from inside. That is, $p^\dagger = p_0 = \text{const}$ (the pressure on NPD from the outside stays constant at p_0 during this process because the electric-field strength remains at $\mathcal{E} = 0$ outside of NPD). The pressure $p^\dagger$ is called the *plate pressure.** With the plates charged sufficiently to balance NPD, the electric field $\mathcal{E}$ inside is called the *osmotic electric field.*

With this introduction, let us now digress to derive the necessary thermodynamic equations. As Koenig* shows, $p^\dagger$ in Fig. 5.3 and p in

* F. O. Koenig, *loc. cit.*

Fig. 5.1 are not equal; in fact, $p^\dagger = p - (D^2/8\pi)$ (Problem 5.8). Hence we must change the variables of Section 5.1 in such a way as to replace p by $p^\dagger$.

We substitute

$$E^\dagger = E + (D^2V/8\pi) \tag{5.52}$$

and

$$p^\dagger = p - (D^2/8\pi) \tag{5.53}$$

into Eq. (5.6), and obtain

$$dE^\dagger = T\,dS - p^\dagger\,dV + J\,dD + \mu_1\,dN_1 + \mu_2\,dN_2, \tag{5.54}$$

where $J = \mathcal{E}V/4\pi$. This introduces $p^\dagger$ as required, but the independent field variable is D rather than $\mathcal{E}$. However, this does not cause any difficulty. Then

$$\begin{aligned} E^\dagger &= TS - p^\dagger V + \mu_1 N_1 + \mu_2 N_2, \\ G &= \mu_1 N_1 + \mu_2 N_2, \\ dG &= -S\,dT + V\,dp^\dagger + J\,dD + \mu_1\,dN_1 + \mu_2\,dN_2. \end{aligned} \tag{5.55}$$

Partial molecular quantities are defined by

$$\bar{\mathrm{s}}_1 = \left(\frac{\partial S}{\partial N_1}\right)_{T,p^\dagger,D,N_2}, \quad \text{etc.}$$

Then, for example,

$$\frac{\partial^2 G}{\partial T\,\partial N_1} = -\bar{\mathrm{s}}_1 = \left(\frac{\partial \mu_1}{\partial T}\right)_{p^\dagger,D,m},$$

where $m = N_2/N_1$ as in Section 4.4. Thus we find

$$d\mu_1 = -\bar{\mathrm{s}}_1\,dT + \bar{\mathrm{v}}_1\,dp^\dagger + \bar{\mathrm{J}}_1\,dD + \left(\frac{\partial \mu_1}{\partial m}\right)_{T,p^\dagger,D} dm. \tag{5.56}$$

For the pure solvent,

$$d\mu_1 = -\mathrm{s}_1\,dT + \mathrm{v}_1\,dp^\dagger + \mathrm{J}_1\,dD, \tag{5.57}$$

where $\mathrm{J}_1 = \mathcal{E}\mathrm{v}_1(T, p^\dagger, D)/4\pi$.

For a very dilute solution in the absence of a field [Eq. (4.94)],

$$\mu_1 = \mu_1^\triangle(p^\dagger, T) - kTm \qquad (m \to 0). \tag{5.58}$$

In the presence of a moderate field,

$$\left(\frac{\partial \mu_1}{\partial D}\right)_{T,p^\dagger,m} = \bar{\mathrm{J}}_1 = \mathrm{J}_1 = \frac{\mathcal{E}\mathrm{v}_1(p^\dagger, T)}{4\pi} \qquad (m \to 0) \tag{5.59}$$

so that

$$\mu_1 = \mu_1^\triangle(p^\dagger, T) - kTm + [\mathrm{v}_1(p^\dagger, T)D^2/8\pi\epsilon_1(p^\dagger, T)] \qquad (m \to 0), \tag{5.60}$$

where ϵ_1 is the dielectric constant of pure solvent.

Now we return to the particular experimental situation that concerns us in this subsection. Our object is to derive the limiting law for the osmotic electric field.* The analogue of Eq. (4.31) is

$$0 = \bar{\text{v}}_1 \, dD + \left(\frac{\partial \mu_1}{\partial m}\right)_{T,p_0,D} dm, \tag{5.61}$$

since μ_1, T, and $p^\dagger = p_0$ are all held constant in the experiment. From Eqs. (5.57) and (5.59),

$$0 = [D\text{v}_1(p_0, T)/4\pi\epsilon_1(p_0, T)] \, dD - kT \, dm \qquad (m \to 0). \tag{5.62}$$

Hence

$$D^2\text{v}_1(p_0, T)/8\pi\epsilon_1(p_0, T) = kTm$$

and

$$\epsilon_1(p_0, T)\mathcal{E}^2/8\pi = \rho_2 kT \qquad (\rho_2 \to 0). \tag{5.63}$$

This is the limiting law for the osmotic electric field.

As a numerical illustration of Eq. (5.63), consider, at 25°C, a 0.1% solution (by weight) of a solute with a molecular weight of 500,000. Then, from $\Pi = \rho_2 kT$, we find that $\Pi = 0.5$ mm H_2O, a small pressure that is very difficult to measure accurately. From Eq. (5.63), we find that $\mathcal{E} = 1200$ v cm^{-1} if $\epsilon_1 = 78.5$, and $\mathcal{E} = 4800$ v cm^{-1} if $\epsilon_1 = 5$. These are sizable fields and are not at all difficult to measure accurately.

Herein lies the possible experimental value of the osmotic electric field: the usual osmotic-pressure method for the determination of molecular weights (or virial coefficients) becomes inaccurate when it is applied to solutes with very high molecular weights. The essential reason for this, from a thermodynamic point of view, is that the chemical potential of the solvent (in, say, a binary solution) depends too sensitively on the pressure. This suggests that the pressure might profitably be replaced in osmotic experiments by a variable on which the solvent chemical potential depends less sensitively, for example, the electric field $\mathcal{E}$. Let us amplify this point a little.

The relative effects of pressure and electric field on the chemical potential of the solvent can be seen from Eq. (5.57) (low field, $\rho_2 \to 0$):

$$d\mu_1 = p_0\text{v}_1(dp_0/p_0) \qquad \text{(conventional osmotic case)} \tag{5.64}$$

$$\begin{aligned} d\mu_1 &= (\text{v}_1 D^2/4\pi\epsilon_1)(dD/D) \\ &= (\text{v}_1\epsilon_1\mathcal{E}^2/4\pi)(d\mathcal{E}/\mathcal{E}) \qquad \text{(electric field case)}. \end{aligned} \tag{5.65}$$

* For higher terms, see T. L. Hill, *loc. cit.*

Under ordinary circumstances, the coefficient of dp_0/p_0 in Eq. (5.64) is of order $10^{-3}kT$ (for a gas it would be kT), while the coefficient of $d\mathcal{E}/\mathcal{E}$ in Eq. (5.65) is about 1000 times smaller ($\epsilon_1 = 80$, $\mathcal{E} = 1000 \text{ v cm}^{-1}$). Thus a larger percentage increase in $\mathcal{E}$ is required than for p_0 to accomplish the same increase in μ_1. It is in this sense that the solvent chemical potential depends less sensitively on $\mathcal{E}$ than on p_0.

Finally, we give a simple alternative derivation of the limiting law, Eq. (5.63). In Fig. 5.3, with ρ_2 small and with no field, $\Pi = \rho_2 kT$. The inside pressure on NPD is $p_0 + \Pi$ and the outside pressure is p_0; hence NPD bows out from the excess pressure. Let us now put a surface charge density $+\sigma$ on plate C_2, and $-\sigma$ on C_1 (or vice versa). Because of the opposite signs of the charges, this will tend to pull NPD back in. NPD will be exactly balanced if σ is chosen so that the electrostatic force per unit area (a pressure) pulling NPD in just equals Π. The electric-field strength at NPD, owing to $-\sigma$ on C_1, is $2\pi\sigma/\epsilon_1$ in magnitude. This quantity, multiplied by σ, the charge per unit area on NPD, gives the electrostatic inward "pressure." Thus

$$2\pi\sigma^2/\epsilon_1 = \epsilon_1 \mathcal{E}^2/8\pi = \Pi = \rho_2 kT. \tag{5.66}$$

5.5 THERMODYNAMICS OF A MAGNETIC FIELD

The thermodynamics of a magnetic field parallels exactly the electric case.* Hence we need make only a few comments. The corresponding basic equations are:

$$D = \epsilon\mathcal{E} = \mathcal{E} + 4\pi P,$$
$$B = \mu H = H + 4\pi I, \tag{5.67}$$

and

$$\frac{P}{\mathcal{E}} = \frac{\epsilon - 1}{4\pi} = \chi_e,$$
$$\frac{I}{H} = \frac{\mu - 1}{4\pi} = \chi_m, \tag{5.68}$$

where B is the magnetic induction, H is the magnetic-field strength, μ is the permeability, I is the magnetization, χ_e is the electric susceptibility, and χ_m is the magnetic susceptibility.

Magnetic materials are less "susceptible" than dielectrics. While ϵ, for a condensed system, may be of order 10^1 or 10^2, in paramagnetism

* For a detailed account, see E. A. Guggenheim, *Proc. Roy. Soc.* (London) **155A,** 49, 70 (1936).

we have $\boldsymbol{\mu} = 1 + O(10^{-3})$ and in diamagnetism $\boldsymbol{\mu} = 1 - O(10^{-6})$. Thus, typically, $\chi_e/\chi_m = O(10^4)$.

Simple model. As an elementary example of a magnetic system, let us consider a model which is formally the same as Langmuir adsorption (Section 2.4), α–β elasticity (Section 3.4), and the electric field model on p. 73 (though the details of polarization and magnetization are different).

Suppose we have a lattice of M equivalent magnetic dipoles (associated, say, with electron or nuclear spins), each of which can exist in only two orientations or states: $\uparrow$ (state B), in the direction of the magnetic field H; or $\downarrow$ (state A), against the field. The potential energy of a dipole or spin is $-mH$ if oriented with the field ($\uparrow$), and $+mH$ if oriented against the field ($\downarrow$), where m is the magnetic moment. The dipoles are assumed not to interact with each other; each dipole behaves independently of the rest. This is a good model for nuclear-spin systems but not for electron-spin systems (e.g., ferromagnetism). Nearest neighbor interactions are needed to simulate ferromagnetism.

Let N be the number of A or $\downarrow$ states and $M - N$ the number of B or $\uparrow$ states. For a given value of N, the total potential energy of the dipoles in the field is

$$mHN - mH(M - N) = (2N - M)mH. \tag{5.69}$$

We define the magnetization by

$$I = (M - 2N)m. \tag{5.70}$$

This is the average excess number of B states over A states, multiplied by m. In this case, I is the analogue of the total moment M in electric field thermodynamics, rather than of P. In the absence of a magnetic field, the two states have the same potential energy (zero), and occur in equal numbers by symmetry; hence $I = 0$ when $H = 0$.

Unlike the electric field model on p. 67, the magnetization here is explicitly quantized: there is only one possible energy level for each state (i.e., there are two levels altogether, $-mH$ and $+mH$).

Corresponding to Eqs. (5.50),

$$\begin{aligned}\mu_A &= \mu'' + kT \ln x + mH \\ \mu_B &= \mu'' + kT \ln (1 - x) - mH,\end{aligned} \tag{5.71}$$

where $x = N/M$ = fraction in A, or $\downarrow$ state = fraction against the field. Then

$$x/(1 - x) = e^{-2mH/kT}. \tag{5.72}$$

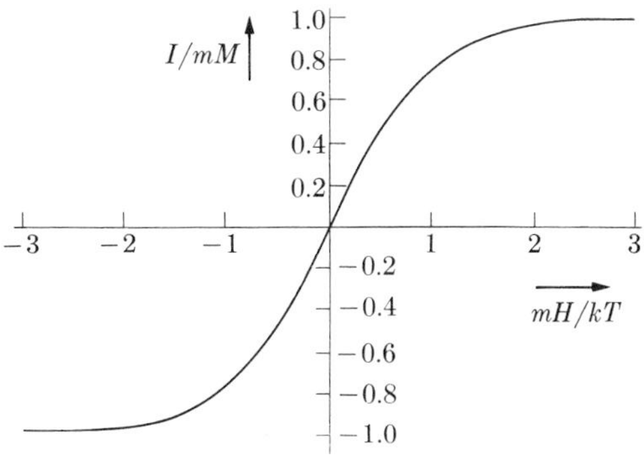

Fig. 5.4. Magnetization (I/mM) of lattice of noninteracting magnetic dipoles as a function of magnetic field (mH/kT).

This resembles Eq. (5.51), except that $K \equiv 1$. When $H \rightarrow +\infty$, $x \rightarrow 0$ (all spins $\uparrow$); when $H \rightarrow -\infty$, $x \rightarrow 1$ (all spins $\downarrow$). Thus there is a saturation effect at high fields. Note that the treatment is not limited to moderate fields as in some parts of this chapter.

The magnetization can be written

$$I/mM = 1 - 2x = \tanh{(mH/kT)} = (mH/kT) - \tfrac{1}{3}(mH/kT)^3 + \cdots \tag{5.73}$$

This function is plotted in Fig. 5.4.

The basic thermodynamic relation is a modification of Eq. (5.36):

$$dE' = T\,dS - I\,dH + \mu\,dM, \tag{5.74}$$

where the collection of M magnetic dipoles is here regarded as a one-component system in equilibrium with respect to the states A and B. For convenience, we can take the functions in Eq. (5.74) to be excess functions over the zero-field ($H = 0$) quantities. That is, $E' = 0$, $S = 0$, and $\mu = 0$ when $H = 0$ (I is already defined to have this property). Then, from (5.69),

$$\begin{aligned} E' &= -IH \\ &= -mMH \tanh{(mH/kT)}. \end{aligned} \tag{5.75}$$

Also, from Eqs. (5.71) and (5.72),

$$\begin{aligned} \mu &= \mu_A(H) - \mu_A(0) = \mu_B(H) - \mu_B(0) \\ &= -kT \ln{[\cosh{(mH/kT)}]}. \end{aligned} \tag{5.76}$$

The entropy then follows from

$$E' = TS + \mu M. \tag{5.77}$$

The self-consistency of these results may be checked using

$$d\mu = -(S/M)\,dT - (I/M)\,dH \tag{5.78}$$

(Problem 5.9).

PROBLEMS

5.1 Use Coulomb's law and an integration to show that the (normal) electric field of an infinite plane sheet of charge, with density σ, is $2\pi\sigma$.

5.2 Calculate the value of $y = \mu_0 D/kT$ for $\mu_0 = 1$ Debye, $D = 1000$ v cm^{-1}, and $T = 300$°K.

5.3 Calculate the ratio $\alpha/(\mu_0^2/3kT)$ for HCl gas at 300°K. Take $\mu_0 = 1.03$ Debye and $\alpha = 2.63$ Å^3 molecule^{-1}.

5.4 Use Eqs. (5.14) and (5.30) to derive Eq. (5.35) for $\mu(\rho, T, D)$ in an imperfect gas.

5.5 Use Eq. (5.15) or (5.16) to find the first few terms in the expansion of $(\partial p/\partial D)_{T,\mu}$ in powers of ρ, for an imperfect gas.

5.6 Start with Eq. (4.40) for μ_2 at $\mathcal{E} = 0$ and show that

$$(\partial\mu_2/\partial\rho_2)_{T,\mathcal{E},\mu_1} = kT/\rho_2,$$

when ρ_2 is small.

5.7 Suppose that, for a protein molecule at 300°K, because of proton migration,

$$g_A = \mu_{0A}^2/3kT \text{ and } g_B = \mu_{0B}^2/3kT,$$

where $\mu_{0A} = 250$ Debye and $\mu_{0B} = 200$ Debye. Calculate the electric field factor in Eq. (5.51) for $\mathcal{E} = 100{,}000$ v cm^{-1} (as in a biological membrane: 50 mv/50 Å).

5.8 Prove that p in Fig. 5.1 and $p^\dagger$ in Fig. 5.3 (for the same system) are related by $p^\dagger = p - (D^2/8\pi)$.

5.9 Use Eq. (5.76) for $\mu(T, H)$ to derive expressions for I and E'. Compare with Eqs. (5.73) and (5.75).

5.10 Suppose a two-dimensional lattice of molecules (a "membrane") is in an external field $\mathcal{E}_0$ perpendicular to the plane of the lattice. Let $\mathcal{E}g(T)$ be the moment of a molecule in a field $\mathcal{E}$, where $\mathcal{E}$ is the local field "felt" by a molecule. The field $\mathcal{E}$ has two contributions: (1) $\mathcal{E}_0$; and (2) the field due to all the other moments $\mathcal{E}g(T)$. Devise an integration (instead of a sum) that takes care of (2), approximately, and hence derive an expression for $\mathcal{E}$ as a function of $\mathcal{E}_0$, $g(T)$, and the two-dimensional density of the lattice molecules $(N/\mathcal{A})$.

5.11 Derive a series, in powers of ρ, for the electric susceptibility $\chi_e = P/\mathcal{E}$ of an imperfect gas.

SUPPLEMENTARY READING

Guggenheim, E. A., *Proc. Roy. Soc.* (London) **155A,** 49, 70 (1936).

Hill, T. L., *Introduction to Statistical Thermodynamics*, Chapter 12 and Section 15.5. Reading, Mass.: Addison-Wesley, 1960.

Hill, T. L., *J. Chem. Phys.* **28,** 61 (1958).

Hill, T. L., *J. Chem. Phys.* **30,** 1161 (1959).

Koenig, F. O., *J. Phys. Chem.* **41,** 597 (1937).

Mayer, J. E., and M. G. Mayer, *Statistical Mechanics*, Chapter 15. New York: Wiley, 1940.

Slater, J. C., *Quantum Theory of Matter*, Chapters 13 and 14. New York: McGraw-Hill, 1951.

CHAPTER 6

THERMODYNAMICS OF SMALL SYSTEMS

This chapter is based on a recent monograph devoted to the thermodynamics of small systems (see Supplementary Reading). Many further details and other aspects of the subject will be found there. Somewhat more statistical mechanics is used in this chapter than in the others, but the level is quite elementary.

6.1 INTRODUCTION

In ordinary thermodynamics, thermodynamic functions are defined and mathematical interrelations between these functions are derived for *macroscopic* (strictly infinite) systems only. Our main object in this chapter is to indicate how the range of validity of these definitions and interrelations can be extended to include small nonmacroscopic systems (e.g., a single macromolecule or colloidal particle).

Let us turn immediately to a simple illustration. Suppose that a certain one-component macroscopic solid has a Gibbs free energy $G = Nf(p, T)$, where N is the number of molecules in the sample and f is a function of p and T only. Several typical interrelations between thermodynamic functions are then

$$\mu = \left(\frac{\partial G}{\partial N}\right)_{p,T} = \frac{G}{N} \tag{6.1}$$

and

$$-S = \left(\frac{\partial G}{\partial T}\right)_{N,p} = N\left(\frac{\partial f}{\partial T}\right)_p, \qquad \left(\frac{\partial \mu}{\partial T}\right)_p = -\frac{S}{N}. \tag{6.2}$$

Now consider a colloidal particle of the same solid, small enough that correction terms must be added to G. For example, suppose that

$$G = Nf(p, T) + a(p, T)N^{2/3} + b(T)\ln N + c(p, T). \tag{6.3}$$

The term in $N^{2/3}$ is a surface free energy, while the last two terms might be due, among other things, to rotation of the colloidal particle. In the limit $N \to \infty$, $G \to Nf$, the macroscopic relationship. But when the system (the colloidal particle) is small and all terms in Eq. (6.3) are retained, macroscopic thermodynamics is no longer applicable and equations such as (6.1) and (6.2) are no longer correct. Hence our aim is to generalize the equations of thermodynamics so that they will be valid for small systems, like the one represented by Eq. (6.3), and will go over into ordinary thermodynamic equations as a limiting case (macroscopic system). Thus we shall see in Sections 6.3 and 6.4, for the above example, that two different chemical potentials $\hat{\mu}$ and μ must be defined (they become equal in a macroscopic system) and that we have, instead of Eqs. (6.1) and (6.2),

$$\hat{\mu} = \frac{G}{N}, \qquad \mu = \left(\frac{\partial G}{\partial N}\right)_{p,T}, \qquad \left(\frac{\partial \hat{\mu}}{\partial N}\right)_{p,T} = \frac{\mu - \hat{\mu}}{N},$$
$$\left(\frac{\partial \hat{\mu}}{\partial T}\right)_{N,p} = -\frac{S}{N}, \qquad \left(\frac{\partial \mu}{\partial T}\right)_{N,p} = -\left(\frac{\partial S}{\partial N}\right)_{p,T}.$$

In addition to "small" terms of order $N^{2/3}$ and $\ln N$, as in Eq. (6.3), other typical small terms are of order $N^{1/2}$ (surface of a two-dimensional system), $N^{1/3}$ (second-order surface effect in three dimensions), unity ("surface" of a one-dimensional system or a small system without surfaces), etc. Small system effects will be particularly noticeable at phase transitions and in critical regions.

Ensemble of small systems. Macroscopic thermodynamics will of course apply to a large sample of small systems (e.g., a macromolecular solution), and macroscopic thermodynamic functions are well defined for such a sample. But we wish to pursue thermodynamics on a smaller scale here: we are interested in thermodynamic functions and interrelationships for a *single* small system, including, in general, variations in the size of the system (for example, N, the degree of polymerization or aggregation, V, the volume, etc.). Allowance for these variations in size is, indeed, the important new feature which would not be included in a conventional macroscopic thermodynamic treatment of a large sample of small systems where only the *number* of small systems (macromolecules, etc.) would be varied.

Our point of departure in the thermodynamics of small systems will, in fact, be to start with the macroscopic thermodynamics of a large sample of *independent* small systems (an "ensemble") and introduce N, V, or other such assigned properties of the small systems as variable parameters. The use of an ensemble gives us a firm macroscopic starting point. We shall obtain in this way the desired fundamental thermodynamic equations for a small system. These equations will involve mean values of fluctuating extensive properties (e.g., the energy E). The mean values will be averages over the ensemble. But experiments will, in general, be done on "ensembles" of small systems, so that the ensemble average is just what is required operationally. Conceptually, however, one would like to think as well in terms of time averages for a single small system. For this purpose we have to borrow from statistical mechanics not only the above idea of using an ensemble, but also the fundamental postulate that the time average of a property for a single system is equal to the corresponding ensemble average. This is the only new postulate necessary to define and use thermodynamic properties for a single small system. Otherwise the foundation of small system thermodynamics is based on macroscopic thermodynamics. From a strictly operational point of view, even this postulate is not necessary if we always understand "average" to mean "ensemble average," and not "time average." However, the equivalence of these two averages is so well established as a statistical-mechanical postulate, for large or small systems, that we shall also adopt the postulate and not make any further distinction between the two averages.

Applications. As with macroscopic thermodynamics, we may anticipate two main classes of applications of small system thermodynamics: (1) as an aid in analyzing, classifying, and correlating equilibrium experimental data on "small systems" such as (noninteracting) colloidal particles, liquid droplets, crystallites, macromolecules, polymers, polyelectrolytes, nucleic acids, proteins, etc.; and (2) to verify, stimulate, and provide a framework for statistical-mechanical analysis of models of finite (i.e., "small") systems. A well-known experimental and theoretical example is the helix–coil transition in synthetic polypeptides. A single polymer chain is the system in this case. There are very appreciable effects of the degree of polymerization N on intensive properties of the system (e.g., the fraction of helical content). In macroscopic thermodynamics, intensive properties are always independent of the size (N here) of a system. For a thermodynamic analysis of such size effects one must therefore turn to small system thermodynamics.

Experimental small systems, with possible rare exceptions, are "condensed" systems: a small solid or liquid particle, a macromolecule, etc. A small system which is a gas, however, is of some interest as a theoretical model.

Statistical mechanics is not restricted to macroscopic systems, and examples of the evaluation of statistical-mechanical partition functions and other properties for finite systems have been fairly commonplace.

Implicit in the above discussion of applications is the following rather obvious remark, which, however, needs emphasizing. Small system thermodynamics can provide equations, especially differential equations, *connecting* thermodynamic functions, but the functions themselves must be measured experimentally or calculated from molecular theory (statistical mechanics). The same comment is of course true of macroscopic thermodynamics.

Operational differences. There are some important respects in which experimental small thermodynamic systems differ operationally from macroscopic systems. (a) In general, as already mentioned, measurements are not made on a single small system, but on a large number of small systems. An example is a very dilute solution of a macromolecule: the "small system" is one macromolecule; the solution contains many macromolecules, but the solution must be very dilute so that the systems do not interact with each other. (b) A macroscopic system immersed in a reservoir may exchange heat, molecules, etc., with the reservoir, but the intermolecular interaction between the system and the reservoir at the surface of contact can be neglected in the thermodynamics of the system. This is, in general, no longer the case for a small system immersed in a solvent (the reservoir). The discussion we give in this chapter does not include solvent effects explicitly. But it can be shown that the equations obtained here are usually valid even when solvent effects are present. All that is required is a reinterpretation of the meaning of various symbols. (c) Certain properties which can be varied experimentally at will in a macroscopic system cannot be so varied with a small system. An example is the volume of a colloidal particle. Another is the length of, or mechanical force f on, a free elastic macromolecule in solution. The only operationally possible case is that of $f = \text{const} = 0$. There are, of course, no such restrictions in investigating the theoretical properties of a statistical-mechanical model of a small system.

Differences in thermodynamic treatment. We have already noted a few differences in the thermodynamic treatment of small and macroscopic systems (ensembles, size effects on intensive properties, etc.). There are two further important differences, which we now want to mention. First, consider, say, a macroscopic system of N molecules, volume V, immersed in a heat bath at temperature T. Consider the same system at the same V and T, but in contact with a reservoir of molecules with the value of the chemical potential μ chosen so that the mean $\overline{N}$ has the same numerical value as N above. Then all thermodynamic functions, and all equations connecting the functions, are the same in the two cases. This is an illustration of the well-known fact that properties and equations in macroscopic thermodynamics are *independent of "environment"* (i.e., isothermal, isobaric, open, isolated, etc.). We shall see below that this is not the case with small systems: it is useful to give a separate discussion for each "environment," and the thermodynamic *functions* are different in each case. Of course, these differences are not of "macroscopic order"; they are significant for small systems, but become negligible if the size of the system is increased indefinitely.

It is, in fact, possible to derive a single set of thermodynamic *equations* applicable to all environments [see Eq. (6.21) *et seq.*]. This is an important result in principle, but for most purposes it is not the most convenient or illuminating approach.

Each environment, incidentally, can be characterized by its "environmental variables." For example, these variables in the two cases mentioned above are N, V, T and μ, V, T, respectively.

The second point is the following. Ordinary thermodynamic equations connect mean values of those extensive quantities which fluctuate (E, N, V, etc., as the case may be). Only mean values are of interest, because fluctuations about the mean values are usually completely negligible in magnitude relative to the mean values themselves. With small systems, however, fluctuations are larger, and hence higher moments of the probability distributions become of interest, as well as the mean values. As one might expect, mean-value thermodynamic equations prove to be the first members of a hierarchy of equations involving moments of different order. But we shall not pursue this subject here.

6.2 ENVIRONMENTAL VARIABLES μ, V, T

As we have mentioned in the introduction, it is profitable to give a separate discussion for each type of environment. But in this chapter, we shall consider just two cases. We derive the basic equations for a μ, V, T system in the present section, and then, quite arbitrarily, devote the remainder of the chapter (including several examples) to N, p, T systems.

Actually, in some respects, a μ, p, T system is the most interesting of all types. But this case is more difficult than the others, so we do not include it here. Another topic we omit is the relation between the treatment of spherical interfaces (drops and bubbles) in Section 1.3, and the thermodynamics of small systems.

We consider a small open one-component system of volume V in contact with a heat and molecule reservoir at T and μ. An experimental example would be a spherical colloidal particle or macromolecule with M surface binding sites (M is the analogue of V), immersed in a solvent at T containing molecules at μ which can be bound on the sites. The bound molecules, characterized by μ, M, T, and not including the colloidal particle itself, are the "system" in this case. This involves the approximation of the "separability" of the colloidal particle from the system. A monatomic fluid at μ and T in a cubical container of volume V, with periodic boundary conditions, is a theoretical example.

In order to begin with a firm macroscopic thermodynamic foundation, we consider an ensemble of $\mathcal{N}$ equivalent, distinguishable, independent systems, each with fixed center of mass, and all characterized by μ, V, T. We let $\mathcal{N} \to \infty$. Hence the ensemble itself is a macroscopic thermodynamic system, however small a single system is. We use distinguishable systems with fixed center of mass to eliminate the translational degrees of freedom of the systems. This restriction is convenient but not essential. Thus we shall be concerned, below, with the "internal" thermodynamic properties of a single system. Rotation of the system will often be of negligible importance, or not taken into account, but it need not be excluded.

For the entire ensemble with a fixed value of $\mathcal{N}$, as a thermodynamic system, we have from macroscopic thermodynamics that

$$dE_t = T\,dS_t - p\mathcal{N}\,dV + \mu\,dN_t$$

or

$$dS_t = (1/T)\,dE_t + (p\mathcal{N}/T)\,dV - (\mu/T)\,dN_t,$$

where $t =$ total refers to properties of the whole ensemble. The term $-p\mathcal{N}\,dV$ is a conventional work term for the ensemble. Each system has the volume V, and any volume change dV is the same for all systems. The pressure p is a mean pressure (time or ensemble average). It can be defined formally by

$$p \equiv -\frac{1}{\mathcal{N}}\left(\frac{\partial E_t}{\partial V}\right)_{S_t, N_t, \mathcal{N}}.$$

The entropy S_t is clearly a function not only of E_t, V, and N_t but also of $\mathcal{N}$ (or E_t is a function of S_t, V, N_t, and $\mathcal{N}$). For example, if we increase $\mathcal{N}$, holding E_t, V, and N_t constant, S_t will increase because the N_t molecules can now spread themselves over a larger number of systems of volume V. Thus the complete expression is

$$dE_t = T\,dS_t - p\mathcal{N}\,dV + \mu\,dN_t + X\,d\mathcal{N} \tag{6.4}$$

or

$$dS_t = (1/T)\,dE_t + (p\mathcal{N}/T)\,dV - (\mu/T)\,dN_t - (X/T)\,d\mathcal{N},$$

where

$$X \equiv \left(\frac{\partial E_t}{\partial \mathfrak{N}}\right)_{S_t,V,N_t} \qquad \text{or} \qquad -\frac{X}{T} \equiv \left(\frac{\partial S_t}{\partial \mathfrak{N}}\right)_{E_t,V,N_t}.$$

The term $X\,d\mathfrak{N}$ in Eq. (6.4) may be regarded as another pV work term, for $d\mathfrak{N}$ implies that we are changing the volume of the ensemble, with S_t and N_t constant, by changing the number of available systems of volume V rather than by changing V for each of the $\mathfrak{N}$ systems. We therefore define a new pressure $\hat{p}$ (read "p hat") by $-\hat{p}V \equiv X$. Clearly, $\hat{p}$ may be considered an *integral* pressure, while p is a *differential* pressure. A moment's reflection shows that there is no distinction between p and $\hat{p}$ for a macroscopic system ($V \to \infty$). But p and $\hat{p}$ will, in general, differ for a small system, and both will deviate by small terms from the macroscopic pressure which would obtain at the same μ and T.

Now suppose we hold μ, V, T constant and double the value of $\mathfrak{N}$. That is, we double the size of the ensemble without changing its nature otherwise. Then E_t, S_t, and N_t will also double in value, while p and X remain constant. Hence, for this macroscopic system (the whole ensemble), E_t is a linear homogeneous function of S_t, N_t, and $\mathfrak{N}$, if μ, V, and T are held constant. The volume V has the status here of a parameter which is necessary, with μ and T, to characterize completely a small system. On integrating Eq. (6.4), we obtain

$$E_t = TS_t + \mu N_t - \hat{p}V\mathfrak{N}. \tag{6.5}$$

Next we define $\overline{E}$, $\overline{N}$, and S by

$$E_t = \mathfrak{N}\overline{E}, \qquad N_t = \mathfrak{N}\overline{N}, \qquad S_t = \mathfrak{N}S. \tag{6.6}$$

The quantities $\overline{E}$ and $\overline{N}$ are time or ensemble average values per system of the ensemble, since E and N fluctuate in an environment characterized by μ, V, T. The quantities $\overline{E}$ and $\overline{N}$ are appropriately considered thermodynamic properties of a single small system. We do not put a bar over S because it is not an average value in the same sense. That is, S does not fluctuate in value but is a property of the complete probability distribution in E and N for a single system; hence S has the same value for each system in the ensemble. These comments about S are extrathermodynamic in nature and not essential to the argument. One can verify (Problem 6.1) that S, defined by $S_t/\mathfrak{N}$, has the usual meaning of an entropy in statistical mechanics. The bars over E and N are optional but help remind one that, unlike V, E and N are not environmental variables in this case.

In general, if an extensive variable fluctuates, it is not an environmental variable; if it has the same value in every system of the ensemble, it *is* an environmental variable.

We now return to the definitions in (6.6). Putting these in Eq. (6.5), we have

$$X = -\hat{p}V = \overline{E} - TS - \mu\overline{N}. \tag{6.7}$$

This verifies the statement that $p = \hat{p}$ for a macroscopic system, for in this case we know that

$$-pV = \overline{E} - TS - \mu\overline{N} \qquad (V \text{ macroscopic}).$$

We substitute Eqs. (6.6) and (6.7) into Eq. (6.4) and find, after cancellation and division by $\mathfrak{N}$,

$$d\overline{E} = T\,dS - p\,dV + \mu\,d\overline{N}, \tag{6.8}$$

$$dS = (1/T)\,d\overline{E} + (p/T)\,dV - (\mu/T)\,d\overline{N}. \tag{6.9}$$

On comparing Eq. (6.8) term by term with

$$\overline{E} = TS - \hat{p}V + \mu\overline{N}, \tag{6.10}$$

we see that $\overline{E}$ is *not* a linear homogeneous function of S, V, and $\overline{N}$ as in macroscopic thermodynamics, since $p \neq \hat{p}$ in general. This is what we should expect for a small system: if we hold μ and T constant and double the value of V, because of edge effects, etc., we shall not exactly double the values of other extensive properties as for a macroscopic system. Similarly, intensive properties such as $\overline{N}/V$, p, $\hat{p}$, etc., will change in value (i.e., they are functions of μ, T *and* V). But in the macroscopic limit, $\hat{p}$ approaches p, $\overline{E}$ becomes a linear homogeneous function of S, V and $\overline{N}$, and all intensive properties become functions of μ and T only. Thus, for small systems, we have to abandon the conventional implications of the terms "extensive" and "intensive" properties. We shall still refer to extensive and intensive variables, however, basing the classification on the macroscopic limit.

Equation (6.8) has exactly the same form and physical significance as for a macroscopic system, and this proves to be the case for all environments. The essential difference between macroscopic and small system thermodynamics, for a μ, V, T system, is exhibited then in Eq. (6.10), where $\hat{p}$ occurs instead of p. Equation (6.10) can be rewritten as

$$\overline{E} = TS - pV + \mu\overline{N} + (p - \hat{p})V, \tag{6.11}$$

where the last term is a correction term which becomes negligible for a macroscopic system.

If we take the differential of both sides of Eq. (6.7) to obtain $d(\hat{p}V)$ and use Eq. (6.8), we find

$$d(\hat{p}V) = S\,dT + p\,dV + \overline{N}\,d\mu. \tag{6.12}$$

This equation is especially useful since the independent variables are also the environmental variables. From Eq. (6.12), we have

$$\left(\frac{\partial \hat{p}V}{\partial T}\right)_{V,\mu} = S, \quad \left(\frac{\partial \hat{p}V}{\partial V}\right)_{T,\mu} = p, \quad \left(\frac{\partial \hat{p}V}{\partial \mu}\right)_{T,V} = \overline{N}. \tag{6.13}$$

The middle equation shows the integral-differential relation between $\hat{p}$ and p already mentioned. For a macroscopic system,

$$\left(\frac{\partial \hat{p}V}{\partial V}\right)_{T,\mu} = \frac{\hat{p}V}{V} = \hat{p} = p.$$

As Eq. (6.12) suggests, it is $\hat{p}$ and not p which is directly related to the grand partition function for a small μ, V, T system. This can be seen as follows. An ensemble of μ, V, T systems is itself an open macroscopic system characterized by the independent variables μ, V_t, T, where $V_t = \mathfrak{N}V$. We have then the usual macroscopic relation

$$TS_t - E_t + \mu N_t = kT \ln \Xi_t,$$

where Ξ_t is the grand partition function for the ensemble of systems. From Eq. (6.5), then,

$$\hat{p}V\mathfrak{N} = kT \ln \Xi_t.$$

But because of the independence, equivalence, and distinguishability of the systems of the ensemble, $\Xi_t = \Xi^{\mathfrak{N}}$, where Ξ is the grand partition function of a single μ, V, T system. Hence

$$\hat{p}V = kT \ln \Xi, \tag{6.14}$$

where

$$\Xi = \sum_N Q(N, V, T) e^{N\mu/kT}.$$

Equation (6.12) can also be written as

$$d\left(\frac{\hat{p}V}{T}\right) = -\overline{E}\,d\left(\frac{1}{T}\right) + \frac{p}{T}\,dV + \overline{N}\,d\left(\frac{\mu}{T}\right). \tag{6.15}$$

Another fundamental relation follows from Eqs. (6.8) and (6.11):

$$d[(p - \hat{p})V] = -S\,dT + V\,dp - \overline{N}\,d\mu, \tag{6.16}$$

or

$$d\left[\frac{(\hat{p}-p)V}{T}\right] = -\overline{E}\,d\left(\frac{1}{T}\right) - V\,d\left(\frac{p}{T}\right) + \overline{N}\,d\left(\frac{\mu}{T}\right). \tag{6.17}$$

The left-hand sides of these equations are zero for a macroscopic system: only two of T, p, and μ can be independent; there are two degrees of freedom. We see here that a small system has one more degree of freedom than the corresponding macroscopic system. An equivalent statement was made above when it was noted that intensive properties are functions of V as well as μ and T for a small system.

If we define*

$$\mathcal{E} = (p - \hat{p})V, \tag{6.18}$$

Eqs. (6.11) and (6.16) become

$$\mathcal{E} = \overline{E} - TS + pV - \mu\overline{N} \tag{6.19}$$

and

$$d\mathcal{E} = -S\,dT + V\,dp - \overline{N}\,d\mu. \tag{6.20}$$

In effect, this manipulation replaces $\hat{p}$ as a variable by $\mathcal{E}$. A corresponding definition of $\mathcal{E}$ can be introduced for any environment [see Eq. (6.35), for example]. Hence, Eqs. (6.19) and (6.20) apply to all environments though the averaging bar notation depends on the environment. However, the thermodynamic functions themselves would be different (in "small" or nonmacroscopic terms) for the same system in different environments.

The "small" quantity $\mathcal{E}$ is negligible for a macroscopic system. It may be positive or negative. $\mathcal{E}$ has the physical significance, for any environment, of a *subdivision potential*, the tendency of an ensemble to increase its number of systems, $\mathfrak{N}$. We can prove this, and also obtain Eqs. (6.19) and (6.20) for any environment, by the following argument.

For *any* environment, in place of Eq. (6.4), we begin with

$$dE_t = T\,dS_t - p\,dV_t + \mu\,dN_t + \mathcal{E}\,d\mathfrak{N}. \tag{6.21}$$

Thus systems are added to the ensemble holding S_t, V_t, and N_t constant, where

$$E_t = \mathfrak{N}E, \qquad V_t = \mathfrak{N}V, \qquad N_t = \mathfrak{N}N, \qquad S_t = \mathfrak{N}S. \tag{6.22}$$

Averaging bars are omitted in order to be able to use a single notation for

* Electric fields do not play a role in this chapter so there should be no confusion with $\mathcal{E}$ in Chapter 5.

all environments. Equation (6.21) *defines* $\mathcal{E}$ as

$$\mathcal{E} \equiv \left(\frac{\partial E_t}{\partial \mathfrak{N}}\right)_{S_t, V_t, N_t}. \tag{6.23}$$

This equation suggests the term "subdivision potential," used above (compare the chemical potential, μ). Integration of Eq. (6.21) gives

$$E_t = TS_t - pV_t + \mu N_t + \mathcal{E}\mathfrak{N} \tag{6.24}$$

and

$$E = TS - pV + \mu N + \mathcal{E}. \tag{6.25}$$

Then substitution of Eqs. (6.22) in (6.21) yields

$$dE = T\,dS - p\,dV + \mu\,dN$$

and, hence,

$$d\mathcal{E} = -S\,dT + V\,dp - N\,d\mu.$$

Comparison of these results with Eqs. (6.8), (6.19), and (6.20) shows that the general definition of $\mathcal{E}$ in Eq. (6.21) is consistent with $\mathcal{E} = (p - \hat{p})V$ for a μ, V, T system.

6.3 THERMODYNAMICS OF *N, p, T* SYSTEMS

This is a closed one-component system in contact with a heat bath, and at pressure p. Examples would be a small colloidal particle or crystallite made up of N molecules, or a linear hydrocarbon molecule with N carbon atoms, both in an inert* solvent. Another example is an incompressible macromolecule under a stretching force f. The environmental variables are N, f, T for such a system.

A special case is a system under an invariable pressure or force of zero. Examples are a colloidal particle in a rarefied gas and a rodlike macromolecule, in a solvent, whose length can change through an alteration in molecular configuration. In the latter case, the length $\overline{L}$ replaces the volume $\overline{V}$ as a dependent thermodynamic variable. If the macromolecule has free ends in solution, $f = 0$. The helix–coil transition in synthetic polypeptides is a specific example, but not a very good one, for the molecule is rodlike only in the helical regions, and furthermore these regions are oriented in different directions. The contour length is not a suitable variable here because this length is not thermodynamically conjugate to a force f exerted on the ends of the chain. The end-to-end length along a

---

* This restriction can be removed.

given direction could be used, but this length does not depend linearly on the fraction of helical content. The most natural and satisfactory way to treat the helix–coil transition is as an isomeric equilibrium. We shall, however, consider, by other methods, some simple models in Section 6.4 which are of the helix–coil type.

Use of the environmental variable N implies that the small system is closed. A polymer molecule made up of N monomers held together by chemical bonds is a clear-cut example. But an aggregate of molecules bound by relatively weak van der Waals forces would be open rather than closed. In this case the environmental variables, at equilibrium, would be μ, p, T. The criterion distinguishing the two cases is whether or not the system maintains $N =$ const, within experimental error, during the time required for the thermodynamic measurements of interest. Experimental N, p, T systems will usually be colloidal aggregates, which are essentially nonvolatile (in a gas), insoluble (in a solvent), or chemically bonded polymers.

Although the system is closed here, primary interest attaches to the effects of varying N. For this, experiments must be done on samples with different values of N.

With the above introduction, we now turn to the thermodynamics. Formally this case is the same as the μ, V, T case just discussed because there are two intensive variables and one extensive variable. As we shall see, we need only replace μ by $-p$, $\overline{N}$ by $\overline{V}$, $-p$ by μ, $-\hat{p}$ by $\hat{\mu}$, and V by N.

For an ensemble of N, p, T systems, the analogue of Eq. (6.4) is

$$dE_t = T\,dS_t - p\,dV_t + \mu\mathfrak{N}\,dN + X\,d\mathfrak{N}, \tag{6.26}$$

where

$$X \equiv \left(\frac{\partial E_t}{\partial \mathfrak{N}}\right)_{S_t,V_t,N}.$$

The physical significance of the $X\,d\mathfrak{N}$ term is that we are adding systems to the ensemble, each containing N molecules, in such a way that $S_t = \mathfrak{N}S$ and $V_t = \mathfrak{N}\overline{V}$ are held constant. This is a chemical potential type of term; so we define $\hat{\mu}$ by $\hat{\mu}N \equiv X$. Whereas μ is a "differential" chemical potential (molecules are added to the ensemble by changing N in each of the $\mathfrak{N}$ systems), $\hat{\mu}$ is an "integral" chemical potential (molecules are added to the ensemble in "packages" of N each). In general, for a small system, μ and $\hat{\mu}$ differ from each other and from the macroscopic chemical potential at the same p and T. Both μ and $\hat{\mu}$ approach this macroscopic value as $N \to \infty$.

Integration of Eq. (6.26), T, p, and N being held constant, gives

$$E_t = TS_t - pV_t + \hat{\mu}N\mathfrak{N}$$

and

$$\overline{E} = TS - p\overline{V} + \hat{\mu}N. \tag{6.27}$$

If we use Eq. (6.27) to eliminate $X = \hat{\mu}N$ in Eq. (6.26), we find

$$d\overline{E} = T\,dS - p\,d\overline{V} + \mu\,dN. \tag{6.28}$$

Equation (6.27) can also be written as

$$\overline{E} = TS - p\overline{V} + \mu N + (\hat{\mu} - \mu)N. \tag{6.29}$$

The last term vanishes for a macroscopic system.

Other fundamental equations are

$$d(\hat{\mu}N) = -S\,dT + \overline{V}\,dp + \mu\,dN, \tag{6.30}$$

$$d[(\hat{\mu} - \mu)N] = -S\,dT + \overline{V}\,dp - N\,d\mu. \tag{6.31}$$

Again we note that there is an extra degree of freedom for a small system.

If we define the Gibbs free energy G by

$$G \equiv \hat{\mu}N = \overline{E} - TS + p\overline{V} = X, \tag{6.32}$$

then

$$\left(\frac{\partial \hat{\mu}N}{\partial N}\right)_{T,p} = \left(\frac{\partial G}{\partial N}\right)_{T,p} = \mu. \tag{6.33}$$

But $G/N = \hat{\mu}$.

The connection with statistical mechanics is

$$-\hat{\mu}N = kT \ln \Delta, \tag{6.34}$$

where

$$\Delta(N,p,T) = \sum_V Q(N,V,T)e^{-pV/kT}.$$

This is the *constant pressure* partition function, analogous to the grand partition function for a μ, V, T system. The proof of Eq. (6.34) is similar to that of Eq. (6.14) (Problem 6.2).

From Eqs. (6.29) and (6.31), we see that

$$\mathcal{E} = (\hat{\mu} - \mu)N. \tag{6.35}$$

It will prove convenient here and elsewhere to use the notation μ and $\hat{\mu}$ whenever these quantities occur alone, but when they appear as a difference, we shall usually write $(\hat{\mu} - \mu)N = \mathcal{E}$.

We define

$$H = \overline{E} + p\overline{V}, \tag{6.36}$$

$$A = \overline{E} - TS. \tag{6.37}$$

Then

$$dH = T\,dS + \overline{V}\,dp + \mu\,dN, \tag{6.38}$$

$$dA = -S\,dT - p\,d\overline{V} + \mu\,dN. \tag{6.39}$$

From Eq. (6.30),

$$\left(\frac{\partial \hat{\mu} N}{\partial T}\right)_{p,N} = -S, \qquad \left(\frac{\partial \hat{\mu}}{\partial T}\right)_{p,N} = -\frac{S}{N}, \tag{6.40}$$

$$\left(\frac{\partial \hat{\mu} N}{\partial p}\right)_{T,N} = \overline{V}, \qquad \left(\frac{\partial \hat{\mu}}{\partial p}\right)_{T,N} = \frac{\overline{V}}{N}, \tag{6.41}$$

$$\left(\frac{\partial \hat{\mu} N}{\partial N}\right)_{T,p} = \mu, \qquad \left(\frac{\partial \hat{\mu}}{\partial N}\right)_{T,p} = \frac{\mu - \hat{\mu}}{N}. \tag{6.42}$$

Consequently,

$$d\hat{\mu} = -(S/N)\,dT + (\overline{V}/N)\,dp - (\mathcal{E}/N^2)\,dN, \tag{6.43}$$

or

$$(\hat{\mu} - \mu)\,dN = -S\,dT + \overline{V}\,dp - N\,d\hat{\mu}. \tag{6.44}$$

Next, we want the analogue of Eq. (6.43) for $d\mu$. We first write the three Maxwell relations which follow from Eq. (6.30):

$$-\left(\frac{\partial S}{\partial p}\right)_{T,N} = \left(\frac{\partial \overline{V}}{\partial T}\right)_{p,N},$$
$$-\left(\frac{\partial S}{\partial N}\right)_{T,p} = \left(\frac{\partial \mu}{\partial T}\right)_{p,N},$$
$$\left(\frac{\partial \overline{V}}{\partial N}\right)_{T,p} = \left(\frac{\partial \mu}{\partial p}\right)_{T,N}. \tag{6.45}$$

We shall also need

$$\left(\frac{\partial \mu}{\partial N}\right)_{T,p} = -\frac{1}{N}\left(\frac{\partial \mathcal{E}}{\partial N}\right)_{T,p}, \tag{6.46}$$

from Eq. (6.31). Then, Eqs. (6.45) and (6.46) give

$$d\mu = -\left(\frac{\partial S}{\partial N}\right)_{T,p} dT + \left(\frac{\partial \overline{V}}{\partial N}\right)_{T,p} dp - \frac{1}{N}\left(\frac{\partial \mathcal{E}}{\partial N}\right)_{T,p} dN. \tag{6.47}$$

This should be compared with Eq. (6.43).

The differential-integral relation between μ and $\hat{\mu}$ is also evident from

$$\hat{\mu} = \frac{G}{N} = \frac{\overline{E}}{N} - T\frac{S}{N} + p\frac{\overline{V}}{N} = \frac{H}{N} - T\frac{S}{N}, \tag{6.48}$$

$$\begin{aligned}\mu = \left(\frac{\partial G}{\partial N}\right)_{T,p} &= \left(\frac{\partial \overline{E}}{\partial N}\right)_{T,p} - T\left(\frac{\partial S}{\partial N}\right)_{T,p} + p\left(\frac{\partial \overline{V}}{\partial N}\right)_{T,p} \\ &= \left(\frac{\partial H}{\partial N}\right)_{T,p} - T\left(\frac{\partial S}{\partial N}\right)_{T,p}\end{aligned} \tag{6.49}$$

and from

$$\left(\frac{\partial \hat{\mu}/T}{\partial T}\right)_{p,N} = -\frac{1}{T^2}\frac{H}{N}, \qquad \left(\frac{\partial \mu/T}{\partial T}\right)_{p,N} = -\frac{1}{T^2}\left(\frac{\partial H}{\partial N}\right)_{T,p}. \tag{6.50}$$

It is helpful to note (a) which terms in an equation are of *macroscopic order* (i.e., are significant in the macroscopic limit) and which terms are *small* (i.e., vanish in the macroscopic limit), and (b) what the macroscopic form of an equation is. Thus, terms involving $\mathcal{E}$ or $\hat{\mu} - \mu$ are always small. The same is true of derivatives of intensive variables holding intensive variables constant, such as $(\partial\mu/\partial N)_{T,p}$. Derivatives involving extensive variables holding intensive variables constant are of macroscopic order but become a simple ratio when $N \to \infty$. For example,

$$\lim_{N\to\infty}\left(\frac{\partial G}{\partial N}\right)_{T,p} = \frac{G}{N}.$$

There are some expressions which are of macroscopic order but which do not appear in ordinary macroscopic thermodynamic equations. These rather resemble indeterminate forms. For example, from Eq. (6.31),

$$\left(\frac{\partial \mathcal{E}}{\partial T}\right)_{p,\mu} = -S, \qquad \left(\frac{\partial \mathcal{E}}{\partial p}\right)_{T,\mu} = \overline{V}, \qquad \left(\frac{\partial \mathcal{E}}{\partial \mu}\right)_{T,p} = -N. \tag{6.51}$$

Hence the dependence of the small term $\mathcal{E}$ on T, p, and μ suffices to determine the *extensive* properties, of macroscopic order, of the system.

Effect of size on intensive variables. We bring together here a number of relations showing the effect of size (measured by N, in this case) on intensive variables, especially with pressure and temperature held constant. Such effects are characteristic of small systems and are absent in macroscopic systems. We have already seen that

$$\left(\frac{\partial \hat{\mu}}{\partial N}\right)_{T,p} = -\frac{\mathcal{E}}{N^2} \quad \text{and} \quad \left(\frac{\partial \mu}{\partial N}\right)_{T,p} = -\frac{1}{N}\left(\frac{\partial \mathcal{E}}{\partial N}\right)_{T,p}. \tag{6.52}$$

Among other intensive properties of interest are those of the form

$Y/N = \text{Y}$, where $Y = S, \overline{V}, \overline{E}$, etc. We find

$$\left(\frac{\partial \text{S}}{\partial N}\right)_{T,p} = \frac{1}{N^2}\left(\frac{\partial \mathcal{E}}{\partial T}\right)_{p,N}, \tag{6.53}$$

$$\left(\frac{\partial \text{V}}{\partial N}\right)_{T,p} = -\frac{1}{N^2}\left(\frac{\partial \mathcal{E}}{\partial p}\right)_{T,N}, \tag{6.54}$$

$$\left(\frac{\partial N/\overline{V}}{\partial N}\right)_{T,p} = \frac{1}{V^2}\left(\frac{\partial \mathcal{E}}{\partial p}\right)_{T,N}, \tag{6.55}$$

$$\left(\frac{\partial \text{E}}{\partial N}\right)_{T,p} = -\frac{1}{N^2}\left[\mathcal{E} - T\left(\frac{\partial \mathcal{E}}{\partial T}\right)_{p,N} - p\left(\frac{\partial \mathcal{E}}{\partial p}\right)_{T,N}\right], \tag{6.56}$$

$$\left(\frac{\partial \text{H}}{\partial N}\right)_{T,p} = -\frac{1}{N^2}\left[\mathcal{E} - T\left(\frac{\partial \mathcal{E}}{\partial T}\right)_{p,N}\right], \tag{6.57}$$

$$\left(\frac{\partial \text{A}}{\partial N}\right)_{T,p} = -\frac{1}{N^2}\left[\mathcal{E} - p\left(\frac{\partial \mathcal{E}}{\partial p}\right)_{T,N}\right]. \tag{6.58}$$

Equation (6.57) is a Gibbs-Helmholtz type of relation. Equations (6.50) are other examples of the same type.

It is interesting to note, but not surprising, that it has been possible to express all the effects of size on intensive variables in this subsection in terms of $\mathcal{E}$ and derivatives of $\mathcal{E}$.

There are a number of other general relations that might be derived, especially concerning heat capacities and the equation of state, but we forego these and turn now to some examples.

6.4 EXAMPLES OF N, p, T SYSTEMS

In this section we illustrate a few of the above thermodynamic functions and equations with simple theoretical models.

Colloidal particle. As our first example we choose the case referred to at the beginning of Section 6.1. Suppose that the Gibbs free energy of a spherical colloidal particle has the form

$$G = N\hat{\mu} = Nf(p, T) + a(p, T)N^{2/3} + b(T)\ln N + c(p, T). \tag{6.59}$$

The term Nf is the macroscopic term, while $aN^{2/3}$ is a surface free energy. The constant a is positive and has the order of magnitude of the surface tension multiplied by the square of the nearest neighbor distance. A more complete treatment would include an $N^{1/3}$ term, arising from the variation of surface tension with curvature. The last two terms in Eq. (6.59) may be attributed to rotation and translation. But our point of view here is simply that Eq. (6.59) is an empirical thermodynamic expression applicable to a small colloidal particle.

From Eqs. (6.40) to (6.42), we have

$$-S = \left(\frac{\partial G}{\partial T}\right)_{p,N} = \frac{\partial f}{\partial T} N + \frac{\partial a}{\partial T} N^{2/3} + \frac{db}{dT} \ln N + \frac{\partial c}{\partial T}, \tag{6.60}$$

$$\overline{V} = \left(\frac{\partial G}{\partial p}\right)_{T,N} = \frac{\partial f}{\partial p} N + \frac{\partial a}{\partial p} N^{2/3} + \frac{\partial c}{\partial p}, \tag{6.61}$$

$$\mu = \left(\frac{\partial G}{\partial N}\right)_{T,p} = f + \tfrac{2}{3} a N^{-1/3} + b N^{-1}. \tag{6.62}$$

Then

$$\mathcal{E} = N(\hat{\mu} - \mu) = \tfrac{1}{3} a N^{2/3} + b(\ln N - 1) + c. \tag{6.63}$$

The energy $\overline{E}$ follows directly from the above functions. These functions can now be used to verify various equations in Section 6.3, for example, Eqs. (6.53), (6.54), etc. This task is left to the reader (Problem 6.5).

Ideal lattice gas. Consider a lattice of M identical and distinguishable sites, N of which are occupied by molecules. These molecules form what is known as a *lattice gas* (see Section 2.4). We omit internal degrees of freedom (vibration, etc.) for simplicity (that is, $q \equiv 1$ in Section 2.4). Also, in an *ideal* lattice gas, we omit intermolecular forces. Hence the only energy possible for the system is $E = 0$. We have, in the notation of Eq. (6.34),

$$Q(N, M) = \frac{M!}{N!(M-N)!} \tag{6.64}$$

and

$$\begin{aligned} \Delta(N, \Phi/kT) &= \sum_{M=N}^{\infty} Q(N, M) e^{-\Phi M/kT} \\ &= \frac{x^N}{(1-x)^{N+1}}, \end{aligned}$$

where $x = e^{-\Phi/kT}$ and Φ (Section 2.4) replaces p. Then

$$-\frac{G}{kT} = -\frac{N\hat{\mu}}{kT} = \ln \Delta = N \ln x - (N+1) \ln (1-x) \tag{6.65}$$

and

$$-\frac{\hat{\mu}}{kT} = \ln \frac{x}{1-x} - \frac{1}{N} \ln (1-x). \tag{6.66}$$

Also, we have

$$-\frac{\mu}{kT}=\left(\frac{\partial - G/kT}{\partial N}\right)_x=\ln\frac{x}{1-x}, \tag{6.67}$$

$$\mathcal{E}=N(\hat{\mu}-\mu)=kT\ln(1-x), \tag{6.68}$$

$$\overline{M}=\left(\frac{\partial G/kT}{\partial\Phi/kT}\right)_N=\frac{N+x}{1-x}, \tag{6.69}$$

or

$$-\ln x=\frac{\Phi}{kT}=-\ln\left(\frac{\overline{M}-N}{1+\overline{M}}\right).$$

This is the equation of state. The macroscopic limit is

$$\frac{\Phi}{kT}=-\ln\left(1-\frac{N}{\overline{M}}\right), \tag{6.70}$$

as in Eq. (2.35).

We find for the entropy, after eliminating x,

$$\begin{aligned} S/k &= (\Phi\overline{M}/kT)-(\hat{\mu}N/kT) \\ &= (1+\overline{M})\ln(1+\overline{M})-(1+N)\ln(1+N) \\ &\quad -(\overline{M}-N)\ln(\overline{M}-N). \end{aligned} \tag{6.71}$$

Stirling's approximation has not been used above. Equations (6.65), (6.66), (6.69), and (6.71) are valid for very small N, even $N = 1$. Equations (6.67) and (6.68), on the other hand, involve a differentiation with respect to the discrete variable N and cannot be taken to arbitrarily small N.

In this model there are no edge effects, rotational effects, etc. Deviations from macroscopic behavior are of order unity relative to $O(N)$ and might be termed "pure" small-number effects.

The terms of order $\ln N$ and, especially, $O(N^{2/3})$ in the previous example are much larger than the small terms here. Thus, suppose we want to begin to take into account small terms when their neglect would lead to a one-percent error. For a surface (boundary) effect in a three-dimensional system, we would then have

$$N^{2/3}/N=0.01, \qquad \text{or} \qquad N=10^6.$$

Hence a system is "small," by this criterion, when $N < 10^6$. For a boundary effect in a two-dimensional system,

$$N^{1/2}/N=0.01; \qquad N<10^4.$$

For a ln N term:

$$\ln N/N = 0.01; \qquad N < 600.$$

For a term of order unity (boundary effect in one dimension, or "pure" effect):

$$1/N = 0.01; \qquad N < 100.$$

Helix–coil transition. We have already mentioned that this subject is best treated as an isomeric equilibrium. But an oversimplified rodlike model provides a nice example of an N, f, T system. We begin with a modified version of one of the special cases treated by Gibbs and DiMarzio.*

Consider a rodlike macromolecule containing N units, each of which can be in two states, H (helix) and C (coil) (compare Section 3.4). For generality we include the possibility of exerting a force f on the ends of the chain, although $f = 0$ is the case of most interest. Rotation of the macromolecule is omitted. Let $j_H(T)$ and $j_C(T)$ be intrinsic partition functions for H and C units, and let the constants l_H and l_C be the lengths of a unit ($l_C > l_H$). The total length, for a rod, is then just the sum of the unit lengths.

We investigate first the special case in which coil regions can exist only at the two ends of the chain. That is, the helix can be "unzippered" from the ends only. A typical sequence of units would then be

$$CCC\overset{*}{H}HHHHHCC.$$

If there are n H units and $N - n$ C units, the left end ($\overset{*}{\mathrm{H}}$) of the H sequence can be in any one of $N - n + 1$ locations, for $1 \leq n \leq N$. This is a configurational degeneracy. This degeneracy is unity when $n = 0$.

The partition function Δ is therefore

$$\begin{aligned}\Delta &= \sum_L Q(N, L, T)e^{fL/kT} \\ &= j_C^N e^{Nl_C f/kT} + \sum_{n=1}^{N} (N - n + 1) j_C^{N-n} j_H^n e^{[(N-n)l_C + nl_H]f/kT},\end{aligned} \tag{6.72}$$

where L is the total length of the macromolecule. The summation is easy, and we find

$$\Delta(N, f, T) = e^{-N\hat{\mu}/kT} = r_C^N \frac{Nr(1 - r) + 1 - 2r + r^{N+2}}{(1 - r)^2}, \tag{6.73}$$

where

$$r_C = j_C(T)e^{fl_C/kT}, \qquad r_H = j_H(T)e^{fl_H/kT}, \qquad r(f, T) = \frac{r_H}{r_C}.$$

---

* J. H. Gibbs and E. A. DiMarzio, *J. Chem. Phys.* **30,** 271 (1959).

In the macroscopic limit, $N \to \infty$,

$$\begin{aligned} \ln \Delta &\to N \ln r_C \qquad \text{if } r < 1 \\ &\to N \ln r_H \qquad \text{if } r > 1. \end{aligned} \tag{6.74}$$

This model thus predicts a first-order phase transition at $r = 1$ when $N = \infty$. This is a consequence of the fact that the model artificially allows only two HC boundaries instead of an indefinite number. As is well known, a first-order transition in a one-dimensional system with forces of finite range, treated exactly, can occur only in the double limit $N \to \infty$, $T \to 0$.

We find, for μ,

$$-\frac{\mu}{kT} = \left(\frac{\partial \ln \Delta}{\partial N}\right)_{T,f} = \ln r_C + \frac{r(1-r) + r^{N+2} \ln r}{Nr(1-r) + 1 - 2r + r^{N+2}}. \tag{6.75}$$

At $r = 1$,

$$-\frac{\hat{\mu}}{kT} = \ln r_C + \frac{1}{N} \ln \frac{N^2 + N + 2}{2} \tag{6.76}$$

$$-\frac{\mu}{kT} = \ln r_C + \frac{2N+1}{N^2 + N + 2}. \tag{6.77}$$

The mean value of n is linearly related to $\overline{L}$ by

$$\overline{L} = (N - \overline{n})l_C + \overline{n} l_H. \tag{6.78}$$

If we write Eq. (6.72) as

$$\Delta = r_C^N \left[1 + \sum_{n=1}^{N} (N - n + 1) r^n\right],$$

then

$$\overline{n} = r \frac{\partial \ln \Delta}{\partial r} \tag{6.79}$$

and

$$\frac{\overline{n}}{N} = \frac{r[N(1-r)(1+r^{N+1}) - 2r + 2r^{N+1}]}{N(1-r)[Nr(1-r) + 1 - 2r + r^{N+2}]}. \tag{6.80}$$

This quantity is the mean fraction of helical units in the chain. It is experimentally observable by optical methods. Figure 6.1 shows a plot of $\overline{n}/N$ against $\ln r$. To illustrate the physical significance of $\ln r$, we take $f = 0$ and suppose that both j_C and j_H have simple energy (e.g., hydrogen bond in H) and entropy (e.g., free rotation in C) factors. Then

$$r = \frac{j_H}{j_C} = \frac{\omega_H e^{-\epsilon_H/kT}}{\omega_C e^{-\epsilon_C/kT}}$$

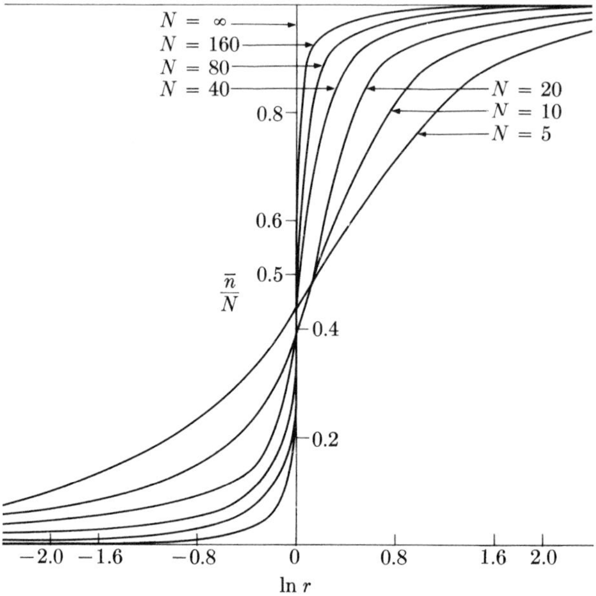

Fig. 6.1. Mean fraction of helical units as a function of ln r (linearly related to $1/T$) for the "unzipper from the ends" model of the helix-coil transition.

or

$$\ln r = \ln \frac{\omega_H}{\omega_C} + \frac{\epsilon_C - \epsilon_H}{kT},$$

where $\omega_H/\omega_C < 1$ and $\epsilon_C - \epsilon_H > 0$. Thus $\ln r$ depends linearly on $1/T$. A related experimental example is shown in Fig. 6.2.

The value of $\bar{n}/N$ at $r = 1$ is

$$\frac{\bar{n}}{N} = \frac{(N+1)(N+2)}{3(N^2+N+2)} \qquad (6.81)$$

$$\rightarrow \tfrac{1}{3} \qquad \text{as} \qquad N \rightarrow \infty.$$

Only the $N = \infty$ curve in Fig. 6.1 falls within the province of macroscopic thermodynamics. The other curves are in the domain of small-system thermodynamics. The effect of N on the intensive property $\bar{n}/N$ is very sizeable in this case.

Next, for purposes of comparison, let us turn to the simplest possible first-order phase-transition model. For a one-dimensional system this case is even more artificial than the above zipper model, as we allow only two of the terms in Eq. (6.72): $n = 0$ or $n = N$. This is an "all-or-none" system: all units are C or all H. This type of model is, however, physically significant for phase transitions in two- or three-dimensional systems.

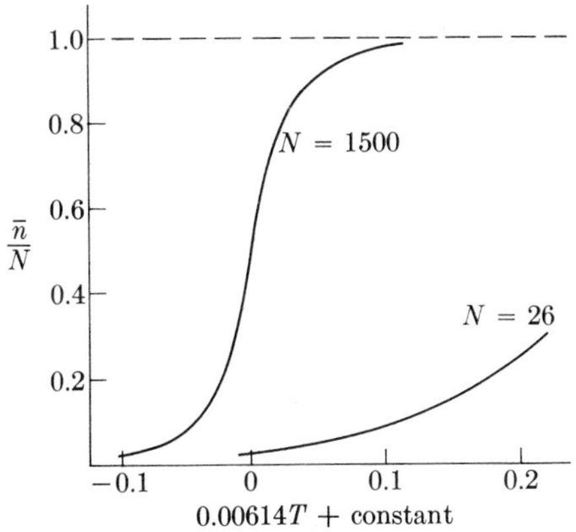

Fig. 6.2. Mean fraction of helical units as a function of T for poly-γ-benzyl-L-glutamate (smooth curves through experimental points). (Data from P. Doty and J. T. Yang, *J. Am. Chem. Soc.* **78,** 498 (1956). See also B. H. Zimm and J. K. Bragg, *J. Chem. Phys.* **31,** 526 (1959).) Usually $\bar{n}/N$ increases with $1/T$ rather than T.

We have, in the same notation as above,

$$\begin{aligned} \Delta = e^{-N\hat{\mu}/kT} &= r_C^N + r_H^N \\ &= r_C^N(1 + r^N). \end{aligned} \tag{6.82}$$

The macroscopic limit is again Eq. (6.74). For the chemical potentials we have

$$\begin{aligned} -\frac{\hat{\mu}}{kT} &= \ln r_C + \frac{1}{N}\ln(1 + r^N) \\ &= \ln r_C + \frac{1}{N}\ln 2 \qquad \text{when} \qquad r = 1; \end{aligned} \tag{6.83}$$

$$\begin{aligned} -\frac{\mu}{kT} &= \ln r_C + \frac{r^N \ln r}{1 + r^N} \\ &= \ln r_C \qquad \text{when} \qquad r = 1. \end{aligned} \tag{6.84}$$

The fraction of helical units is

$$\begin{aligned} \frac{\bar{n}}{N} &= \frac{r}{N}\frac{\partial \ln \Delta}{\partial r} = \frac{r^N}{1 + r^N} \\ &= \tfrac{1}{2} \qquad \text{when} \qquad r = 1. \end{aligned} \tag{6.85}$$

This quantity is shown as a function of $\ln r$ in Fig. 6.3. Again there are relatively large effects of N on the behavior of the system. This is characteristic of a phase transition.

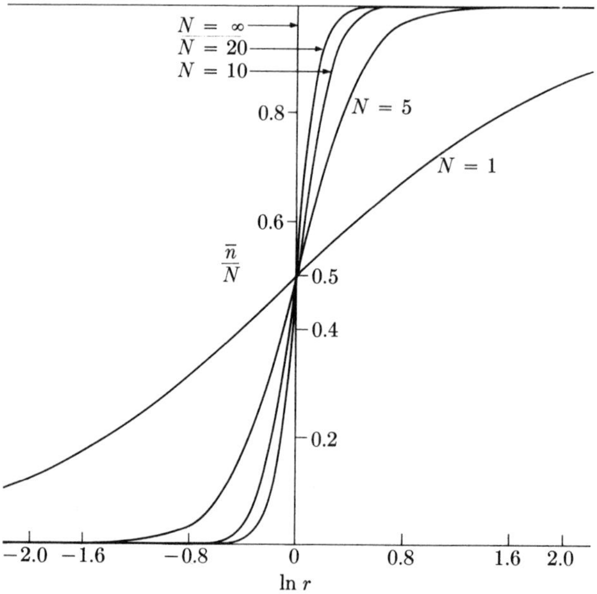

Fig. 6.3. Mean fraction of helical units as a function of ln r (linearly related to $1/T$) for the "all-or-none" model of the helix-coil transition. The $N = 1$ curve also represents Eq. (6.88).

Because of the simplicity of the above results, it is especially easy to check thermodynamic equations with them. Suggested examples, which are left to the reader, are Eqs. (6.50) and (6.54).

Finally, again for comparison, suppose each unit can be C or H, independently. The partition function is

$$\Delta = \sum_{n=0}^{N} \frac{N! r_C^{N-n} r_H^n}{(N-n)!n!} = (r_C + r_H)^N. \tag{6.86}$$

Then

$$\mu = \hat{\mu} = -kT \ln (r_C + r_H) \tag{6.87}$$

and

$$\bar{n}/N = r/(1 + r). \tag{6.88}$$

Except for notation, this is the same as Eq. (3.34). These expressions for μ, $\hat{\mu}$, and $\bar{n}/N$ are independent of N: for any N, this system behaves thermodynamically like a macroscopic system. Equation (6.88) is included in Fig. 6.3.

The three cases considered in this subsection are unrealistic but instructive models of a helix–coil or α–β system. There are, in reality, cooperative interactions between neighboring units in systems of this type. These interactions are taken into account in an extreme way here by allowing only three sequences (coil–helix–coil) in the zipper model and only one sequence (all coil or all helix) in the phase-transition model. The independent-unit model, on the other hand, does not take interactions between neighboring units into account at all.

6.5 FIRST-ORDER PHASE TRANSITIONS IN *N*, *p*, *T* SYSTEMS

An experimental macroscopic system may show discontinuities in various thermodynamic functions below a critical temperature, corresponding to a first-order phase transition. In theoretical work, these discontinuities are "sharp" only in the limit of an infinite system. Small systems will exhibit, instead, more or less gradual changes which approach discontinuities more closely the larger the system.

The exact treatment of first-order phase transitions is an important topic in macroscopic thermodynamics. This topic exists, as an exact branch of thermodynamics, only by virtue of the occurrence of sharp discontinuities in properties of macroscopic systems. Since such discontinuities are absent in small systems, there is no corresponding exact thermodynamics of first-order phase transitions.

From a formalistic and rigorous point of view, the thermodynamics of a *single*-phase small system should be used under all circumstances. If a phase transition is known to occur in a macroscopic system, it is ignored in the corresponding small system. Thus, for example, the treatment of a one-phase N, p, T system in Section 6.3 is valid for a small N, p, T system whether or not the infinite system shows phase transitions.

Of course, even in macroscopic thermodynamics it is quite legitimate to take a similar "black-box" attitude and ignore the possible existence of more than one phase in a system. In this case any phase transition which does in fact occur will be correctly taken into account implicitly, though not explicitly. But for a small system there is no choice: an *exact* treatment must take care of any phase transition implicitly; an exact, explicit analysis does not exist because of the absence of any discontinuities or sharply defined points or regions.

The above comments are, of course, purely thermodynamic in nature. One can investigate the nature of a phase transition, in various ways, exactly and explicitly for N finite or infinite by a statistical-mechanical analysis of a model.

Contrary to the above rather sterile position concerning the exact thermodynamics of phase transitions in small systems, it *is* possible to give an explicit *approximate* thermodynamic treatment of first-order phase transitions in a small N, p, T system. Furthermore, this approximation is probably excellent except near the critical point or for N too small. The remainder of this section will be devoted to this subject.

Phase transitions with other environmental variables require separate discussion. It should be mentioned here, though, that the μ, V, T case (Section 6.2) is formally identical with the present N, p, T case.

Nature of the "two-state" approximation. This approximation, once established, will be handled by thermodynamic methods. But the argument justifying the approximation comes from statistical mechanics.*

The normalized probability that an N, p, T system will be observed to have a volume V is

$$P(V) = \frac{Q(N, V, T)e^{-pV/kT}}{\Delta}, \tag{6.89}$$

where Δ is the N, p, T partition function,

$$\Delta(N, p, T) = \sum_V Q(N, V, T)e^{-pV/kT}. \tag{6.90}$$

At an "ordinary" point (i.e., not near a critical point or phase transition) the function $P(V)$ has a single peak about $\overline{V}$, as shown in Fig. 6.4(a). For a macroscopic system, the peak in Fig. 6.4(a) approaches a δ-function. But, for a small system, the fluctuations in V about $\overline{V}$ become appreciable. At a critical point, $P(V)$ probably has a flat top, as shown schematically in Fig. 6.4(b). At the middle of a phase transition (phases A and B; $\overline{V}_A > \overline{V}_B$), on the other hand, $P(V)$ has two separated peaks, as in Fig. 6.4(c). These become δ-functions at $\overline{V}_A$ and $\overline{V}_B$ for a macroscopic system. In the transition region, but not at its middle, the two peaks remain at $\overline{V}_A$ and $\overline{V}_B$, but they have different heights and areas.

According to Fig. 6.4(c), an N, p, T system in a phase-transition region may be observed to have a volume near $\overline{V}_A$ or near $\overline{V}_B$ [the range of fluctuations about these values depends on the size of the system, just as in Fig. 6.4(a)], but the probability of observing intermediate values of V, say, $V = \overline{V}$, is negligible. Thus the phase-transition region may be regarded

---

* The following discussion is based on appendix 9 of T. L. Hill, *Statistical Mechanics* (New York: McGraw-Hill, 1956). The reader interested in a more detailed argument should consult this reference. A μ, V, T system, with $P(N)$, is discussed in *Statistical Mechanics*, instead of an N, p, T system, with $P(V)$. But these two cases are formally identical. See also T. L. Hill, *J. Chem. Phys.*, **23,** 812 (1955).

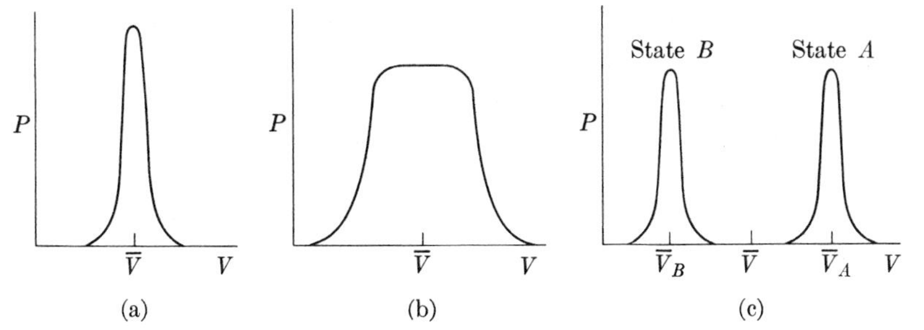

Fig. 6.4. The function $P(V)$. (a) At an "ordinary point"; (b) at a critical point; (c) at the middle of a first-order phase transition. In all these curves, N, p, and T are constant.

as a composite of two "ordinary" states A and B. A given system in the ensemble may be assumed to be either in state A or in state B, but not in an intermediate state. This is the origin of the term "two-state approximation."

The physical reason why intermediate states are unimportant is that, while states A and B are both pure phases, an intermediate state, say, $V = \overline{V}$, must have both phases A and B present, with an *interface* between them. The interface contributes an extra free energy to the system (see Chapter 1) and introduces a corresponding unfavorable Boltzmann factor. Specifically, for a three-dimensional system, in the notation of Fig. 6.4(c),

$$P(\overline{V}_A)/P(\overline{V}) = O(e^{aN^{2/3}/kT}), \tag{6.91}$$

where a is a positive constant of order kT, proportional to the interfacial tension, and $N^{2/3}$ is the approximate number of molecules at the interface. The magnitude of the ratio in Eq. (6.91) determines the degree of validity of the two-state approximation. The ratio is not large if N is very small or if the system is near a critical point (where $a \longrightarrow 0$). In a two-dimensional system, $N^{2/3}$ is replaced by $N^{1/2}$. In a one-dimensional system, this quantity becomes $N^{0/1}$ or unity. A one-dimensional system with forces of finite range does not exhibit a first-order transition, as is well known. At a "transition" in a one-dimensional system, according to Eq. (6.91), $P(V)$ will have more or less of a flat top as in Fig. 6.4(b), and the two-state approximation is not applicable.

A real, macroscopic N, p, T system at a phase transition (e.g., ice plus water in a heat bath) would not always be observed as all ice or all water because of the length of time required to switch from one state to the other. This time would be relatively short for small systems.

There are many approximate statistical mechanical theories of phase transitions (e.g., the van der Waals equation) which lead to a p–V or μ–N "loop" from the canonical ensemble. These theories are characterized by the fact that the system, in the canonical ensemble, is always forced to have a uniform density throughout V: two phases are never present at the same time. In the N, p, T ensemble for such a theory, the function $P(V)$ appears as in Fig. 6.4(c). It is easy to show that

$$P(\overline{V}_A)/P(\overline{V}) = O(e^N) \tag{6.92}$$

except near the critical point, where a flat top as in Fig. 6.4(b) is found. Thus the two-state approximation may be employed with theories of this type except when N is very small or near a critical point.

Some deductions from the approximation. We now accept the two-state approximation and deduce some of its thermodynamic consequences. The observed small system p–$\overline{V}$ curve is shown schematically as ADB in Fig. 6.5. The same curve is included in Fig. 6.6 along with the schematic $N = \infty$ curve, which shows a sharp transition. In Fig. 6.5, ACF is the extrapolation of the state A curve, or ACF may possibly be available as a metastable experimental curve. This is the way the system would behave, based on the state A peak only in Fig. 6.4(c): all systems in the ensemble stay in state A. The extrapolation is well defined for a theoretical model, but it may be somewhat ambiguous if only an experimental curve ADB

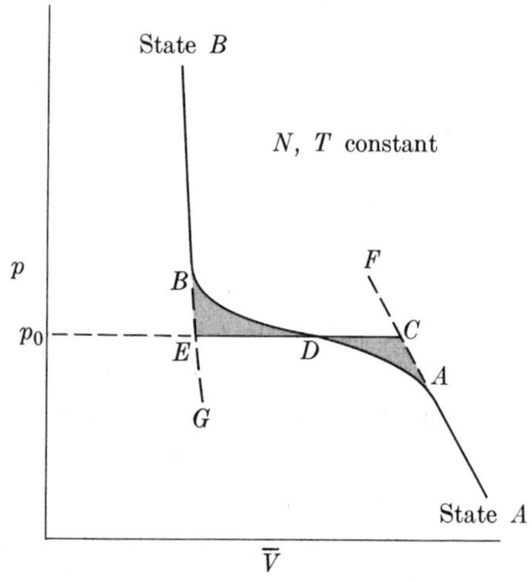

Fig. 6.5. Schematic $p - \overline{V}$ isotherm for small system at a temperature such that the macroscopic system has a first-order phase transition. BDA is the experimental curve.

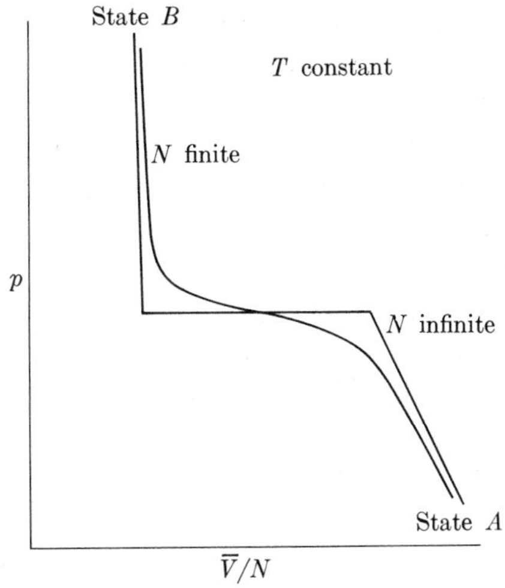

Fig. 6.6. "Sharp" phase transition in an infinite system and the corresponding somewhat smoothed-out transition in a finite system.

is available. In this case, the theorems deduced below will aid in locating the correct extrapolation. The same comments apply, of course, to the extrapolation BEG.

Let $G_A = N\hat{\mu}_A$ and $G_B = N\hat{\mu}_B$ be the Gibbs free energies of states A (curve ACF in Fig. 6.5) and B (BEG in Fig. 6.5), respectively. Both G_A and G_B are functions of N, p, and T, but we shall be concerned for the moment only with the p dependence (N and T held constant). Consider an ensemble of $\mathfrak{N}$ distinguishable N, p, T systems. Each system, in the present approximation, can be either in state A or in state B. If $\mathfrak{N}_A$ systems are in state A and $\mathfrak{N}_B$ in state B, then the total Gibbs free energy of the ensemble is

$$G_t = \mathfrak{N}_A G_A + \mathfrak{N}_B G_B - kT \ln (\mathfrak{N}!/\mathfrak{N}_A!\mathfrak{N}_B!) = \mathfrak{N}G = \mathfrak{N}N\hat{\mu}, \quad (6.93)$$

where the factorial expression is the number of different arrangements of the A and B systems.

The equilibrium value of $\mathfrak{N}_A$ may be found by minimizing G_t with respect to $\mathfrak{N}_A$, holding p, T, N, and $\mathfrak{N}$ constant. We put $\mathfrak{N}_B = \mathfrak{N} - \mathfrak{N}_A$, use the simple Stirling approximation (since $\mathfrak{N} \to \infty$), and find

$$\frac{\mathfrak{N}_A}{\mathfrak{N}_B} = \frac{e^{-G_A/kT}}{e^{-G_B/kT}} = \left(\frac{e^{-\hat{\mu}_A/kT}}{e^{-\hat{\mu}_B/kT}}\right)^N. \quad (6.94)$$

Here $\hat{\mu}_A$ and $\hat{\mu}_B$ are considered known functions of p (N and T constant). Thus, for any p, we can calculate $\mathfrak{N}_A/\mathfrak{N}_B$. If p is chosen so that $\hat{\mu}_A = \hat{\mu}_B$

exactly, then $\mathfrak{N}_A = \mathfrak{N}_B$. We denote this value of p by p_0. If p is slightly different from p_0 so that, say, $\hat{\mu}_B > \hat{\mu}_A$ by a very small fraction of kT, then, according to Eq. (6.94), $\mathfrak{N}_A \gg \mathfrak{N}_B$ when N is very large, and essentially all systems are in state A. The form of Eq. (6.94) thus makes it clear how the large magnitude of N in a macroscopic system leads to the discontinuous behavior shown by the "N infinite" curve in Fig. 6.6. On the other hand, when N is small, say, 20, 100, or 1000, the transition from $\mathfrak{N}_A = \mathfrak{N}_B$ at $p = p_0$ to $\mathfrak{N}_A \cong \mathfrak{N}$ or $\mathfrak{N}_B \cong \mathfrak{N}$ as p is decreased or increased, respectively, is more gradual. The smaller the value of N, the greater the range in p over which the transition is extended.

The equilibrium between state A and state B, for small N, is intermediate in nature between an isomeric chemical equilibrium ($N = 1$) and a macroscopic phase equilibrium ($N = \infty$). Fluctuations about the equilibrium value of $\mathfrak{N}_A$ are negligible, incidentally, because $\mathfrak{N} \to \infty$.

The pressure p_0 is a function of N and T. As $N \to \infty$, p_0 approaches the pressure at which the two macroscopic phases are in equilibrium at temperature T.

From Eq. (6.93) we can write

$$G(N, p, T) = P_A G_A + P_B G_B + kT(P_A \ln P_A + P_B \ln P_B), \qquad (6.95)$$

where $P_A = \mathfrak{N}_A/\mathfrak{N}$ is the probability of a system being in state A and $P_B = 1 - P_A$. In this equation, G_A and G_B are functions of N, p, and T, as are also P_A and P_B through Eq. (6.94). We also have, on division by N,

$$\hat{\mu}(N, p, T) = P_A \hat{\mu}_A + P_B \hat{\mu}_B + (kT/N)(P_A \ln P_A + P_B \ln P_B). \qquad (6.96)$$

If we now differentiate Eq. (6.95) with respect to p, using

$$\left(\frac{\partial G_A}{\partial p}\right)_{N,T} = \overline{V}_A, \qquad \left(\frac{\partial G_B}{\partial p}\right)_{N,T} = \overline{V}_B$$

and

$$\left(\frac{\partial P_A}{\partial p}\right)_{N,T} = \frac{1}{kT}(\overline{V}_B - \overline{V}_A)P_A P_B,$$

$$\left(\frac{\partial P_B}{\partial p}\right)_{N,T} = \frac{1}{kT}(\overline{V}_A - \overline{V}_B)P_A P_B, \qquad (6.97)$$

which follow from Eq. (6.94), we find

$$\left(\frac{\partial G}{\partial p}\right)_{N,T} = \overline{V} = P_A \overline{V}_A + P_B \overline{V}_B \qquad (6.98)$$

as expected. Similarly,

$$\left(\frac{\partial G}{\partial N}\right)_{p,T} = \mu = P_A \mu_A + P_B \mu_B. \qquad (6.99)$$

Thus the experimental curve $\overline{V}(p)$ in Fig. 6.5 (ADB) is a simple linear combination of the extrapolated or metastable curves $\overline{V}_A(p)$ (ACF) and $\overline{V}_B(p)$ (BEG), with weights $P_A(p)$ and $P_B(p)$ from Eq. (6.94): the ensemble is a mixture of systems in state A and state B.

In particular, at $p = p_0$, $\overline{V}$ is midway between $\overline{V}_A$ and $\overline{V}_B$:

$$\overline{V}(p_0) = \tfrac{1}{2}\overline{V}_A(p_0) + \tfrac{1}{2}\overline{V}_B(p_0). \tag{6.100}$$

Thus we have the following theorem: if the experimental curve $\overline{V}(p)$ and the extrapolated curves $\overline{V}_A(p)$ and $\overline{V}_B(p)$ are available, then adjustment of a line segment parallel to the $\overline{V}$ axis, which connects the two extrapolated curves, until the line segment is bisected by the $\overline{V}(p)$ curve will locate that value of p, p_0, at which $\hat{\mu}_A = \hat{\mu}_B$. For example, in Fig. 6.5, D bisects the line EC, and $\hat{\mu}_A$ at C is equal to $\hat{\mu}_B$ at E.

It should be noted that the theorem is based on the two-state approximation; that the equality of $\hat{\mu}_A$ and $\hat{\mu}_B$ resembles the macroscopic phase equilibrium condition, but here C and E are not points on the experimental curve ADB; that this theorem is an "equal-distance" (that is, $ED = DC$) theorem in contrast to the well-known Maxwell "equal-area" theorem; and that metastable but not unstable parts of curves are involved.

It turns out that μ is fundamental in determining chemical equilibria in small systems, while here we see that phase equilibria depend on $\hat{\mu}$. The reason is obvious: in the former case individual molecules change their state, while in the latter whole systems change their state (in the two-state approximation).

Figure 6.7 shows a schematic plot of $\hat{\mu}$ against p, as calculated from Eq. (6.96). The labeling is the same as in Fig. 6.5. Thus AF is the function

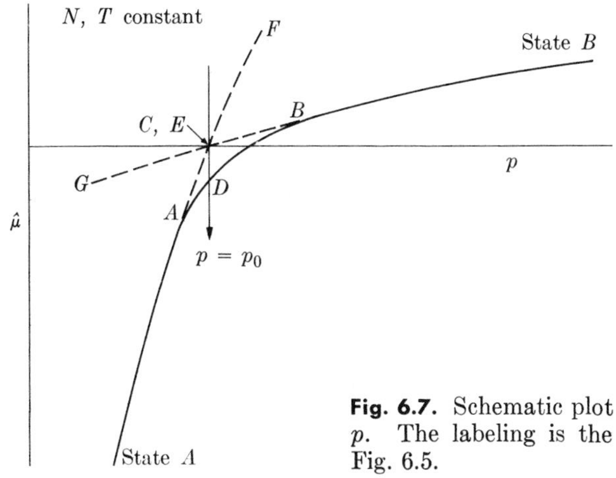

Fig. 6.7. Schematic plot of $\hat{\mu}$ against p. The labeling is the same as in Fig. 6.5.

$\hat{\mu}_A(p)$, while BG is $\hat{\mu}_B(p)$. The observed curve ADB in Fig. 6.7 approaches $ACEB$ more closely as $N \to \infty$ (of course the curves AC and EB would themselves change somewhat as $N \to \infty$, as implied by Fig. 6.6). This can be put quantitatively: according to Eq. (6.96), the distance CD in Fig. 6.7 is $(kT/N) \ln 2$.

In addition to the equal-distance theorem, there is also an equal-area theorem, which we now state and prove. The theorem is the following: the line segment defined in the equal-distance theorem (i.e., placed so that it is bisected by the experimental curve) will produce two equal areas between the extrapolated and experimental curves (i.e., area $ACD =$ area BED in Fig. 6.5). The proof is very simple. Let p_A be any pressure at or below point A in Fig. 6.5. At such a pressure extrapolated (ACF) and experimental (ADB) curves have merged. Similarly, let p_B be any pressure at or above point B in Fig. 6.5. Then we have to show that

$$\int_{p_A}^{p_0} (\overline{V}_A - \overline{V})\, dp = \int_{p_0}^{p_B} (\overline{V} - \overline{V}_B)\, dp, \tag{6.101}$$

or

$$\int_{p_A}^{p_0} \overline{V}_A\, dp + \int_{p_0}^{p_B} \overline{V}_B\, dp = \int_{p_A}^{p_B} \overline{V}\, dp,$$

or

$$G_A(p_0) - G_A(p_A) + G_B(p_B) - G_B(p_0) = G(p_B) - G(p_A).$$

But by the equal-distance theorem, $G_A(p_0) = G_B(p_0)$. Also,

$$G_A(p_A) = G(p_A)$$

since $P_A = 1$ at $p = p_A$ in Eq. (6.95). Similarly, $G_B(p_B) = G(p_B)$. Hence the theorem is proved. The converse follows by reversing the argument: if the areas are made equal, then the pressure thus defined is that at which $\hat{\mu}_A = \hat{\mu}_B$.

We now have two independent ways of finding the pressure $p = p_0$ at which $\hat{\mu}_A = \hat{\mu}_B$: we can adjust the line EC so that it is bisected by the experimental curve; or we can adjust it so that two equal areas ACD and BED are formed. If the extrapolations are uncertain, the redundancy in these two methods can be used as a check to correct the extrapolations.

Equations of the Clausius-Clapeyron type. Using the theorems discussed above, we can locate points (C and E in Fig. 6.5) on the two extrapolated or metastable curves at which $\hat{\mu}_A = \hat{\mu}_B$. The two states represented by points C and E have the same values of N, p, T and $\hat{\mu}$. If conditions are varied, the equality of these four variables at C and E must be maintained. Thus variations in N, p, and T must satisfy $d\hat{\mu}_A = d\hat{\mu}_B$; hence only two of N, p, and T are independent.

It should be emphasized that we are discussing here the "equilibrium" between points on two metastable curves for a small system. Or, on the equilibrium curve, we are considering the point $\mathfrak{N}_A = \mathfrak{N}_B$ only. Because the system is small, there is an additional independent variable N which does not appear in the corresponding macroscopic problem.

From $d\hat{\mu}_A = d\hat{\mu}_B$ and Eq. (6.43) we have*

$$-\mathrm{s}_A\,dT + \mathrm{v}_A\,dp + \left(\frac{\mu_A - \hat{\mu}_A}{N}\right) dN = -\mathrm{s}_B\,dT + \mathrm{v}_B\,dp + \left(\frac{\mu_B - \hat{\mu}_B}{N}\right) dN, \tag{6.102}$$

where $\mathrm{s}_A = S_A/N$, etc. Then

$$\left(\frac{\partial p}{\partial T}\right)_N = \frac{\Delta \mathrm{s}}{\Delta \mathrm{v}} = \frac{\Delta \mathrm{H}}{T\,\Delta \mathrm{v}}, \tag{6.103}$$

$$\left(\frac{\partial T}{\partial N}\right)_p = \frac{\Delta \mu}{N\,\Delta \mathrm{s}} = \frac{\Delta \mu}{\Delta S} = -\frac{T\,\Delta \mathcal{E}}{N\,\Delta H}, \tag{6.104}$$

$$\left(\frac{\partial p}{\partial N}\right)_T = -\frac{\Delta \mu}{N\,\Delta \mathrm{v}} = -\frac{\Delta \mu}{\Delta \overline{V}} = \frac{\Delta \mathcal{E}}{N\,\Delta \overline{V}}, \tag{6.105}$$

where Δ means the value at point C (state A) minus the value at point E (state B) and where we have used

$$N\hat{\mu} = H - TS, \qquad \Delta\hat{\mu} = 0, \qquad \Delta H = T\,\Delta S \tag{6.106}$$

$$\mathcal{E} = N(\hat{\mu} - \mu), \qquad \Delta \mathcal{E} = -N\,\Delta\mu. \tag{6.107}$$

Equation (6.103) resembles the familiar Clausius-Clapeyron equation, but Eqs. (6.104) and (6.105) are new for small systems. The left-hand sides of Eqs. (6.103) through (6.105) are measurable, as is also $\Delta \mathrm{v}$. Hence $\Delta \mathrm{s}$ and $\Delta\mu$ may be calculated.

Since the process $B \rightarrow A$ referred to above occurs in a closed system at constant p and T, the reversible heat $Q = \Delta H = T\,\Delta S$. But this would not ordinarily be an operational heat, because two metastable states are involved and the solvent is not included.

Only two of Eqs. (6.103) through (6.105) are independent in view of

$$\left(\frac{\partial p}{\partial T}\right)_N = -\frac{(\partial p/\partial N)_T}{(\partial T/\partial N)_p}. \tag{6.108}$$

If we take the direction of the transition such that $\Delta \mathrm{s} > 0$ (that is, state A is the high-temperature phase) then $(\partial p/\partial T)_N$ has the same sign as $\Delta \mathrm{v}$ and $(\partial T/\partial N)_p$ has the same sign as $\Delta\mu$.

---

* The pressure p in Eqs. (6.102) through (6.107) is denoted by p_0 above and in Fig. 6.5.

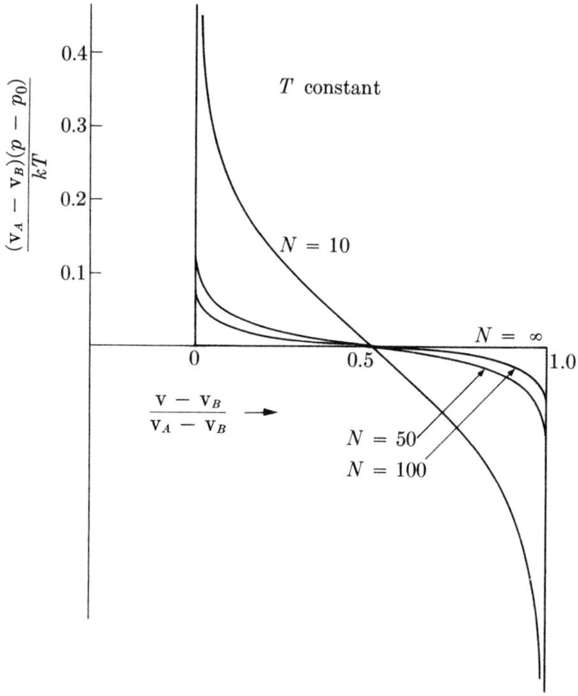

Fig. 6.8. Plot of (essentially) p versus v in a simple model of a first-order phase transition.

Simple example. Here we consider the simplest conceivable illustration of the two-state approximation. Suppose A and B are two condensed phases with v_A and v_B, $v_A > v_B$, independent of p and N. Therefore, in Fig. 6.5, the curves ACF and BEG are both vertical lines. Also, in Fig. 6.7, ACF and BEG are straight lines with slopes v_A and v_B, respectively. Let $\hat{\mu}$ be the common value of $\hat{\mu}_A$ and $\hat{\mu}_B$ when $p = p_0$ (p_0 is also assumed independent of N). Then integration of $\partial\hat{\mu}_A/\partial p = v_A$ gives

$$\hat{\mu}_A = \hat{\mu} + v_A(p - p_0).$$

Similarly,

$$\hat{\mu}_B = \hat{\mu} + v_B(p - p_0).$$

Equation (6.94) becomes

$$\frac{P_A}{1 - P_A} = \exp\left[-\frac{N(v_A - v_B)(p - p_0)}{kT}\right]. \tag{6.109}$$

Because v_A and v_B are assumed to be independent of N, the only N dependence on the right-hand side is that explicitly indicated. Since

$P_A = (\mathrm{v} - \mathrm{v}_B)/(\mathrm{v}_A - \mathrm{v}_B)$, a plot (Fig. 6.8) of

$$\frac{(\mathrm{v}_A - \mathrm{v}_B)(p - p_0)}{kT} \quad \text{versus} \quad \frac{\mathrm{v} - \mathrm{v}_B}{\mathrm{v}_A - \mathrm{v}_B} \tag{6.110}$$

can easily be calculated from Eq. (6.109). This is essentially a p versus v diagram for this simple model, corresponding to Fig. 6.5. Several values of N are included in the figure, which demonstrates quantitatively how the transition becomes sharper as N increases.

Comparison shows that Eqs. (6.85) ("all-or-none" helix–coil model) and (6.109) are formally identical. This is not surprising in view of the models. The correspondences in the two equations are:

$$P_A \leftrightarrow \frac{\overline{n}}{N}, \qquad \exp\left[-\frac{(\mathrm{v}_A - \mathrm{v}_B)(p - p_0)}{kT}\right] \leftrightarrow r.$$

Thus Fig. 6.8 is also a plot of $-\ln r$ against $\overline{n}/N$. Hence, Figs. 6.3 and 6.8 are identical except for a rotation of one figure by 90°.

Example: crystallite melting. We investigate next the effect of the size of a crystallite on the temperature and pressure at which it melts. The pressure could be exerted by an inert fluid reservoir in which the small systems are insoluble. We use a simplified version of the model in Eqs. (6.59) through (6.62), for both solid and liquid, in that the only small term we retain is the surface term. We shall seek only first-order departures from macroscopic behavior.

Suppose p_∞ and T_∞ are values of p and T at which the two macroscopic phases are in equilibrium. We consider first the effect of a finite N on the equilibrium T, holding p constant at p_∞. We use Eq. (6.104) for this purpose. From Eq. (6.62) we have

$$\Delta\mu = \Delta f(p_\infty, T) + \tfrac{2}{3}N^{-1/3}\,\Delta a(p_\infty, T), \tag{6.111}$$

where $\Delta\mu = \mu_L - \mu_S$ (L = liquid, S = solid), etc. The temperature here is the equilibrium T: this is the value of T at which the two metastable states are in equilibrium ($\hat{\mu}_L = \hat{\mu}_S$) at the given N and p_∞; it is also the value of T at which half the crystallites have melted at N and p_∞. We also have, from Eq. (6.59),

$$\Delta\hat{\mu} = 0 = \Delta f(p_\infty, T) + N^{-1/3}\,\Delta a(p_\infty, T). \tag{6.112}$$

It should be noted that $\Delta f(p_\infty, T_\infty) = 0$ but $\Delta f(p_\infty, T) \neq 0$. On elimination of Δf between Eqs. (6.111) and (6.112), we obtain

$$\Delta\mu = -\tfrac{1}{3}N^{-1/3}\,\Delta a(p_\infty, T). \tag{6.113}$$

Equation (6.60) gives

$$\Delta s = -\frac{\partial\,\Delta f(p_\infty, T)}{\partial T} - N^{-1/3}\frac{\partial\,\Delta a(p_\infty, T)}{\partial T}. \qquad (6.114)$$

We may now substitute Eqs. (6.113) and (6.114) into Eq. (6.104). But we are interested in first-order effects only. Hence we expand Δa and $\partial\Delta f/\partial T$ about T_∞, keeping just the first terms, and we omit the $N^{-1/3}$ term in Δs. With these simplifications,

$$\left(\frac{\partial T}{\partial N}\right)_{p_\infty} = -\frac{N^{-4/3}\,\Delta a(p_\infty, T_\infty)}{3\,\Delta s_\infty}, \qquad (6.115)$$

where $\Delta s_\infty = -(\partial\Delta f/\partial T)_\infty$ is the macroscopic entropy of fusion. Integration of this equation gives the desired result,

$$T = T_\infty + \frac{N^{-1/3}\,\Delta a(p_\infty, T_\infty)}{\Delta s_\infty}. \qquad (6.116)$$

An alternative simpler derivation of Eq. (6.116) is the following. In Eq. (6.112), expand Δf about T_∞:

$$\begin{aligned}\Delta f(p_\infty, T) &= \left(\frac{\partial\,\Delta f}{\partial T}\right)_{T_\infty}(T - T_\infty) + \cdots \\ &= -\Delta s_\infty(T - T_\infty) + \cdots\end{aligned}$$

We also expand Δa about T_∞ and keep the leading term only. Equation (6.112) then becomes identical with Eq. (6.116).

Completely analogous arguments lead to

$$p = p_\infty - \frac{N^{-1/3}\,\Delta a(p_\infty, T_\infty)}{\Delta v_\infty} \qquad (6.117)$$

for the first-order effect of N on the equilibrium pressure at constant $T = T_\infty$.

Now a is proportional to the surface tension* γ. In fact, we may set the surface free energy $aN^{2/3}$ in Eq. (6.59) equal to $\gamma\mathcal{A}$, where $\mathcal{A}$ is the surface area. If we assume a spherical shape for the crystallite,

$$aN^{2/3} = \gamma\mathcal{A} = \gamma(6\pi^{1/2}Nv)^{2/3}$$

or

$$\begin{aligned}a &= \gamma(6\pi^{1/2}v)^{2/3}, \\ \Delta a &= 6^{2/3}\pi^{1/3}\,\Delta(\gamma v^{2/3}). \qquad (6.118)\end{aligned}$$

Suppose, as an example, that γ_S is sufficiently larger than γ_L to make Δa negative. Since Δs_∞ is positive, Eq. (6.116) then predicts that the

* Strictly, interfacial tension between small system and inert fluid.

crystallite has a lower melting point than the bulk solid. If $\Delta a > 0$, the crystallite melting point will be higher than that of the bulk solid. As for the rough order of magnitude of the effect, Δa is of order kT, Δs_∞ is of order k, and hence the correction term in Eq. (6.116) is of order $TN^{-1/3}$. It could easily be larger than this by a factor of 100 or more.

If Δa is negative and Δv_∞ is positive, Eq. (6.117) predicts that the pressure on a crystallite must be increased in order to maintain its melting point at the bulk value T_∞. The order of magnitude of the correction term is $pN^{-1/3}$.

PROBLEMS

6.1 Let $ijk \cdots$ represent a possible quantum state for an ensemble of $\mathfrak{N}$ equivalent, distinguishable, and independent systems, where i designates the quantum state of the first system, j the second, etc. Let $p_{ijk\cdots}$ be the probability of observing the ensemble in this state. Given that the ensemble entropy is

$$S_t = -k \sum_{ijk\cdots} p_{ijk\cdots} \ln p_{ijk\cdots},$$

prove that $S_t = \mathfrak{N}S$, where

$$S = -k \sum_i p_i \ln p_i$$

and p_i is the probability of observing a single system in state i.

6.2 Derive Eq. (6.34) for the partition function Δ by a method analogous to that used for Eq. (6.14).

6.3 Discuss the ideal lattice gas of p. 98 in a μ/T, M system, using the grand partition function, Eq. (6.14).

6.4 Prove that

$$\left(\frac{\partial T}{\partial N}\right)_{p,\mathrm{v}} = -\frac{1}{N^2}\left(\frac{\partial \mathcal{E}}{\partial \mathrm{s}}\right)_{T,N}.$$

6.5 Verify the general equations (6.53) and (6.54) using the functions for a colloidal particle on p. 98.

6.6 In an N, p, T phase transition, show that, at $p = p_0$,

$$\left(\frac{\partial \mathrm{v}}{\partial p}\right)_T \cong -\frac{N(\mathrm{v}_A - \mathrm{v}_B)^2}{4kT}.$$

6.7 Given that, in the two-state approximation, $\overline{V}$ is plotted against T (N, p constant), show that there is an equal-distance theorem but not an equal-area theorem.

6.8 Prove, in the two-state approximation, that

$$\left(\frac{\partial \hat{\mu}}{\partial T}\right)_N = -\frac{\Delta(\mathrm{s}/\mathrm{v})}{\Delta(1/\mathrm{v})}.$$

6.9 Derive the basic equations for the two-state approximation in a μ, V, T system at a phase transition. Prove that

$$\left(\frac{\partial \mu}{\partial V}\right)_T = -\frac{\Delta p}{\Delta N} = -\frac{\Delta \mathcal{E}}{V\,\Delta \overline{N}}.$$

6.10 Consider the same small system with three different sets of environmental variables: (1) N_0, V_0, T; (2) μ, V_0, T, where μ is chosen so that $\overline{N}(\mu, V_0, T) = N_0$; and (3) N_0, p, T, where p is chosen so that $\overline{V}(N_0, p, T) = V_0$. If S_1, S_2, and S_3 are the respective entropies of the three systems, what can be said in general about the relative magnitudes of S_1, S_2, and S_3?

SUPPLEMENTARY READING

Hill, T. L., *Thermodynamics of Small Systems*, Parts I and II. New York: Benjamin, 1963, 1964.

CHAPTER 7

INTRODUCTION TO IRREVERSIBLE THERMODYNAMICS

It is not possible, in a single chapter, to present this subject in a way that is simultaneously deductive, general, and elementary. Our aim will therefore be much more modest: merely to indicate something of the nature of the problem, primarily by means of a study of simple models or examples and varied methods of attack. With this chapter as a background, the reader should be ready to undertake a more systematic study (see Supplementary Reading).

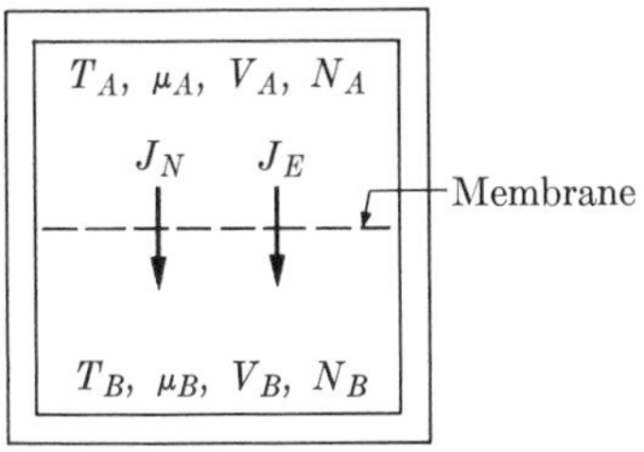

Fig. 7.1. Nonequilibrium one-component discontinuous system.

7.1 DISCONTINUOUS ONE-COMPONENT SYSTEM (I)

In this section we adopt a general thermodynamic approach for the investigation of a particular type of nonequilibrium system, shown in Fig. 7.1. The method is easy to generalize to more components, chemical reactions, etc. We shall content ourselves with establishing the notation and general ideas in this section, and then return to the same system in Section 7.4 to extend the discussion a little further. Sections 7.2 and 7.3 constitute a digression which serves to introduce kinetic and stochastic methods in the study of perhaps the simplest possible explicit model of the type of system shown in Fig. 7.1. Somewhat more complicated models will be considered in later sections.

In Fig. 7.1, parts A and B are large one-component *equilibrium* systems containing the same kind of molecule, but A and B are not in equilibrium with each other, for, in general, $\mu_A \neq \mu_B$ and $T_A \neq T_B$. The two parts, A and B, are separated by a thin rigid membrane which, in general, allows transport of molecules and heat from one side to the other, as a consequence of the disequilibrium between the two sides. The total system, $A + B$, is isolated. Thus

$$\begin{gathered} E_A + E_B = E = \text{const}, \\ N_A + N_B = N = \text{const}, \\ V_A = \text{const}, \qquad V_B = \text{const}, \qquad V_A + V_B = V = \text{const}. \end{gathered} \tag{7.1}$$

So long as any net transport takes place between A and B,

$$dS = dS_A + dS_B > 0 \tag{7.2}$$

for an infinitesimal process. At equilibrium, $dS = 0$.

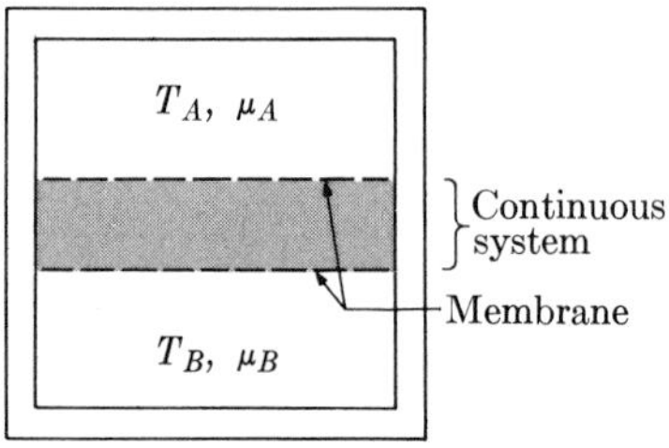

Fig. 7.2. An example of a "continuous" nonequilibrium system.

Because of the discontinuity in properties at the membrane, $A + B$ is called a *discontinuous* irreversible system. Except for Section 7.6, in which we discuss homogeneous chemical reactions, and Section 7.9, all systems considered in this chapter are discontinuous. An example of a *continuous* system, which has gradual changes in properties, is shown in Fig. 7.2. More advanced mathematical methods are necessary to treat this kind of system.

Because V_A and V_B are constant, we have, for the separate subsystems, in any infinitesimal process,

$$\begin{aligned} dE_A &= T_A\,dS_A + \mu_A\,dN_A, \\ dE_B &= T_B\,dS_B + \mu_B\,dN_B. \end{aligned} \tag{7.3}$$

Then, for the entropy change,

$$\begin{aligned} dS &= dS_A + dS_B \\ &= dE_B\left(\frac{1}{T_B} - \frac{1}{T_A}\right) + dN_B\left(\frac{\mu_A}{T_A} - \frac{\mu_B}{T_B}\right) \geq 0, \end{aligned} \tag{7.4}$$

where we have used $dE_A = -dE_B$ and $dN_A = -dN_B$. We can also write this as

$$\frac{dS}{dt} = \dot{S} = J_E\left(\frac{1}{T_B} - \frac{1}{T_A}\right) + J_N\left(\frac{\mu_A}{T_A} - \frac{\mu_B}{T_B}\right) \geq 0, \tag{7.5}$$

where

$$J_E = \frac{dE_B}{dt} = -\frac{dE_A}{dt} \quad \text{and} \quad J_N = \frac{dN_B}{dt} = -\frac{dN_A}{dt}, \tag{7.6}$$

and where $\dot{S}$ is the rate of entropy production, J_E is the flux in energy in the direction $A \to B$, and J_N is the flux in molecules in the direction $A \to B$. While (7.4) is an equation of classical thermodynamics, nonthermodynamic considerations of mechanism and kinetics enter the analysis beginning with Eq. (7.5), because the actual rates J_E and J_N will clearly depend not only on the properties of A and B, but also on the nature of the membrane and on the details of transport of heat and molecules across it.

The quantities in parentheses in Eq. (7.5) are called thermodynamic forces, and are denoted by X:

$$X_E = \frac{1}{T_B} - \frac{1}{T_A}, \qquad X_N = \frac{\mu_A}{T_A} - \frac{\mu_B}{T_B}. \tag{7.7}$$

Thus

$$\dot{S} = J_E X_E + J_N X_N \geq 0. \tag{7.8}$$

By convention, the X's are defined in Eq. (7.7) in such a way that there is a positive sign in front of each JX product in Eq. (7.8). The separate products may be positive or negative; but the *sum* cannot be negative.

The X's are called forces for the rather obvious reason that when they differ in value from zero, fluxes across the membrane are induced (the membrane permitting, of course).

Two important special cases of Eq. (7.8) are: (a) if $J_N = 0$, then $\dot{S} = J_E X_E$, and J_E and X_E have the same sign (heat flow in a temperature gradient); and (b) if $X_E = 0$, then $\dot{S} = J_N X_N$, and J_N and X_N have the same sign (isothermal molecular flow in a chemical-potential gradient).

Equation (7.8) includes, but is not restricted to, situations in which A and B are almost in equilibrium with each other; the combined system, $A + B$, may be arbitrarily far from equilibrium. However, as we shall soon see, the *conventional* discipline of irreversible thermodynamics, founded by Lars Onsager, is restricted to *near* equilibrium.

At a steady state (for which A and B must be very large if $A + B$ is isolated), all quantities in Eq. (7.8) are independent of time. At equilibrium, they are all zero. If the system is approaching equilibrium, they are all, in the most general case, functions of time.

Generalization. If the combined system is closed but not isolated,

$$dS = d_eS + d_iS = \sum (DQ/T) + d_iS, \tag{7.9}$$

where d_eS is the entropy change associated with heat exchange between the combined system and its surroundings (e = external), while d_iS is the contribution to dS owing to irreversible processes taking place inside the combined system (i = internal). The summation sign is meant to indicate that heat exchange with the surroundings may take place in different parts of the combined system (at different temperatures). According to the second law,

$$dS \geq d_eS \qquad \text{or} \qquad d_iS \geq 0. \tag{7.10}$$

This is the generalization of the statement $dS \geq 0$ for an isolated system. Depending on the particular circumstances, d_iS may be related to an appropriate free energy change, etc. In any case, Eq. (7.4) still follows, except that dS is replaced by d_iS. Hence, in these more general circumstances, $\dot{S}$ is to be understood to mean d_iS/dt.

Actually, the fact that Eq. (7.8) is more general than the derivation given here is rather obvious intuitively. The transport takes place at and near the membrane, and occurrences here are "unaware" of the nature of far-away contacts between the combined system and its surroundings. Of course, if Eq. (7.8) were to be integrated over a significant interval of time, we must know the details of these contacts, the volumes V_A and V_B, etc.

As a simple illustration of a nonisolated combined system, suppose $T_A = T_B = T = \text{const}$ in Fig. 7.1, and that the entire system is in contact with a heat bath at T. Otherwise, conditions are as described at the outset. Then, since T and V are constant, the criterion for equilibrium and the approach to equilibrium is $dA \leq 0$, where $A = E - TS$. Now

$$dA_A = \mu_A\, dN_A \qquad \text{and} \qquad dA_B = \mu_B\, dN_B \qquad (V_A,\ V_B,\ T \text{ constant}).$$

Hence,

$$-\frac{dA}{T} = -\frac{1}{T}\left(dA_A + dA_B\right) = dN_B\left(\frac{\mu_A}{T} - \frac{\mu_B}{T}\right) \geq 0. \tag{7.11}$$

This is the appropriate version of Eq. (7.4) for this case. The relation to d_iS is immediate:

$$dE = DQ = T\, d_eS = T(dS - d_iS) \qquad (V \text{ constant})$$

so that

$$d_iS = dS - \frac{dE}{T} = -\frac{dA}{T} \qquad (V,\ T \text{ constant}). \tag{7.12}$$

Fluxes expressed in powers of forces. Since fluxes are induced by forces, and since the J's $= 0$ when the X's $= 0$, we might expect to be able to expand the J's in powers of the X's, with linear terms appearing as the leading terms in the series. This is confirmed experimentally. Such a series is a McLaurin expansion, similar to the expansion of, say, $f(x, y)$ when $f(0, 0) = 0$:

$$f(x, y) = \left(\frac{\partial f}{\partial x}\right)_{\substack{x=0\\y=0}} x + \left(\frac{\partial f}{\partial y}\right)_{\substack{x=0\\y=0}} y + \cdots \tag{7.13}$$

In the present example, we have

$$\begin{aligned} J_N &= L_{NN}X_N + L_{NE}X_E + \cdots, \\ J_E &= L_{EN}X_N + L_{EE}X_E + \cdots, \end{aligned} \tag{7.14}$$

where the L's are coefficients. With just the linear terms retained, as in Eq. (7.14), we are restricting the discussion to *near-equilibrium* systems. Just as the coefficients in Eq. (7.13) are evaluated at $x = 0$, $y = 0$, the L's are properties of the *equilibrium* state ($X_N = 0$, $X_E = 0$). Of course, if we kept higher powers of the X's in Eqs. (7.14), their coefficients would also be properties of the equilibrium state. Since the L's "control" the amount of flux for a given set of forces, they obviously depend not only on the properties of the macroscopic systems A and B at equilibrium, but also on the nature of the membrane at equilibrium. In later sections, we shall derive explicit formulas for the L's applicable to particular models.

From a purely thermodynamic point of view, the L's are to be measured experimentally, just as we measure virial coefficients in the virial expansion of the pressure. The basically experimental nature of this subject should not be lost sight of despite our preoccupation in this chapter with illustrative models.

The same set of L's applies to all nonequilibrium states in the neighborhood of the same equilibrium state. Thus, special choices of X's and J's may be used to make general deductions about the L's. For example, if $X_E = 0$, X_N and J_N have the same sign [see Eq. (7.8)]. Therefore, from Eq. (7.14), L_{NN} must always be positive. Similarly, from the special case $X_N = 0$, we can deduce that L_{EE} is always positive. In general, all "diagonal" L's are positive. On the other hand, "off-diagonal" L's (L_{NE} and L_{EN}, in this case) may be positive or negative.

The physical significance of the terms $L_{NN}X_N$ and $L_{EE}X_E$ are obvious: a flux arises in response to its "own" force. The other terms, which are referred to as "cross" or "coupling" or off-diagonal, represent the indirect effect of one force on a different flux.

It is easy to see, in special cases, how such an effect can come about. Suppose, for example, that we have isothermal diffusion of *two* components between parts A and B, and suppose further that the components can cross the membrane either alone or when complexed together. Because of the latter mechanism, the two fluxes are obviously "coupled" and this will be reflected by nonzero off-diagonal L's. If the two components diffused completely independently of each other, the off-diagonal L's would be zero.

In the particular example (7.14), if $X_E = 0$, that is, if $T_A = T_B$, but $X_N \neq 0$, there will be a flux in both N and E because molecular transport is necessarily accompanied by transport of the energy of the molecules themselves. Thus $L_{EN} \neq 0$.

We make one further comment about the expansion (7.14), with higher terms included. If the membrane is symmetrical with respect to sides A and B, the J's must change sign but not magnitude if the X's change sign but not magnitude. Therefore, for a symmetrical membrane, the expansion (7.14) contains only odd powers of the X's.

Fundamental postulate. We now come to the fundamental postulate of (near-equilibrium) irreversible thermodynamics. This is a statement that cannot be deduced from equilibrium thermodynamics alone. That is, something really new is added. As applied to the particular system being considered in this section, the postulate states that $L_{NE} = L_{EN}$. Off-hand, one would not have expected this "coincidence." This is called a reciprocal relation. Onsager first encountered reciprocal relations while working out properties of models. He then provided a general proof of their existence based on statistical mechanics. From the thermodynamic point of view, the postulate is to be tested experimentally* (and has been, to some extent).

Since we have developed the argument in this section for a particular case (Fig. 7.1), we should restate the postulate in somewhat more general terms: if, for a discontinuous system, forces $X_1, X_2, \ldots, X_n$ and corresponding fluxes $J_1, J_2, \ldots, J_n$ are defined in such a way that

$$\dot{S} = J_1X_1 + J_2X_2 + \cdots + J_nX_n \geq 0, \tag{7.15}$$

then, in the linear relations

$$\begin{aligned} J_1 &= L_{11}X_1 + L_{12}X_2 + \cdots + L_{1n}X_n, \\ J_2 &= L_{21}X_1 + L_{22}X_2 + \cdots + L_{2n}X_n, \\ &\vdots \\ J_n &= L_{n1}X_1 + L_{n2}X_2 + \cdots + L_{nn}X_n, \end{aligned} \tag{7.16}$$

---

* See, for example, D. G. Miller, *Chem. Rev.* **60,** 15 (1960).

which hold near equilibrium, the L matrix is symmetric. That is, $L_{ij} = L_{ji}$ (a reciprocal relation). Chemical reactions may be included in this formulation, as we shall see in Sections 7.6 and 7.8.

We mention again that, though Eq. (7.15) holds far from equilibrium, the linear equations (7.16) are applicable only near equilibrium (higher terms in the expansion of the J's in powers of the X's must be negligible). This limitation is often serious, as for example in biology. Generalizations of the Onsager postulate to states arbitrarily far from equilibrium (or even to include the next expansion terms) have not been found as yet.

At a steady state (near equilibrium), all quantities in Eqs. (7.16) are time-independent. If the system is approaching equilibrium, the J's and X's are functions of time (but not the L's). At equilibrium, all the J's and X's are equal to zero.

In general, for a given system which requires the introduction of n fluxes and forces, various choices or definitions of the J's and X's, all satisfying Eq. (7.15), may be made. We shall encounter examples of this later.

Near equilibrium, forces such as $\Delta(1/T)$ and $\Delta(\mu/T)$ in Eq. (7.7) will be written as $\delta(1/T)$ and $\delta(\mu/T)$, and treated as differentials.

In the elementary case of one flux and one force,

$$\dot{S} = JX \geq 0, \qquad J = LX. \tag{7.17}$$

There is no reciprocal relation in this case, of course.

Having introduced some of the general ideas of irreversible thermodynamics through the thermodynamic example shown in Fig. 7.1, we turn in the next two sections to a detailed kinetic and stochastic analysis of a very simple model with only one flux and force, as in Eq. (7.17). In Sections 7.5 to 7.8, we shall encounter explicit examples of reciprocal relations.

7.2 SIMPLE MEMBRANE MODEL

In this section we examine the properties of a simple explicit kinetic model of membrane transport. Our object is to illustrate some of the ideas of the preceding section at the molecular level. However, by no means will this be an analysis based on first principles; we shall take the possible elementary events and corresponding rate constants (or transition probabilities) as given, and not examine *their* theory at all.

The system we consider first is shown in Fig. 7.3. A symmetrical membrane separates bath A from bath B; the baths are assumed to be very large. Both baths contain the same solvent and solute, and have the same temperature T. The solute, but not the solvent, can pass through the mem-

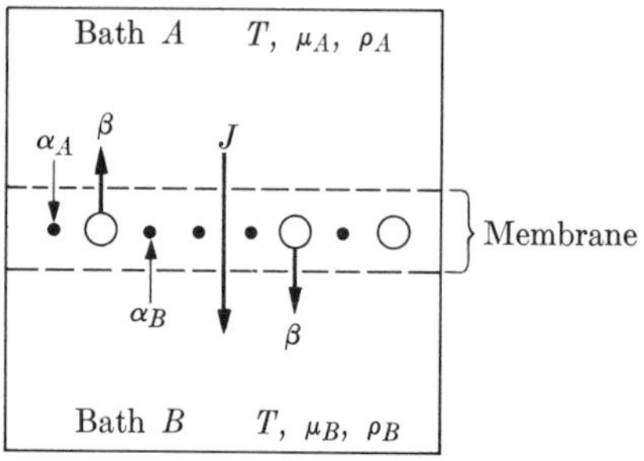

Fig. 7.3. Simple membrane transport model.

brane. The mechanism of membrane transport is by means of adsorption on and desorption from a large number, M, of equivalent and independent sites, as indicated in the figure.

There are four possible events: binding on a site from bath A; binding from bath B; and desorption into either bath. There is no diffusion *on* the membrane (no jumping from site to site); or, at least, if diffusion exists we do not and need not acknowledge it explicitly. The rate constants for the four events listed above are α_A, α_B, β, and β respectively. These "constants" are all functions of T. The constant α_A (or α_B) is assumed to be proportional to $\lambda_A = e^{\mu_A/kT}$ (or λ_B). If the solutions are dilute,

$$\mu_i = \mu_i' + kT \ln \rho_i \qquad (i = A \text{ or } B), \tag{7.18}$$

where ρ_i is the concentration in bath i. In this case, α_i is proportional to ρ_i. The desorption constant β depends on the nature of the membrane and solvent, but not on ρ_A or ρ_B; it includes a desorption activation energy factor (see Section 7.7). At equilibrium, $\mu_A = \mu_B$ and $\alpha_A = \alpha_B$.

The reader will recognize the above as a kinetic Langmuir model (see Section 2.4).

Let $N_0(t)$ be the number of empty sites and let $N(t)$ be the number of occupied sites at time t, where $N_0 + N = M$. Then

$$\frac{dN_0}{dt} = -\frac{dN}{dt} = (\beta N - \alpha_A N_0) + (\beta N - \alpha_B N_0). \tag{7.19}$$

This equation makes the definition of the rate constants explicit (see also Section 7.3). The first (second) pair of parentheses in Eq. (7.19) concerns two events, a binding from bath $A(B)$ and its inverse.

At equilibrium, there is *detailed balance*—that is, each elementary process and its inverse occur at the same rate. Thus, when this system is at equilibrium ($\alpha_A = \alpha_B = \alpha$),

$$\frac{N^e}{N_0^e} = \frac{N^e}{M - N^e} = \frac{\alpha}{\beta}, \tag{7.20}$$

where the superscript e refers to the equilibrium state. The membrane itself is an equilibrium subsystem with $\lambda = e^{\mu/kT} = \lambda_A = \lambda_B$. If $q(T)$ is the partition function of a molecule bound on a membrane site, the connection between the kinetics and statistical mechanics of this model is $\alpha/\beta = q\lambda$ [see Eq. (2.37)]. Whether or not the system is at equilibrium, $\alpha_A/\beta = q\lambda_A$ and $\alpha_B/\beta = q\lambda_B$.

Let us define the flux J as the rate at which molecules enter bath B. That is, $J = \beta N - \alpha_B N_0$. There is only one independent flux (instead of two, as in Fig. 7.1) because the system is isothermal. In general, J is a function of time. At steady state, the constant J is also equal to the rate at which molecules leave bath A. At equilibrium, $J = 0$.

Steady state. Although it is easy to integrate Eq. (7.19) to find $N(t)$ (see Section 7.3), we confine the discussion below to the situation at steady state ($\alpha_A \neq \alpha_B$; $t = \infty$). In this case, the quantities in parentheses in Eq. (7.19) are not separately zero, as at equilibrium, but their sum is zero: $dN_0/dt = 0$. Therefore,

$$\frac{N^\infty}{M - N^\infty} = \frac{\alpha_A + \alpha_B}{2\beta} \tag{7.21}$$

or

$$\frac{N^\infty}{M} = \frac{\alpha_A + \alpha_B}{\alpha_A + \alpha_B + 2\beta}, \tag{7.22}$$

where the superscript ∞ refers to the steady state ($t = \infty$). In effect, the membrane is in equilibrium with an average bath with $\alpha = (\alpha_A + \alpha_B)/2$, or $\lambda = (\lambda_A + \lambda_B)/2$. This remark will be amplified in the next section.

The steady-state flux is

$$J^\infty = \beta N^\infty - \alpha_B N_0^\infty = \frac{M\beta(\alpha_A - \alpha_B)}{\alpha_A + \alpha_B + 2\beta}. \tag{7.23}$$

This is the flux for an arbitrary steady state, not necessarily near equilibrium. The "force" here is proportional to $\alpha_A - \alpha_B$, $\lambda_A - \lambda_B$, or $\rho_A - \rho_B$ (dilute solutions). If expressed in terms of the conventional force

$$X = (\mu_A - \mu_B)/T$$

[see Eq. (7.7)], J^∞ becomes a series in odd powers of X (Problem 7.1). To get just the linear (near-equilibrium) term in X, we write

$$\frac{\delta\alpha}{\alpha} = \frac{\delta\lambda}{\lambda} = \frac{\delta\mu}{kT} = \frac{X}{k}, \tag{7.24}$$

where $\delta\alpha = \alpha_A - \alpha_B$, etc., so that

$$J^\infty = \frac{M\alpha\beta(\delta\alpha/\alpha)}{2(\alpha + \beta)} = \frac{M\alpha\beta X}{2k(\alpha + \beta)} = LX, \tag{7.25}$$

with

$$L = M\alpha\beta/2k(\alpha + \beta). \tag{7.26}$$

Equation (7.25) applies to steady states *near* equilibrium only (the next term, in X^3, must be negligible). In Eq. (7.26), we have our first explicit formula for a linear flux-force coefficient. We see that L depends on equilibrium properties of the baths (α, β) and of the membrane (M, β); L may also be written as $\beta N^e/2k$.

The entropy production, at steady state, is

$$\dot{S}^\infty = J^\infty X = LX^2, \tag{7.27}$$

where the form LX^2 applies only near equilibrium. If we write

$$\dot{S}^\infty = J^\infty(\delta\mu/T)$$

and consider the solutions dilute, the nature of the entropy production is easy to understand. At steady state, the entropy of the membrane is, of course, constant and hence makes no contribution to $\dot{S}^\infty$. If, for example, J^∞ and $\delta\mu$ are both positive, then entropy is being produced within this system at steady state because solute molecules are being transported from a higher concentration bath (ρ_A, μ_A) with a *lower* partial molecular entropy ($\bar{\text{s}}_A$) to a lower concentration bath (ρ_B, μ_B) with a *higher* partial molecular entropy ($\bar{\text{s}}_B$):

$$\mu = \bar{\text{E}} - T\bar{\text{s}} + p\bar{\text{v}}, \qquad \delta\mu = -T\,\delta\bar{\text{s}} \qquad \text{(dilute solute)}$$

$$\delta\mu = \mu_A - \mu_B > 0, \qquad \delta\bar{\text{s}} = \bar{\text{s}}_A - \text{s}_B < 0.$$

Therefore

$$\dot{S}^\infty = J^\infty(-\delta\bar{\text{s}}), \tag{7.28}$$

where $-\delta\bar{\text{s}}$ is the entropy increase per molecule transported and J^∞ is the rate of transport. We might add that, for bath A, $d_iS^A/dt = -J^\infty\bar{\text{s}}^A$, while for bath B, $d_iS^B/dt = J^\infty\bar{\text{s}}^B$. The sum of these is (7.28).

Membrane in contact with one bath. This is a variation on the preceding model. The system is shown in Fig. 7.4. Bath A and the membrane are as before, but bath B is missing. The subscript A is no longer necessary. In effect, the membrane itself becomes the second macroscopic part, "B," of the discontinuous system. Bath A is at equilibrium and is very large; its properties are independent of time. The membrane starts ($t = 0$) out of equilibrium with the bath but comes to equilibrium with it at $t = \infty$. No steady state is possible. The membrane has an eventual equilibrium state for any choice of α and β. We denote the chemical potential of the (dilute)

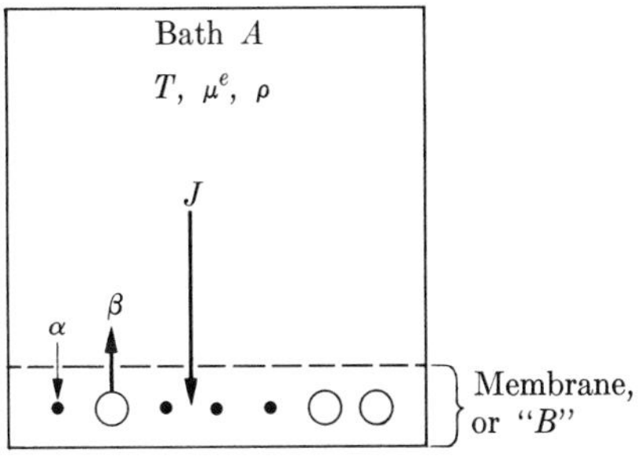

Fig. 7.4. Simple model of a discontinuous system.

solute in the bath as μ^e, where $\mu^e = \mu' + kT \ln \rho$, because μ^e is necessarily the eventual equilibrium value of the chemical potential of the bound molecules on the membrane. The flux J is defined as the net rate at which molecules are adsorbed on the membrane.

We have, in place of Eq. (7.19),

$$\frac{dN_0}{dt} = -\frac{dN}{dt} = -J = \beta N - \alpha N_0. \tag{7.29}$$

At equilibrium,

$$\frac{N^e}{M - N^e} = \frac{\alpha}{\beta} = q\lambda^e = qe^{\mu^e/kT}. \tag{7.30}$$

Using this, Eq. (7.29) can be rewritten as

$$J(t) = \frac{d[N(t) - N^e]}{dt} = -(\alpha + \beta)[N(t) - N^e]. \tag{7.31}$$

Therefore, if $N(0)$ is the value of N at $t = 0$,

$$N(t) - N^e = [N(0) - N^e]e^{-(\alpha+\beta)t}. \tag{7.32}$$

Note that $J(t)$ may be positive or negative, depending on the choice of α/β and $N(0)/M$.

Actually, we are more interested in the differential equation (7.31) than in its solution, (7.32), for (7.31) is essentially the flux-force relation; N^e, in Eq. (7.31), is related to the chemical potential in the bath through Eq. (7.30). If we assume that the bound molecules are in internal equilibrium at t (i.e., the membrane itself is an equilibrium system at t) as well as at $t = \infty$, then a chemical potential $\mu(t)$ will be determined by $N(t)$ through the relation [see Eq. (7.30)]

$$\frac{N(t)}{M - N(t)} = qe^{\mu(t)/kT}. \tag{7.33}$$

We shall examine the assumption of internal equilibrium for $t < \infty$ in the next section; it is not always valid. If we now combine Eqs. (7.30), (7.31), and (7.33), and define $X(t) = [\mu^e - \mu(t)]/T$, then one can show (Problem 7.2) that the expansion of J in powers of X, about the equilibrium state, starts off with a linear and then a quadratic term. The quadratic term appears in this case because this system is not symmetrical with respect to A and "B." The operational meaning of replacing X by $-X$ in $J(X)$ (this tests whether J is an odd function of X) is that μ^e (bath) is held constant while μ (membrane) is changed from $\mu^e - XT$ to $\mu^e + XT$. On the other hand, when we change the sign of X in Eq. (7.23), the properties of the baths A and B are exchanged.

Near equilibrium

$$J(t) = (\alpha + \beta)\ \delta N(t),$$

where $\delta N = N^e - N$, and from Eq. (7.33),

$$\frac{X}{k} = \frac{\delta\mu}{kT} = \frac{M\ \delta N}{N^e(M - N^e)} = \frac{(\alpha + \beta)^2\ \delta N}{\alpha\beta M}.$$

Therefore

$$J(t) = LX(t) \tag{7.34}$$

with

$$L = M\alpha\beta/k(\alpha + \beta). \tag{7.35}$$

From Eq. (7.32), the time dependence of both $J(t)$ and $X(t)$ is $\sim e^{-(\alpha+\beta)t}$.

Despite the factor of two in the denominator of Eq. (7.26), Eqs. (7.34) and (7.25) actually agree, as one might expect. The fluxes are defined in the same way, but X in Eq. (7.34) is one-half of X in Eq. (7.24). (Near equilibrium, the membrane has a chemical potential intermediate between those of the two baths.)

Near equilibrium, since $\dot{S}(t) = LX(t)^2$ and $X(t) \sim e^{-(\alpha+\beta)t}$, both $\dot{S}(t)$ and $S^e - S(t)$ are positive and depend on t as $e^{-2(\alpha+\beta)t}$.

7.3 STOCHASTIC TREATMENT OF SIMPLE MEMBRANE MODEL

We now return to the first model considered in the last section (Fig. 7.3) and give a more detailed analysis using stochastic methods. As will be seen, this is a more powerful approach capable of answering more detailed questions about the behavior of the system (given the same model).

The first new feature is that we study here an *ensemble* of systems rather than a single system. We are interested in the evolution, in time, of the whole ensemble. Alternatively, one can think of the ensemble behavior as representing the results of an experiment conducted over and over again on a single system. A third point of view (the most realistic) is that we are, in fact, following only a single system in a single experiment but (1) we may start with imprecise information about the state of the system and, in any case, (2) the system has certain probabilities of evolving in different ways. It requires a stochastic treatment to handle all the possibilities.

In brief, the method of Section 7.2 ("deterministic kinetics") is capable of following mean values only; here we study the complete probability distribution. Of course, for most purposes, if the system is macroscopic, it is only the mean values that we have any interest in (relative fluctuations are extremely small). But there are important exceptions (for example, the questions of internal equilibrium and phase transitions).

Let $P_N(t)$ (where $N = 0, 1, \ldots, M$) be the fraction of systems in the ensemble with, or the probability that any one system chosen at random has, exactly N adsorbed molecules at time t. "System" means the membrane of M sites, with N adsorbed molecules, in the remainder of this section. In more complicated models we would have to include other variables along with N; but here we are fortunate to have only one variable to contend with. The ensemble starts off at $t = 0$ with some given probability distribution $P_N(0)$. Our first object is to derive a differential equation for $P_N(t)$ which, together with the boundary condition just mentioned, determines $P_N(t)$ for any t, at least in principle. Actually, in this brief discussion we shall be concerned only with special cases and properties of $P_N(t)$.

We now characterize the model in stochastic terms. Let $\alpha_A\,dt$ be the probability a particular empty site in a system will adsorb a molecule from bath A in the infinitesimal period dt; let $\beta\,dt$ be the probability that any particular adsorbed molecule will desorb into bath A in dt, etc. (see Fig. 7.3). Then the probability that a system with exactly N adsorbed molecules will adsorb one more molecule (so that $N \to N + 1$) from bath A in dt is $(M - N)\alpha_A\,dt$; the probability it will desorb one (so that $N \to N - 1$) into bath A in dt is $N\beta\,dt$, etc. These expressions rest on the fact that dt is infinitesimal so that at most one event can occur in dt, and also on the additivity of the probabilities of independent events.

To find an equation for dP_N/dt, we calculate first the probability $P_N(t + dt)$ that a system has N particles at $t + dt$, given $P_N(t)$ at t for all

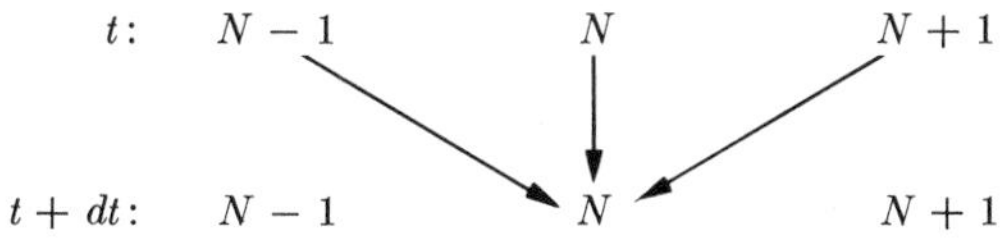

Figure 7.5

N. As Fig. 7.5 indicates schematically, a system may have N particles at $t + dt$ starting from $N - 1$, N, or $N + 1$ at t.

The probability that a system with $N - 1$ molecules at t will acquire an additional one in dt is $P_+ = [M - (N - 1)](\alpha_A + \alpha_B)\,dt$. The probability that a system with $N + 1$ at t will lose one in dt is

$$P_- = 2(N + 1)\beta\,dt.$$

The probability that a system with N at t will still have N at $t + dt$ is $P_* = 1 - (M - N)(\alpha_A + \alpha_B)\,dt - 2N\beta\,dt$. The desired probability $P_N(t + dt)$ is then

$$P_N(t + dt) = P_{N-1}(t)P_+ + P_{N+1}(t)P_- + P_N(t)P_*.$$

We substitute the above expressions for P_+, P_-, and P_*, form the quotient

$$\frac{P_N(t + dt) - P_N(t)}{dt} = \frac{dP_N(t)}{dt},$$

and thus find

$$\frac{dP_N(t)}{dt} = -[(\alpha_A + \alpha_B)(M - N) + 2\beta N]P_N(t) + (\alpha_A + \alpha_B)(M - N + 1)P_{N-1}(t) + 2\beta(N + 1)P_{N+1}(t). \tag{7.36}$$

This is called the "master equation" for this system. It governs the time evolution of the ensemble, and determines its final state at $t = \infty$.

In the equilibrium case, $\alpha_A = \alpha_B = \alpha$ and P_N^e is independent of t. Detailed balance at equilibrium requires that the inverse transitions

$$N \to N + 1 \text{ (bath } A) \qquad \text{and} \qquad N + 1 \to N \text{ (bath } A)$$

have the same probability per unit time. That is,

$$\alpha(M - N)P_N^e = \beta(N + 1)P_{N+1}^e. \tag{7.37}$$

There are altogether four such pairs of transitions and four detailed balance relations included in the terms of Eq. (7.36), at equilibrium. However, the other three relations are equivalent to Eq. (7.37). This equation is a recursion formula sufficient (together with $\sum_N P_N^e = 1$) to provide a complete solution for P_N^e. After writing the first few ($N = 0, 1, 2, \ldots$) members of the set (7.37), one finds easily

$$P_N^e = \frac{M!(\alpha/\beta)^N}{N!(M - N)![1 + (\alpha/\beta)]^M}. \tag{7.38}$$

This result is independent of the initial distribution, $P_N(0)$, as we should expect.

We pointed out, following Eq. (7.20), that $\alpha/\beta = q\lambda$. Therefore

$$P_N^e = \frac{M!(q\lambda)^N}{N!(M-N)!(1+q\lambda)^M}. \tag{7.39}$$

This ought to agree with the corresponding expression from equilibrium statistical mechanics, and it does. For, in an open system with [see Eqs. (2.28), (6.14), and (6.89)]

$$Q(N, M, T) = \frac{M!q^N}{N!(M-N)!} \tag{7.40}$$

and grand partition function

$$\Xi(\lambda, M, T) = \sum_{N=0}^{M} Q(N, M, T)\lambda^N = (1+q\lambda)^M, \tag{7.41}$$

the probability that a system contains N particles is

$$P_N^e = \frac{Q(N, M, T)\lambda^N}{\Xi}. \tag{7.42}$$

This is the same as Eq. (7.39).

At steady state, $\alpha_A \neq \alpha_B$ and P_N^∞ is independent of time. The right-hand side of Eq. (7.36) is equal to zero, but we do not have detailed balance. However, the solution is still easy. The first few equations ($N = 0, 1, 2, \ldots$) should be written out, noting that in the $N = 0$ case the term $2\beta N P_N$ and the term involving P_{N-1} must be omitted. One sees that the solution is the same as in Eq. (7.38), except that α is replaced by $(\alpha_A + \alpha_B)/2$. That is,

$$P_N^\infty = \frac{M![(\alpha_A + \alpha_B)/2\beta]^N}{N!(M-N)!\{1 + [(\alpha_A + \alpha_B)/2\beta]\}^M}. \tag{7.43}$$

This confirms the remark made following Eq. (7.22) to the effect that the steady-state membrane is "in equilibrium with an average bath."

A "normal" time-dependent distribution is another important special solution of the master equation, (7.36), as we shall see. Consider the case where every site in the ensemble is equivalent and stochastically independent. Then, if $p(t)$ is the probability that any one site is occupied at t, for a whole system

$$P_N(t) = \frac{M!p(t)^N[1 - p(t)]^{M-N}}{N!(M-N)!}. \tag{7.44}$$

This we call a "normal" distribution. When M is large, the distribution is Gaussian. Equations (7.38) (equilibrium) and (7.43) (steady state) are obviously examples (at $t = \infty$).

Not all distributions are normal, however. The two distributions shown in Fig. 7.6 illustrate this. Either of these might well be used as the initial distribution, $P_N(0)$. It is clear, for example, that in the system represented by Fig. 7.6(b), the sites are *not* stochastically independent. There is the restraint or interrelation between the sites that, of the M sites in each system of the ensemble, exactly $M/2$ are occupied. The distribution $P_N(0)$ in Fig. 7.6(b) would be normal, however, if the delta-function peak were situated at $N = 0$ [$p(0) = 0$], or $N = M$ [$p(0) = 1$].

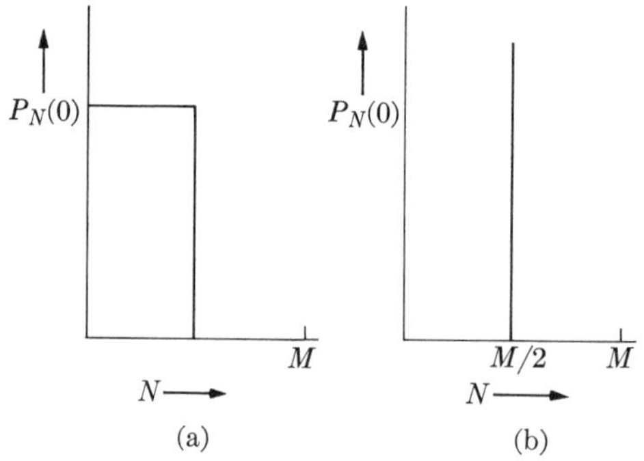

Fig. 7.6. Two examples of non-normal initial distributions.

As already pointed out, an equilibrium or steady-state distribution is of the form (7.44). As we shall see, if we start with any normal distribution at $t = 0$, the ensemble evolves through a succession of normal distributions to $t = \infty$. In other words, for any $p(0)$, a function $p(t)$ exists such that Eq. (7.44) satisfies the master equation, (7.36), for all t. Physically, this corresponds to having a membrane in steady state (or equilibrium) contact with a pair of baths (α'_A, α'_B) and then, at $t = 0$, suddenly switching the membrane into contact with a different pair of baths (α_A, α_B). The system evolves from [see Eq. (7.43)]

$$p(0) = \frac{(\alpha'_A + \alpha'_B)/2\beta}{1 + [(\alpha'_A + \alpha'_B)/2\beta]} \tag{7.45}$$

to

$$p^{\infty} = \frac{(\alpha_A + \alpha_B)/2\beta}{1 + [(\alpha_A + \alpha_B)/2\beta]} \tag{7.46}$$

through a series of similar (i.e., normal) states. In connection with Eq. (7.33), we note that this system is in internal equilibrium at any t. Equation (7.46) is the same as Eq. (7.22), though the notation is different.

Let us now prove the assertions made above. We shall show that Eq. (7.44) is a solution of the master equation and find $p(t)$. Differentiation of Eq. (7.44) with respect to t yields

$$\frac{dP_N}{dt} = \frac{M!}{N!(M-N)!} \times [-(M-N)p^N(1-p)^{M-N-1} + Np^{N-1}(1-p)^{M-N}]\frac{dp}{dt}.$$

This is the left-hand side of Eq. (7.36) in this special case. Next, we observe that if we put Eq. (7.44) in the right-hand side of Eq. (7.36), the resulting expression can be rearranged to read

$$\frac{M!}{N!(M-N)!}[-(M-N)p^N(1-p)^{M-N-1} + Np^{N-1}(1-p)^{M-N}] \times [(\alpha_A + \alpha_B)(1-p) - 2\beta p].$$

Therefore, Eq. (7.44) satisfies the master equation, where $p(t)$ is a solution of

$$dp/dt = (\alpha_A + \alpha_B)(1-p) - 2\beta p \tag{7.47}$$

or of

$$d(p - p^\infty)/dt = -(\alpha_A + \alpha_B + 2\beta)(p - p^\infty). \tag{7.48}$$

The explicit solution is

$$p(t) - p^\infty = [p(0) - p^\infty]e^{-(\alpha_A+\alpha_B+2\beta)t} \tag{7.49}$$

with p^∞ given by Eq. (7.46).

Equation (7.47) is a special case of Eq. (7.19). The stochastic derivation of Eq. (7.19) will be given next.

The rate equation for the mean. We shall not pursue the question of solutions of the master equation any further here, but turn instead to a derivation of the rate equations for the mean and variance of the distribution $P_N(t)$.

The basic equations for the mean are

$$\overline{N}(t) = \sum_N NP_N(t) \quad \text{and} \quad \frac{d\overline{N}}{dt} = \sum_N N\frac{dP_N(t)}{dt}. \tag{7.50}$$

According to the second of these equations, if we multiply the right-hand side of the master equation, (7.36), by N and sum over N, we obtain an expression for $d\overline{N}/dt$. In this procedure we encounter the sums

$$\sum_N P_{N-1}(M-N+1)N \quad \text{and} \quad \sum_N P_{N+1}(N+1)N.$$

It is convenient to rewrite these as

$$\sum_N P_N(M - N)(N + 1) \qquad \text{and} \qquad \sum_N P_N N(N - 1).$$

There are slight complications at $N = 0$ and $N = M$ which can be ignored without error (Problem 7.3). We then find, after some cancellation,

$$d\overline{N}/dt = (\alpha_A + \alpha_B)(M - \overline{N}) - 2\beta\overline{N}. \tag{7.51}$$

This is the same as Eq. (7.19), except that averaging is made explicit here. The present derivation is more general, however, because we have not had to assume that M is a large number [as was done implicitly in writing Eq. (7.19)]. Equation (7.47) is a special case, restricted to systems with a normal distribution.

Equation (7.51) is easy to integrate:

$$\overline{N}(t) - \overline{N}^\infty = [\overline{N}(0) - \overline{N}^\infty]e^{-(\alpha_A+\alpha_B+2\beta)t}. \tag{7.52}$$

The rate equation for the variance. Aside from the mean, the most interesting property of $P_N(t)$ for us is the variance $\sigma^2(t)$:

$$\sigma^2 = \overline{(N - \overline{N})^2} = \overline{N^2} - (\overline{N})^2. \tag{7.53}$$

Let us derive an equation for $d\sigma^2/dt$, by the method just used for $d\overline{N}/dt$. We start with

$$\begin{aligned} \frac{d\sigma^2}{dt} &= \frac{d\overline{N^2}}{dt} - 2\overline{N}\,\frac{d\overline{N}}{dt} \\ &= \sum_N N^2\,\frac{dP_N}{dt} - 2\overline{N}\,\frac{d\overline{N}}{dt}. \end{aligned} \tag{7.54}$$

The summation has to be calculated; the other term we already have from Eq. (7.51). We therefore multiply the right-hand side of the master equation by N^2 and sum over N. This time the sums

$$\sum_N P_{N-1}(M - N + 1)N^2 \qquad \text{and} \qquad \sum_N P_{N+1}(N + 1)N^2$$

occur. We rewrite them as

$$\sum_N P_N(M - N)(N + 1)^2 \qquad \text{and} \qquad \sum_N P_N N(N - 1)^2.$$

Again there is cancellation of various terms and we obtain finally

$$\frac{d\sigma^2}{dt} = (\alpha_A + \alpha_B)(M - \overline{N}) + 2\beta\overline{N} - 2(\alpha_A + \alpha_B + 2\beta)\sigma^2. \tag{7.55}$$

Using Eq. (7.52), it is easy to solve Eq. (7.55) for $\sigma^2(t)$. But we leave this to the reader (Problem 7.4).

At steady state, $d\overline{N}/dt = 0$ [see Eq. (7.21)] and $d\sigma^2/dt = 0$. Hence

$$\sigma_\infty^2 = \frac{\overline{N}^\infty(M - \overline{N}^\infty)}{M}. \tag{7.56}$$

From the equilibrium statistical mechanics of this open system (Problem 7.5),

$$\begin{aligned} \overline{N}^e &= \frac{Mq\lambda}{1 + q\lambda} \\ \sigma_e^2 &= \lambda \frac{\partial \overline{N}^e}{\partial \lambda} \\ &= \frac{Mq\lambda}{(1 + q\lambda)^2} = \frac{\overline{N}^e(M - \overline{N}^e)}{M}. \end{aligned} \tag{7.57}$$

Since equilibrium is a steady state, this is a self-consistency check on Eq. (7.56).

Equation (7.55) can be put in a more illuminating form. Let $f_\infty(\overline{N}^\infty)$ be the function of $\overline{N}^\infty$ on the right-hand side of Eq. (7.56): this is the functional dependence of σ^2 on $\overline{N}$ at $t = \infty$. At any time t,

$$f_\infty(\overline{N}(t)) = \frac{\overline{N}(t)[M - \overline{N}(t)]}{M} \tag{7.58}$$

is the value that $\sigma^2(t)$ would have if the variance at t had the *steady state* functional relation to the mean at t. It is easy to show, from Eqs. (7.51) and (7.55), that

$$\frac{d}{dt}[\sigma^2(t) - f_\infty(\overline{N}(t))] = -2(\alpha_A + \alpha_B + 2\beta)[\sigma^2(t) - f_\infty(\overline{N}(t))]. \tag{7.59}$$

Then

$$\sigma^2(t) - f_\infty(\overline{N}(t)) = [\sigma^2(0) - f_\infty(\overline{N}(0))]e^{-2(\alpha_A+\alpha_B+2\beta)t}. \tag{7.60}$$

If we compare Eqs. (7.52) and (7.60), we see that, as t increases, the variance approaches its steady-state relation to the mean at twice the rate that the mean approaches its steady-state value. It can be shown* that the third and higher moments of $P_N(t)$ behave essentially like the variance in this respect. In other words, the probability distribution $P_N(t)$ approaches the steady-state *shape* corresponding to $\overline{N}(t)$ twice as fast as $\overline{N}(t)$ approaches its steady-state value. In the equilibrium case ($\alpha_A = \alpha_B$), appropriate language to describe this is that the system comes into *internal* equilibrium before it reaches final equilibrium with the baths† [see Eq. (7.33)].

---

* See T. L. Hill and I. W. Plesner, *J. Chem. Phys.* **43,** 267 (1965).

† There are abnormal cases that have to be excepted. See Hill and Plesner, *loc. cit.*

If we start with any normal distribution, $\sigma^2(0) = f_\infty(\overline{N}(0))$ (Problem 7.6). Therefore, for any t, $\sigma^2(t) = f_\infty(\overline{N}(t))$.

We shall return to this model again in Section 7.9.

7.4 DISCONTINUOUS ONE-COMPONENT SYSTEM (II)

We come back now to the system treated in Section 7.1 (see Fig. 7.1) and consider three additional short topics, all of some importance.

Entropy production in terms of forces. Near equilibrium, the entropy production shown in Eq. (7.8) may be expressed in terms of forces rather than in terms of forces *and* fluxes. To accomplish this, we substitute Eqs. (7.14) (with $L_{EN} = L_{NE}$) in Eq. (7.8) and find

$$\dot{S} = L_{NN}X_N^2 + 2L_{NE}X_NX_E + L_{EE}X_E^2 \geq 0. \tag{7.61}$$

This function of the X's is a positive-definite quadratic form. Therefore (see Problem 7.7)

$$L_{NN}L_{EE} - L_{NE}^2 > 0. \tag{7.62}$$

The physical meaning of this relation is that the "indirect" or off-diagonal terms in Eqs. (7.14) cannot dominate the flux expressions. The "direct" or diagonal terms, $L_{NN}X_N$ and $L_{EE}X_E$, are the principal ones. This is intuitively reasonable.

Let us summarize the information we have about the L's: L_{NN} and L_{EE} are positive; $L_{EN} = L_{NE}$; L_{NE} may be positive or negative; and the inequality (7.62) must hold.

The generalization of Eqs. (7.61) and (7.62) to any number of fluxes and forces is taken up in Problem 7.7.

Entropy production and steady states. Hitherto in this chapter and, indeed, in the sections following this one as well, the term *steady state* means, in general, a system with all forces held at constant nonzero values. The fluxes are therefore also all constant and, in general, nonzero. Experimentally, such a steady state may be realized, for example, by using very large baths, A and B, so that bath properties do not change appreciably with time.

Equilibrium is a special case in which all forces and fluxes are constant and have the value zero.

Another type of steady state is one in which, with relatively small baths A and B, some but not all the forces are held constant, say, $X_1, X_2, \ldots, X_r$ but not $X_{r+1}, \ldots, X_n$. Experimentally, the constant forces have to be maintained by contact of A and B with other reservoirs. A steady state will then be reached when the two baths, A and B, have adjusted their properties so that the fluxes $J_{r+1}, \ldots, J_n$ all have the value zero. This must obviously be the case because any other final state would be unstable: if one of these J's is nonzero, the flux will eventually erase itself by alteration, in this finite system, of the values of the unrestricted forces.

The absolute minimum value of the entropy production $\dot{S}$ is zero, and this value is attained only at equilibrium. If we use finite baths A and B, and no restraints on any of the forces, with the passage of time, $\dot{S}$ will decrease to its final equilibrium value of zero. There is a very interesting generalization of this statement to near-equilibrium steady-state systems of the type just introduced: if the forces $X_1, \ldots, X_r$ are held constant, the system evolves with time to a steady state as already discussed, and this steady state corresponds to the lowest possible value of $\dot{S}$ consistent with the restraints $X_1 = \text{const}, \ldots, X_r = \text{const}$. This is a conditional minimum in $\dot{S}$ rather than an absolute minimum.

We prove this statement in our simple N, E case, and leave the more general problem to the reader (Problem 7.8). Let us take, say, $X_E = \text{const}$ (that is, $\delta T = \text{const}$), but put no restraint on X_N. Then, a steady state will finally be reached when X_N adjusts its value so that molecular flow stops, $J_N = 0$. Let us now see that if we minimize $\dot{S}$ with respect to X_N holding X_E constant, the conditional minimum corresponds to the steady state just described ($X_E = \text{const}$, $J_N = 0$). We differentiate Eq. (7.61) with respect to X_N, holding X_E constant, and find

$$\frac{\partial \dot{S}}{\partial X_N} = 0 = 2L_{NN}X_N + 2L_{NE}X_E = 2J_N. \tag{7.63}$$

Thus $J_N = 0$ at the conditional minimum. To verify that this is in fact a minimum and not a maximum, we note that $\partial^2\dot{S}/\partial X_N^2 = 2L_{NN} > 0$.

Equations (7.14) become, at this steady state,

$$\begin{aligned} 0 &= L_{NN}X_N + L_{NE}X_E, \\ J_E &= L_{NE}X_N + L_{EE}X_E. \end{aligned} \tag{7.64}$$

Therefore, the steady-state value of X_N is

$$X_N = -(L_{NE}/L_{NN})X_E, \tag{7.65}$$

and the steady-state flux J_E (this is pure heat flow, since $J_N = 0$) is

$$J_E = \left(L_{EE} - \frac{L_{NE}^2}{L_{NN}}\right) X_E. \tag{7.66}$$

According to (7.62), the coefficient of X_E here is positive, as we should expect.

If we substitute Eq. (7.65) into Eq. (7.61) to find the conditional minimum value of $\dot{S}$, we obtain

$$\dot{S}_{\text{min}} = \left(L_{EE} - \frac{L_{NE}^2}{L_{NN}}\right) X_E^2 = J_E X_E \geq 0. \tag{7.67}$$

In summary, for this finite system, if we hold δT constant, where δT is small, and let molecular and heat flow take place until a steady state is reached (at which there is still heat flow but no longer any molecular flow), then during the time evolution of the system, $\dot{S}$ decreases to its minimum possible value consistent with the restraint $\delta T = \text{const}$ (see Problem 7.18). This is given by Eq. (7.67). Only if $\delta T = 0$ does $\dot{S}$ reach its absolute minimum value of zero (equilibrium).

Section 7.9 is closely related to the subject of this subsection.

Alternate choices of forces and fluxes. Let us first make a different choice of forces, without regard to the requirement (7.15), which is, however, part of the fundamental postulate of irreversible thermodynamics.

We have been using, as in Eq. (7.7), $X_E = -\delta(1/T) = \delta T/T^2$ and $X_N = \delta(\mu/T)$ for the forces. A rather obvious alternative choice to make is $\delta T/T^2$ and $\delta\mu/T$ (we divide by T simply to keep the same dimensions as before). Then from

$$J_N = L_{NN}\left[\frac{\delta\mu}{T} - \mu\left(\frac{\delta T}{T^2}\right)\right] + L_{NE}\left(\frac{\delta T}{T^2}\right),$$

$$J_E = L_{NE}\left[\frac{\delta\mu}{T} - \mu\left(\frac{\delta T}{T^2}\right)\right] + L_{EE}\left(\frac{\delta T}{T^2}\right),$$

we find that

$$\begin{aligned} J_N &= L_{NN}\left(\frac{\delta\mu}{T}\right) + (L_{NE} - \mu L_{NN})\left(\frac{\delta T}{T^2}\right), \\ J_E &= L_{NE}\left(\frac{\delta\mu}{T}\right) + (L_{EE} - \mu L_{NE})\left(\frac{\delta T}{T^2}\right). \end{aligned} \tag{7.68}$$

Obviously, this particular choice of forces and fluxes has destroyed the reciprocal relation (the cross coefficients are not equal). We also note, from

$$\dot{S} = J_E\left(\frac{\delta T}{T^2}\right) + J_N\left[\frac{\delta\mu}{T} - \mu\left(\frac{\delta T}{T^2}\right)\right], \tag{7.69}$$

that

$$\dot{S} \neq J_E\left(\frac{\delta T}{T^2}\right) + J_N\left(\frac{\delta\mu}{T}\right). \tag{7.70}$$

Hence these fluxes and forces are not consistent with (7.15).

The moral of the above simple exercise is that indiscriminate choices of forces and fluxes cannot be made if we wish to stay within the framework of conventional irreversible thermodynamics.

We can, however, keep the new forces selected above and retrieve the situation by defining new fluxes. The form of Eq. (7.69) suggests immediately that we use J_N and $J'_E = J_E - \mu J_N$, for then

$$\dot{S} = J'_E\left(\frac{\delta T}{T^2}\right) + J_N\left(\frac{\delta\mu}{T}\right), \tag{7.71}$$

which has the desired form. As a check, we see that Eqs. (7.68) become

$$\begin{aligned} J_N &= L_{NN}\left(\frac{\delta\mu}{T}\right) + (L_{NE} - \mu L_{NN})\left(\frac{\delta T}{T^2}\right) \\ J'_E &= (L_{NE} - \mu L_{NN})\left(\frac{\delta\mu}{T}\right) + (L_{EE} - 2\mu L_{NE} + \mu^2 L_{NN})\left(\frac{\delta T}{T^2}\right), \end{aligned} \tag{7.72}$$

with a reciprocal relation restored.

In general, for a given system, various definitions of fluxes and forces are possible, all consistent with Eq. (7.15). From among these, the choice actually made is usually based on the physical significance of the fluxes and forces, and on convenience.

7.5 MODEL WITH COUPLING. DIAGRAM METHOD

In Section 7.2 we considered a very simple model for steady-state transport across a membrane. Here we analyze a related but more complicated model, using a diagram method* with wide applicability to steady-state transport problems. This model will also serve to illustrate coupling between two forces and fluxes, and will show a reciprocal relation.

General remarks. Before discussing the specific model, we make a few remarks to give some indication of the generality of the method.

Consider a system (membrane) of M independent and equivalent units each of which can exist in s different states. Transitions between pairs of these states can occur, obeying unimolecular kinetics. Thus, for example, if at time t a system has N_i units in state i, and a transition $i \rightarrow j$ is possible, then the probability that some one of these N_i units will undergo this process (so that $N_i \rightarrow N_i - 1$, $N_j \rightarrow N_j + 1$) in a time interval dt is $\kappa_{ij} N_i\, dt$, where the rate constant or transition probability κ_{ij} is independent of t. If we consider an ensemble of these systems, we can derive

* See T. L. Hill and O. Kedem, *J. Theoret. Biol.* **10,** 399 (1966); T. L. Hill, *J. Theoret. Biol.* **10,** 442 (1966).

by stochastic theory, as in Section 7.3, an expression for each of the $d\overline{N}_i/dt$ in terms of the various $\overline{N}_j$. These are linear first-order differential equations that may be obtained most easily merely by inspection of the particular model (as in Section 7.2). At steady state (which is all we consider) we have $d\overline{N}_i/dt = 0$ for all i so that we are concerned with the solution of linear algebraic equations only. The averages are ensemble averages. From here on, for simplicity of notation, we shall omit the bar denoting an average.

For any given model, the most conventional choices of rate constants would be such as to lead to eventual equilibrium in the system at $t = \infty$. However, we are primarily interested here in cases in which one or more of an "equilibrium set" of rate constants are altered in value so that the system reaches a nonequilibrium steady state at $t = \infty$.

In the model below, we study isothermal steady state transport of two components across a membrane between two large reservoirs. But we wish to emphasize that the diagram analysis to be used may be applied to any "unimolecular system" of the general type described above, for example, to combined heat and molecular transport across membranes, to unimolecular chemical kinetics in gas or solvent,* etc. In the case of heat transport, different membrane energy levels are different "states" (see Section 7.7, for example).

Our main interest is in steady-state fluxes, but one needs first the steady-state values of the N_i, denoted by N_i^∞ (equilibrium values of the N_i will be indicated by N_i^e). Of course, the N_i^∞ may be found in a straightforward way, in any particular case, by solution of a set of linear algebraic equations. But if the model is at all complicated, this may involve a great deal of tedious labor. One of our objects in this section is to show how the solution of the algebraic equations can be found, alternatively, from an enumeration of a certain class of diagrams. Furthermore, the solution in terms of diagrams has a certain intuitive appeal, and leads directly to the fluxes.

The model. Two kinds of molecules are being transported isothermally, between two baths, across a membrane. The transport channels (units) are pairs of sites for binding component 1. Component 2 molecules can be bound only on already bound molecules of component 1. There are M independent units in a system; each unit may exist in any one of the five

---

* See, for example, E. L. King and C. Altman, *J. Phys. Chem.* **60,** 1375 (1956). This application is to enzyme kinetics.

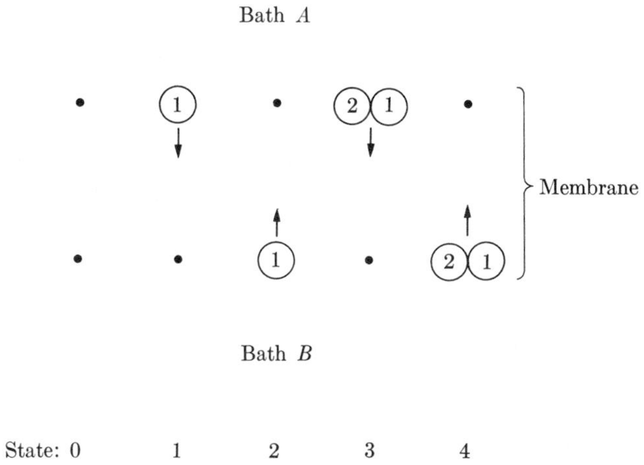

Fig. 7.7. Possible states for each unit in membrane.*

states shown in Fig. 7.7. For example, state 0 has both sites empty; state 1 has a molecule of component 1 bound on the A side of the membrane; etc. The (average) number of units in state i is N_i; $\sum_i N_i = M$.

The arrows in Fig. 7.7 indicate a jump of a molecule from a site on one side of the membrane to a site on the other side. Alternatively, the same formal model could apply to a quite different physical picture, no doubt of more importance in biological membranes. Thus state 1 might represent, say, a macromolecule, with a bound molecule of component 1, in a configuration such that the bound molecule is accessible to bath A. State 2 might represent a second macromolecular configuration such that the bound molecule is accessible to bath B. The bound molecule need not "jump" at all; instead, the macromolecule undergoes some kind of configuration change, not necessarily a large one.

Similarly, the complex 1 + 2 in states 3 and 4 may, from the first point of view, "jump" from one site to another, or, in the alternative picture, there may be a macromolecular configuration change which alters availability of the bound complex from one bath to the other. In either case, component 1 serves as a "carrier" (in biochemical terminology) for component 2. Or, one can think of the "bare" macromolecule as the carrier for component 1 *and* component 2; but component 2 is transported only when the macromolecule is "activated" first by the binding of component 1.

---

* Adapted from T. L. Hill, "Diagram Method for Unimolecular Systems," *J. Theoret. Biol.* **10,** 442 (1966), p. 444.

Figure 7.8 is the *basic diagram* for this model. Each number at a vertex (point of intersection) represents a state and each line represents a possible transition (in either direction) between states. The rate constants are shown beside the appropriate lines. The curved arrows indicate a direction and hence show the particular rate constant that belongs to a given process; for example, α_{B1} for $0 \rightarrow 2$, β_{B2} for $4 \rightarrow 2$, κ_1 for $1 \rightarrow 2$, etc. Figure 7.8 should be related, in detail, to Fig. 7.7.

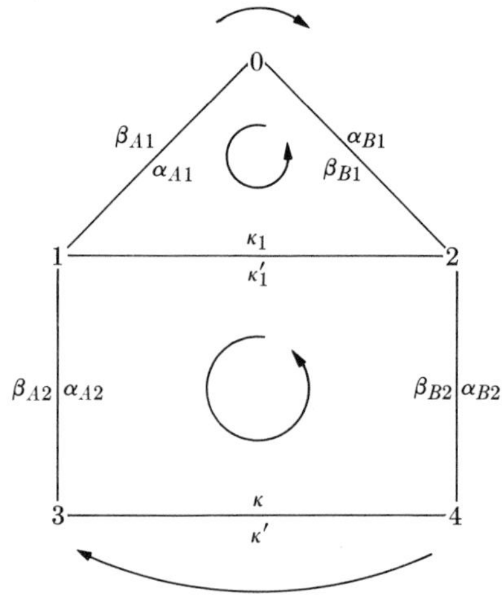

Fig. 7.8. Basic diagram for Fig. 7.7.*

As in Section 7.2, the α's are rate constants for adsorption (from a bath); they are proportional to bath concentrations (if these are assumed small). The β's are desorption rate constants. The κ's are internal "jump" constants. Since, in general, $\beta_{A1} \neq \beta_{B1}$ and $\beta_{A2} \neq \beta_{B2}$, the membrane is asymmetrical. Although not necessary, for simplicity we assume in this model that, at equilibrium, $\alpha_{A1} = \alpha_{B1}$ and $\alpha_{A2} = \alpha_{B2}$. Then, to obtain a nonequilibrium steady state at $t = \infty$, we have to choose (by altering bath concentrations) $\alpha_{A1} \neq \alpha_{B1}$ or $\alpha_{A2} \neq \alpha_{B2}$, or both. The β's and κ's are the same for steady state as for equilibrium.

Detailed balance at equilibrium imposes two conditions on the β's and κ's (steady state *or* equilibrium). Thus, from the triangular "cycle" (or closed path) 0210 in Fig. 7.8, we have

$$\alpha_1 N_0^e = \beta_{B1} N_2^e, \qquad \kappa_1' N_2^e = \kappa_1 N_1^e, \qquad \beta_{A1} N_1^e = \alpha_1 N_0^e \tag{7.73}$$

* *Ibid.*, p. 445

or

$$\frac{N_0^e}{N_2^e} \cdot \frac{N_2^e}{N_1^e} \cdot \frac{N_1^e}{N_0^e} = \frac{\beta_{B1}}{\alpha_1} \cdot \frac{\kappa_1}{\kappa_1'} \cdot \frac{\alpha_1}{\beta_{A1}} = \frac{\beta_{B1}\kappa_1}{\beta_{A1}\kappa_1'} = 1. \tag{7.74}$$

Similarly, from the square cycle 12431,

$$\kappa_1\kappa'\beta_{A2}/\kappa_1'\kappa\beta_{B2} = 1. \tag{7.75}$$

Relations of this type may be written merely by inspection of the basic diagram: the product of rate constants around a cycle in one direction is equal to the product of constants in the opposite direction (for equilibrium).

The differential equation for N_0 is

$$\frac{dN_0}{dt} = (\beta_{A1}N_1 - \alpha_{A1}N_0) + (\beta_{B1}N_2 - \alpha_{B1}N_0), \tag{7.76}$$

with similar expressions for dN_1/dt, etc. Each pair of terms on the right corresponds to a line in the basic diagram, Fig. 7.8. Thus dN_1/dt is equal to three pairs of terms, and there are three lines emanating from state 1 in the diagram. At steady state, Eq. (7.76) becomes

$$(\beta_{A1}N_1^\infty - \alpha_{A1}N_0^\infty) + (\beta_{B1}N_2^\infty - \alpha_{B1}N_0^\infty) = 0. \tag{7.77}$$

At equilibrium, each pair of terms is separately equal to zero [see Eqs. (7.73)].

We obtain an equation like (7.77) for each state. Thus, in this example, we have a set of five linear equations in the five N_i^∞. But only four of these equations are independent. The fifth *independent* equation, necessary to solve for the N_i^∞, is $\sum_i N_i^\infty = M$. The solution will give each N_i^∞/M as a function of rate constants.

Now, instead of solving five equations with five unknowns in the conventional way, as an alternative we can write the solution using diagrams, as follows. (The proof* is too detailed to be given here; but the reader should check the method on a simpler model—see Problem 7.9.) The first step is to construct the complete set of *partial diagrams*, each of which contains the maximum possible number of lines (four here) that can be included in the diagram without forming a cycle (closed path). There are eleven such partial diagrams in this case, shown in Fig. 7.9.

If one more line is introduced into any vacant position in any of these partial diagrams, a cycle is produced.

* See T. L. Hill, *J. Theoret. Biol.* **10,** 442 (1966).

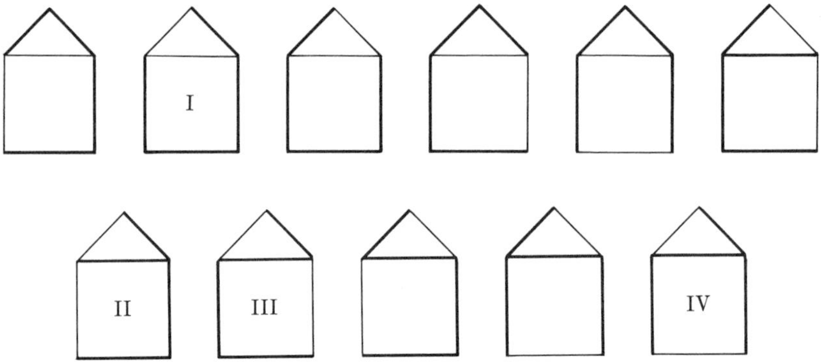

Fig. 7.9. Partial diagrams.*

At least one line goes to each vertex (state) in a partial diagram (otherwise more lines could be introduced without forming a cycle).

The next step is to introduce arrows (i.e., a directionality for each line) into the partial diagrams of Fig. 7.9 in five different ways, one way for each state (vertex). For example, consider state 1. Figure 7.10 shows the eleven *directional diagrams* for this state, as obtained from Fig. 7.9. The recipe for introducing arrows is simple: all connected paths in Fig. 7.10 are made to "flow" *toward* and *end at* vertex 1. It will be noted that in the flow toward the ultimate vertex (vertex 1 in Fig. 7.10), "streams" may converge but they never diverge (for this would require a cycle in the partial diagram).

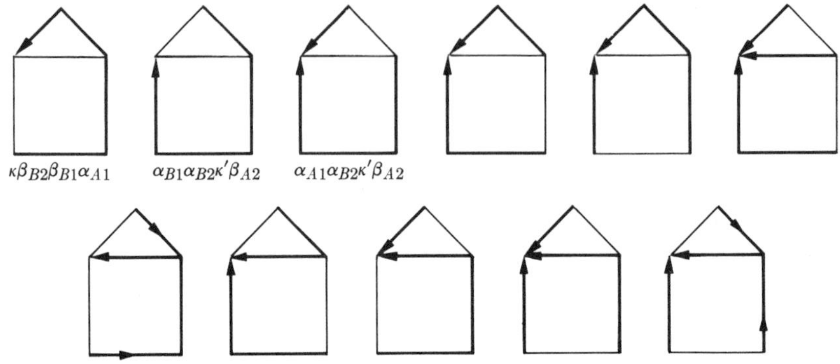

Fig. 7.10. Directional diagrams for state 1.*

---

* Reprinted by permission from T. L. Hill, "Diagram Method for Unimolecular Systems," *J. Theoret. Biol.* **10,** 442 (1966), p. 446.

There is a set of eleven directional diagrams for each of the five states. In each case, all streams flow toward—and end at—the particular state being considered.

Now each directional line or arrow in Fig. 7.10 corresponds to a rate constant; the key for assigning constants to directional lines is provided by Fig. 7.8. Using this key, each directional diagram in Fig. 7.10 represents a product of four rate constants, one for each arrow, as indicated under the first three of these diagrams.

Considering each directional diagram as a product of rate constants, the final step is the following: each N_i^∞ is proportional to the sum of the directional diagrams belonging to state i. But, since $\sum_i N_i^\infty = M$,

$$N_i^\infty = \frac{M \times \text{sum of directional diagrams of state } i}{\text{sum of directional diagrams of } all \text{ states}}. \tag{7.78}$$

In the above example, there are $5 \times 11 = 55$ directional diagrams altogether. Therefore, for state 1, say,

$$N_1^\infty = \frac{M(\kappa\beta_{B2}\beta_{B1}\alpha_{A1} + \alpha_{B1}\alpha_{B2}\kappa'\beta_{A2} + 9 \text{ other terms})}{(\kappa\beta_{B2}\beta_{B1}\alpha_{A1} + \alpha_{B1}\alpha_{B2}\kappa'\beta_{A2} + 53 \text{ other terms})}. \tag{7.79}$$

The result (7.78) is intuitively reasonable because the steady-state occupation of the ith state, N_i^∞, is proportional to the sum of products of rate constants along different routes leading *toward* state i. That is, we would expect in a general way that the larger the rate constants leading *toward* state i, the larger the relative population of state i at $t = \infty$.

Equation (7.78) is, of course, also the solution for N_i^e in the special case that the rate constants correspond to equilibrium at $t = \infty$.

Fluxes for the model. Steady-state fluxes are associated with cycles. A *cyclic diagram* is obtained from a directional diagram by adding one arrow (i.e., multiplying by a rate constant) in a direction such as to complete a closed path of arrows, all in the same direction. Cyclic diagrams occur in

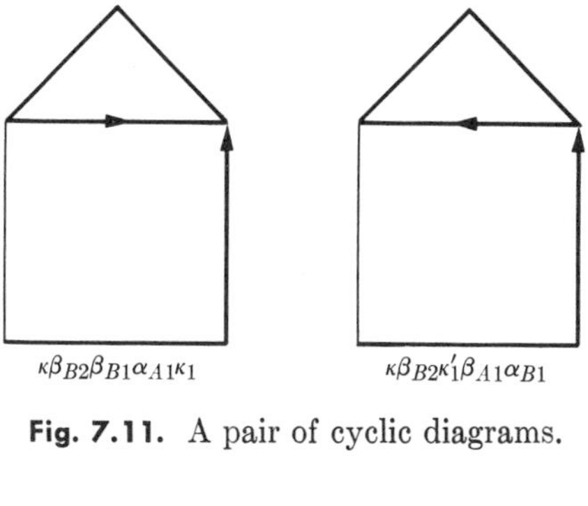

Fig. 7.11. A pair of cyclic diagrams.

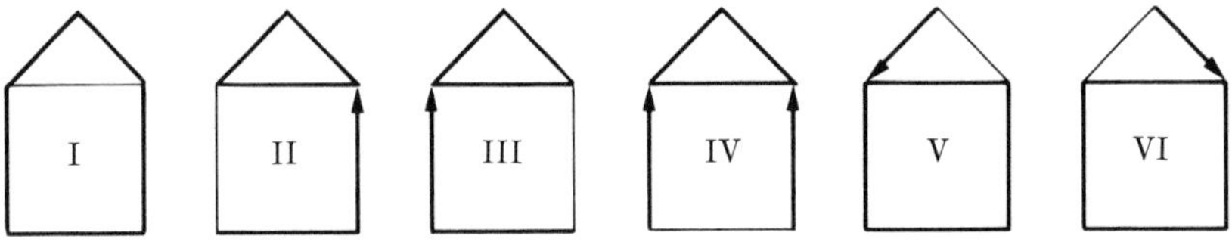

Fig. 7.12. Flux diagrams.*

pairs, as shown in Fig. 7.11. These differ only in the direction of traversal of the cycle. The algebraic difference between such a pair of cyclic diagrams is a *flux diagram.* The difference may be taken in two ways, of course. All possible flux diagrams for this model are shown in Fig. 7.12. For example, from Fig. 7.11, the algebraic value of flux diagram II in Fig. 7.12 (if we attach the positive sign to the counterclockwise direction around the cycle) is

$$\mathrm{II} = (\alpha_{A1}\kappa_1\beta_{B1} - \beta_{A1}\alpha_{B1}\kappa_1')\kappa\beta_{B2}. \tag{7.80}$$

If i and j are adjacent states in a basic diagram, then the net steady-state rate of conversion of units in state j into units in state i is

$$\kappa_{ji}N_j^\infty - \kappa_{ij}N_i^\infty.$$

We denote this rate, which is the steady-state flux along the line i–j in the direction $j \to i$, by $J_{j\to i}^\infty$. Then, in view of the relation between directional and flux diagrams, we have (details of the proof are left to the reader;† see Problem 7.10)

$$J_{j\to i}^\infty = \frac{M \times \text{sum of } j \to i \text{ flux diagrams}}{\text{sum of directional diagrams of all states}}, \tag{7.81}$$

where a flux diagram is considered a $j \to i$ flux diagram if the line i–j is included in the cycle of the flux diagram. Explicitly, to establish the algebraic sign,

$$(j \to i \text{ flux diagram}) = (j \to i \text{ cyclic diagram}) - (i \to j \text{ cyclic diagram}) \tag{7.82}$$

For example, in computing $J_{0\to1}^\infty$ for our present model, the $0 \to 1$ flux diagrams are I, II, III, and IV in Fig. 7.12. Incidentally, these can be generated by adding the line 0–1 to those partial diagrams in Fig. 7.9 with the 0–1 line missing (also labeled I to IV). The sign chosen in Eq. (7.80) for flux diagram II is correct for $J_{0\to1}^\infty$.

---

* *Ibid.*, p. 452.

† Or, see T. L. Hill, *J. Theoret. Biol.* **10**, 442 (1966).

A flux diagram may be derived from a partial diagram by adding one line as just mentioned. Alternatively, we can define a flux diagram as a diagram that contains one and only one cycle (with arrows omitted since the cycle is traversed in both directions) plus one or more streams (with arrows included) flowing into the cycle at one or more points of the cycle. Streams may converge, but may not diverge on their way toward the cycle. The number of lines used in a flux diagram is one more than the number of lines used in a partial diagram. A flux diagram is related to a cycle in the same way that a directional diagram is related to a state. The flux-diagram sum in Eq. (7.81) is the sum over all those diagrams of the type just described whose cycle includes the line i–j. Each flux diagram makes an additive contribution to the total flux.

Nonvanishing steady-state fluxes are possible only for systems whose basic diagrams contain one or more cycles. Alteration of an equilibrium set of rate constants in a basic diagram with no cycles can only lead to a new equilibrium state at $t = \infty$. If the basic diagram has one or more cycles, the rate constant alteration must occur in one of the cycles in order to produce a nonequilibrium steady state.

Different flux diagrams that contain the *same* cycle may be collected and added together. Thus Eq. (7.81) may be rewritten as

$$J_{j\to i}^{\infty} = \frac{M \times \text{sum of } j \to i \text{ cycles}}{\text{sum of directional diagrams for all states}}, \tag{7.83}$$

where, in this algebraic context, *cycle* means the sum of all possible flux diagrams based on the cycle in question (the algebraic sign is determined by the direction $j \to i$). This sum of flux diagrams determines the relative contribution made by the cycle to the total flux $J_{j\to i}^{\infty}$. This is an intuitively reasonable result in essentially the same way that Eq. (7.78) is. The flux contributed by a cycle would be expected to be larger the greater the difference in the product of the rate constants going around the cycle in the two different directions, and the larger the rate constants leading *toward* ("feeding into") the cycle from other parts of the diagram.

Let us return now to explicit consideration of the model being investigated in this section. The basic diagram, Fig. 7.8, admits of three cycles, shown in Fig. 7.13. The flux $J_{0\to 1}^{\infty}$, for example, has contributions from cycles a and b because these two cycles make use of the line 0–1. Thus

$$J_{0\to 1}^{\infty} = \frac{M \text{ (cycle } a + \text{cycle } b)}{55 \text{ terms in Eq. (7.79)}}, \tag{7.84}$$

where

$$\text{cycle } a = \text{I}, \qquad \text{cycle } b = \text{II} + \text{III} + \text{IV (Fig. 7.12)}. \tag{7.85}$$

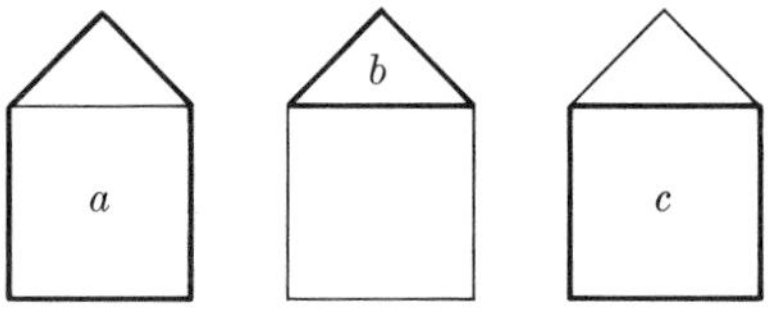

Fig. 7.13. Cycles.*

The explicit algebraic expressions, using Fig. 7.8, are

$$\begin{aligned} \text{I} &= \alpha_{A1}\alpha_{A2}\kappa\beta_{B2}\beta_{B1} - \beta_{A1}\alpha_{B1}\alpha_{B2}\kappa'\beta_{A2}, \\ \text{II} &= (\alpha_{A1}\kappa_1\beta_{B1} - \beta_{A1}\alpha_{B1}\kappa_1')\kappa\beta_{B2}, \\ \text{III} &= (\alpha_{A1}\kappa_1\beta_{B1} - \beta_{A1}\alpha_{B1}\kappa_1')\kappa'\beta_{A2}, \\ \text{IV} &= (\alpha_{A1}\kappa_1\beta_{B1} - \beta_{A1}\alpha_{B1}\kappa_1')\beta_{A2}\beta_{B2}. \end{aligned} \tag{7.86}$$

But, in view of the detailed balance conditions (7.74) and (7.75),

$$\begin{aligned} \text{cycle } a &= (\alpha_{A1}\alpha_{A2} - \alpha_{B1}\alpha_{B2})\kappa\beta_{B2}\beta_{B1}, \\ \text{cycle } b &= (\alpha_{A1} - \alpha_{B1})\kappa_1\beta_{B1}(\kappa\beta_{B2} + \kappa'\beta_{A2} + \beta_{A2}\beta_{B2}). \end{aligned} \tag{7.87}$$

In the equilibrium case, these α differences are equal to zero and $J^{\infty}_{0\to 1} = 0$.

The flux $J^{\infty}_{1\to 2}$ is proportional to cycle b + cycle c; the flux $J^{\infty}_{1\to 3}$ is proportional to cycle a + cycle c; etc. Also, of course, at steady state,

$$\begin{aligned} J^{\infty}_{2\to 0} &= J^{\infty}_{0\to 1}, \\ J^{\infty}_{1\to 3} &= J^{\infty}_{3\to 4} = J^{\infty}_{4\to 2}, \\ J^{\infty}_{0\to 1} &= J^{\infty}_{1\to 2} + J^{\infty}_{1\to 3}, \\ J^{\infty}_{1\to 2} + J^{\infty}_{4\to 2} &= J^{\infty}_{2\to 0}. \end{aligned} \tag{7.88}$$

The explicit expression for cycle c (direction $1 \to 3$) is

$$\begin{aligned} \text{cycle } c &= \text{V} + \text{VI (Fig. 7.12)} \\ &= (\alpha_{A2} - \alpha_{B2})\kappa\kappa_1'\beta_{B2}(\alpha_{A1} + \alpha_{B1}). \end{aligned} \tag{7.89}$$

Thermodynamic fluxes. There is a steady-state flux, between the baths and across the membrane, in the two components 1 and 2. We denote these fluxes by J_1^{∞} and J_2^{∞} in the direction $A \to B$ (as in Section 7.2). The rate at which component 1 molecules leave bath A is $J^{\infty}_{0\to 1}$. Therefore $J_1^{\infty} = J^{\infty}_{0\to 1}$. Similarly, $J_2^{\infty} = J^{\infty}_{1\to 3}$. Thus the steady-state fluxes J_1^{∞} and J_2^{∞} are given by

$$J_1^{\infty}\Sigma/M = \text{cycle } a + \text{cycle } b, \quad J_2^{\infty}\Sigma/M = \text{cycle } a + \text{cycle } c, \tag{7.90}$$

where Σ is the sum of 55 terms in the denominator of Eq. (7.79).

---

* Reprinted by permission from T. L. Hill, "Diagram Method for Unimolecular Systems," *J. Theoret. Biol.* **10,** 442 (1966), p. 452.

The "forces"* [compare Eq. (7.23)] that produce steady-state fluxes in this model are $\alpha_{A1} - \alpha_{B1}$ and $\alpha_{A2} - \alpha_{B2}$. The first of these occurs in cycle b and the second in cycle c. *Both* forces are operative in cycle a; it is this feature that tells us, without benefit of explicit algebra, that there will be coupling between the two forces and fluxes. Since a cycle makes the same contribution to the flux (in the same direction) along all lines making up the cycle, either force in cycle a will cause a flux in *both* components. Furthermore, the words "same contribution" used above lead to the reciprocal relation, as we shall see.

In general, any model whose basic diagram contains one or more cycles that involve two or more forces will show coupling between the forces and fluxes. A more complicated example, illustrating so-called active transport, will be discussed in Section 7.8. The origin of reciprocal relations, in terms of cycles, will be pursued further there.

We return now to Eqs. (7.90). Let us arbitrarily choose bath B as the "reference bath" and write

$$\text{cycle } a = \left(\frac{\alpha_{A1}\alpha_{A2}}{\alpha_{B1}\alpha_{B2}} - 1\right) a, \qquad a = \kappa\beta_{B2}\beta_{B1}\alpha_{B1}\alpha_{B2}, \tag{7.91}$$

$$\text{cycle } b = \left(\frac{\alpha_{A1}}{\alpha_{B1}} - 1\right) b, \quad b = \kappa_1\beta_{B1}(\kappa\beta_{B2} + \kappa'\beta_{A2} + \beta_{A2}\beta_{B2})\,\alpha_{B1}, \tag{7.92}$$

$$\text{cycle } c = \left(\frac{\alpha_{A2}}{\alpha_{B2}} - 1\right) c, \quad c = \kappa\kappa_1'\beta_{B2}(\alpha_{A1} + \alpha_{B1})\alpha_{B2}. \tag{7.93}$$

Then we introduce the identity

$$\frac{\alpha_{A1}\alpha_{A2}}{\alpha_{B1}\alpha_{B2}} - 1 = \left(\frac{\alpha_{A1}}{\alpha_{B1}} - 1\right)\left(\frac{\alpha_{A2}}{\alpha_{B2}} - 1\right) + \left(\frac{\alpha_{A1}}{\alpha_{B1}} - 1\right) + \left(\frac{\alpha_{A2}}{\alpha_{B2}} - 1\right)$$

in Eq. (7.91) and use

$$\alpha_{A1} = (\alpha_{A1} - \alpha_{B1}) + \alpha_{B1}$$

in Eq. (7.93), so that

$$c = \left[2 + \left(\frac{\alpha_{A1}}{\alpha_{B1}} - 1\right)\right] c', \qquad c' = \kappa\kappa_1'\beta_{B2}\alpha_{B1}\alpha_{B2}. \tag{7.94}$$

Equations (7.90) for the fluxes then become

$$\frac{J_1^\infty \Sigma}{M} = \left(\frac{\alpha_{A1}}{\alpha_{B1}} - 1\right)(a + b) + \left(\frac{\alpha_{A2}}{\alpha_{B2}} - 1\right) a + \left(\frac{\alpha_{A1}}{\alpha_{B1}} - 1\right)\left(\frac{\alpha_{A2}}{\alpha_{B2}} - 1\right) a \tag{7.95}$$

$$\frac{J_2^\infty \Sigma}{M} = \left(\frac{\alpha_{A1}}{\alpha_{B1}} - 1\right) a + \left(\frac{\alpha_{A2}}{\alpha_{B2}} - 1\right)(a + 2c')$$
$$+ \left(\frac{\alpha_{A1}}{\alpha_{B1}} - 1\right)\left(\frac{\alpha_{A2}}{\alpha_{B2}} - 1\right)(a + c'). \tag{7.96}$$

---

* Quotes are used because these are not the conventional thermodynamic forces $(\delta\mu_i/T)$.

These are the fluxes at an arbitrary steady state, not necessarily near equilibrium. The coefficients of the "forces" are properties of the steady state, not of an equilibrium state. Note further that α_{A1} and α_{A2} are included in $\sum$ (i.e., "reference bath" B has not been introduced in $\sum$ as it has been in the right-hand side of the two equations above). Note also that even in the above form the coefficients of linear "force" terms obey a reciprocal relation.

Near equilibrium, we put

$$\frac{\alpha_{Ai}}{\alpha_{Bi}} - 1 = \frac{\delta\alpha_i}{\alpha_i} = \frac{X_i}{k} \qquad (i = 1, 2), \tag{7.97}$$

as in Eq. (7.24), drop nonlinear terms in the X's, and obtain

$$\begin{aligned} J_1^\infty &= \left[\frac{M(a^e + b^e)}{\sum^e k}\right] X_1 + \left[\frac{Ma^e}{\sum^e k}\right] X_2, \\ J_2^\infty &= \left[\frac{Ma^e}{\sum^e k}\right] X_1 + \left[\frac{M(a^e + 2c'^e)}{\sum^e k}\right] X_2, \end{aligned} \tag{7.98}$$

where the equilibrium forms of a, b, c', and $\sum$, which appear here, are found by setting $\alpha_{Ai} = \alpha_{Bi} = \alpha_i$ $(i = 1, 2)$. There is a reciprocal relation, $L_{12} = L_{21}$, which is a direct consequence of the facts (1) that cycle a is the only cycle containing two forces and (2) that a flux around this cycle contributes equal fluxes to components 1 and 2.

Special case. If the four κ's are comparable in size but all very large compared to the α's and β's, a^e becomes negligible relative to b^e and c'^e in Eqs. (7.98): there is no longer any coupling. Internal equilibrium is

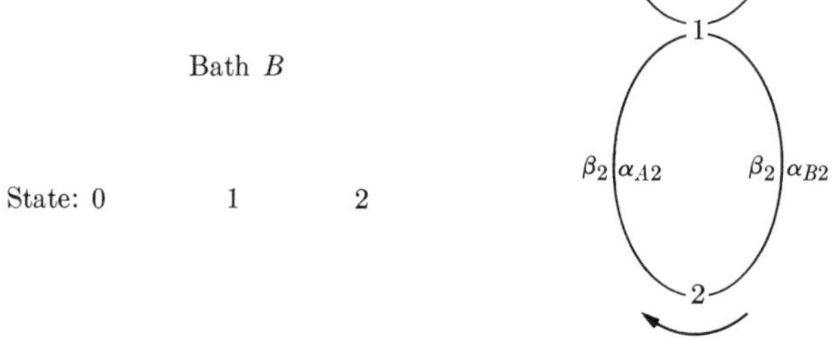

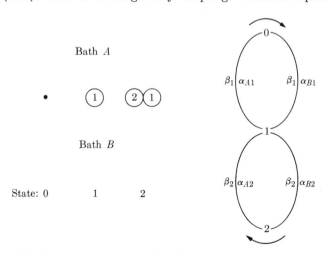

Fig. 7.14. Membrane transport model with two components and no coupling.

obtained in the membrane at steady state. Component 2 is "carried" by the equilibrium population of component 1; transport of component 2 is no longer influenced by a chemical-potential gradient in component 1.

A closely related model is shown in Fig. 7.14. The symmetrical membrane consists of only a single row of sites for binding component 1 (from either bath). Component 2 is bound (from either bath) only on component 1, as before. The basic diagram, which is included in the figure, is a collapsed version of Fig. 7.8. There are two cycles (top half; bottom half). Each cycle involves only one force. Hence, despite the apparent interdependence of the transport of the two components, there is no coupling. From a physical point of view, the reason for this is that the interaction between the two components in this model has no directional aspect, one way or the other, normal to the membrane.

Derivation of the steady-state flux expressions for this model is left to the reader* (Problem 7.9).

7.6 CHEMICAL REACTIONS

The discussion given here will not be very extensive. We begin with a few general relations and then consider three examples. A chemical reaction will also appear in the model treated in Section 7.8, coupled with molecular transport.

Consider first a very large *isolated* homogeneous thermodynamic system, in equilibrium *except* with respect to one or more chemical reactions (the reactions are slow relative to the rate of heat and molecular transport within the system). In the time interval dt, the reactions proceed toward equilibrium to an infinitesimal extent. Then the basic equation

$$dE = T\,dS - p\,dV + \sum_i \mu_i\,dN_i \tag{7.99}$$

leads to the expression for entropy production,

$$\frac{dS}{dt} = \dot{S} = -\sum_i \frac{\mu_i}{T}\frac{dN_i}{dt} \geq 0, \tag{7.100}$$

since E and V are constant. Components j not involved in a chemical reaction will have $dN_j/dt = 0$ here. If we introduce the concentrations $\rho_i = N_i/V$,

$$\frac{\dot{S}}{V} = -\sum_i \frac{\mu_i}{T}\frac{d\rho_i}{dt} \geq 0. \tag{7.101}$$

To go further, we need to introduce the actual reactions explicitly.

* Or, see T. L. Hill and O. Kedem, *J. Theoret. Biol.* **10,** 399 (1966), Model 6.

Alternatively, we may derive the same result, Eq. (7.100), as follows. Suppose the closed system is held at constant p and T, rather than being isolated. Such an arrangement is of more interest experimentally. Then the pertinent general equation, for an infinitesimal change in state, is

$$dG = -S\,dT + V\,dp + \sum_i \mu_i\,dN_i. \tag{7.102}$$

This becomes

$$-\frac{d(G/T)}{dt} = -\sum_i \frac{\mu_i}{T}\frac{dN_i}{dt} \geq 0, \tag{7.103}$$

since p and T are constant. We also have [compare Eq. (7.12)]

$$dH = DQ = T\,d_eS = T(dS - d_iS) \qquad (p \text{ constant})$$

and

$$d_iS = dS - \frac{dH}{T} = -\frac{dG}{T} \qquad (p,\, T \text{ constant}). \tag{7.104}$$

Therefore, on combining Eqs. (7.103) and (7.104), the entropy production is

$$\frac{d_iS}{dt} = \dot{S} = -\sum_i \frac{\mu_i}{T}\frac{dN_i}{dt} \geq 0, \tag{7.105}$$

which is the same as Eq. (7.100).

Simple isomeric reaction. Suppose that the only chemical reaction is the isomeric one, $A \rightleftarrows B$. Then, since $\rho_A + \rho_B =$ const (the system is closed),

$$\begin{aligned}\frac{\dot{S}}{V} &= -\left(\frac{\mu_A}{T}\frac{d\rho_A}{dt} + \frac{\mu_B}{T}\frac{d\rho_B}{dt}\right) \geq 0 \\ &= J\mathsf{A} \geq 0,\end{aligned} \tag{7.106}$$

where

$$J = \text{reaction flux } (A \rightarrow B) = \frac{d\rho_B}{dt} = -\frac{d\rho_A}{dt} \tag{7.107}$$

and

$$\mathsf{A} = \text{affinity (reaction force)} = \frac{\mu_A - \mu_B}{T}. \tag{7.108}$$

Thus the conventional form of the entropy production, *flux* $\times$ *force*, is obtained for this chemical reaction. The affinity and flux have the same sign; both quantities vanish at equilibrium.

Let us now consider an explicit simple mechanism:

$$A \underset{\kappa'}{\overset{\kappa}{\rightleftarrows}} B,$$

where κ and κ' are rate constants. This is formally very similar to the case on p. 129, at the end of Section 7.2:

$$\text{empty sites} \underset{\beta}{\overset{\alpha}{\rightleftarrows}} \text{occupied sites}.$$

We assume that components A and B are dilute, with total concentration $\rho_0 = \rho_A + \rho_B$. The flux is

$$J = \frac{d\rho_B}{dt} = -\frac{d\rho_A}{dt} = \kappa\rho_A - \kappa'\rho_B. \tag{7.109}$$

At equilibrium,

$$\frac{\rho_B^e}{\rho_A^e} = \frac{\kappa}{\kappa'} = K = \text{equilibrium constant}$$

$$\rho_A^e = \rho_0/(1+K), \qquad \rho_B^e = \rho_0 K/(1+K).$$

Also, since $\mu_A^e = \mu_B^e$,

$$\mu_A' + kT \ln \rho_A^e = \mu_B' + kT \ln \rho_B^e$$

and

$$\mu_B' - \mu_A' = -kT \ln K.$$

These relations are useful below.

Equation (7.109) can also be written in the form

$$J = \frac{d(\rho_B - \rho_B^e)}{dt} = (\kappa + \kappa')(\rho_B^e - \rho_B), \tag{7.110}$$

which is, of course, easy to solve explicitly. In Eq. (7.110), which applies arbitrarily far from equilibrium, the "force" is a concentration difference.

Near equilibrium, we substitute

$$\rho_A = \rho_A^e - (\rho_B - \rho_B^e)$$

and

$$\rho_B = \rho_B^e + (\rho_B - \rho_B^e)$$

into

$$\mu_A - \mu_B = (\mu_A' + kT \ln \rho_A) - (\mu_B' + kT \ln \rho_B),$$

retain linear terms in $\rho_B^e - \rho_B$, and find that

$$\mathsf{A} = \frac{\mu_A - \mu_B}{T} = \frac{k(\kappa+\kappa')^2(\rho_B^e - \rho_B)}{\kappa\kappa'\rho_0}. \tag{7.111}$$

Thus, near equilibrium, Eq. (7.110) becomes

$$J = L\mathsf{A}, \tag{7.112}$$

where

$$L = \frac{\rho_0\kappa\kappa'}{k(\kappa+\kappa')}. \tag{7.113}$$

This should be compared with Eq. (7.35). Alternative forms for L are

$$L = \frac{\kappa\rho_A^e}{k} = \frac{\kappa'\rho_B^e}{k}, \tag{7.114}$$

where $\kappa\rho_A^e$ and $\kappa'\rho_B^e$ are the opposing elementary rates at equilibrium [see Eq. (7.109)].

A more complicated reaction. Let the only reaction be

$$\nu_A A + \nu_B B \rightleftarrows \nu_C C,$$

where ν_A, ν_B, and ν_C are the stoichiometric coefficients (small integers). Define the flux J as the number of units of reaction, from left to right, per unit time per unit volume. One "unit of reaction" occurs when ν_A molecules of A and ν_B molecules of B form ν_C molecules of C. Then

$$J = \frac{1}{\nu_C}\frac{d\rho_C}{dt} = -\frac{1}{\nu_A}\frac{d\rho_A}{dt} = -\frac{1}{\nu_B}\frac{d\rho_B}{dt}. \tag{7.115}$$

Equation (7.101) becomes, in this case,

$$\dot{S}/V = J\mathsf{A} \geq 0, \tag{7.116}$$

if we define the affinity as

$$\mathsf{A} = \frac{\nu_A\mu_A + \nu_B\mu_B - \nu_C\mu_C}{T}. \tag{7.117}$$

This is the generalization of Eq. (7.108). We shall not go beyond this purely thermodynamic result in this case.

Triangular isomeric reactions. As a final example, suppose that three dilute species react according to the mechanism

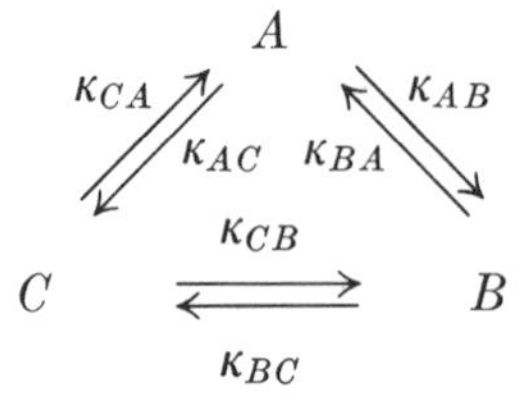

Then the kinetic equations are

$$\begin{aligned}
\frac{d\rho_A}{dt} &= (\kappa_{BA}\rho_B - \kappa_{AB}\rho_A) + (\kappa_{CA}\rho_C - \kappa_{AC}\rho_A),\\
\frac{d\rho_B}{dt} &= (\kappa_{CB}\rho_C - \kappa_{BC}\rho_B) + (\kappa_{AB}\rho_A - \kappa_{BA}\rho_B),\\
\frac{d\rho_C}{dt} &= (\kappa_{AC}\rho_A - \kappa_{CA}\rho_C) + (\kappa_{BC}\rho_B - \kappa_{CB}\rho_C).
\end{aligned} \tag{7.118}$$

Only two of these are independent, however, since

$$\rho_A + \rho_B + \rho_C = \rho_0 = \text{const.}$$

At $t = \infty$, the system reaches equilibrium, where (detailed balance)

$$\kappa_{BA}\rho_B^e = \kappa_{AB}\rho_A^e, \qquad \kappa_{CA}\rho_C^e = \kappa_{AC}\rho_A^e, \qquad \kappa_{CB}\rho_C^e = \kappa_{BC}\rho_B^e. \tag{7.119}$$

Therefore the κ's must be related by

$$\kappa_{AB}\kappa_{BC}\kappa_{CA} = \kappa_{AC}\kappa_{CB}\kappa_{BA}.$$

If we define deviations from equilibrium $x_A = \rho_A - \rho_A^e$, etc., then

$$\begin{aligned} \frac{dx_A}{dt} &= (\kappa_{BA}x_B - \kappa_{AB}x_A) + (\kappa_{CA}x_C - \kappa_{AC}x_A), \\ \frac{dx_B}{dt} &= (\kappa_{CB}x_C - \kappa_{BC}x_B) + (\kappa_{AB}x_A - \kappa_{BA}x_B), \\ \frac{dx_C}{dt} &= (\kappa_{AC}x_A - \kappa_{CA}x_C) + (\kappa_{BC}x_B - \kappa_{CB}x_C). \end{aligned} \tag{7.120}$$

Also,

$$x_A + x_B + x_C = 0.$$

Again, only two of Eqs. (7.120) are independent.

The affinities are defined by

$$\mathsf{A}_{ij} = (\mu_i - \mu_j)/T \qquad (i, j = A, B, C). \tag{7.121}$$

Only two of these are independent. Thus this system has two forces (affinities) and two fluxes.

Near equilibrium, we use

$$\begin{aligned} \mu_A &= \mu'_A + kT \ln \rho_A = \mu'_A + kT \ln \left[\rho_A^e\left(1 + \frac{x_A}{\rho_A^e}\right)\right] \\ &= \mu'_A + kT \ln \rho_A^e + \frac{kTx_A}{\rho_A^e}, \end{aligned} \tag{7.122}$$

with similar expressions for species B and C. Since $\mu_A^e = \mu_B^e = \mu_C^e$, the affinities become, near equilibrium,

$$\mathsf{A}_{ij} = \frac{\mu_i - \mu_j}{T} = \frac{kx_i}{\rho_i^e} - \frac{kx_j}{\rho_j^e}.$$

But, if we multiply the above by $\kappa_{ij}\rho_i^e/k$,

$$\frac{\kappa_{ij}\rho_i^e\mathsf{A}_{ij}}{k} = \kappa_{ij}x_i - \frac{\kappa_{ij}\rho_i^e x_j}{\rho_j^e} = \kappa_{ij}x_i - \kappa_{ji}x_j. \tag{7.123}$$

Therefore, near equilibrium, Eqs. (7.120) can be written

$$\begin{aligned} \frac{dx_A}{dt} &= \left(\frac{\kappa_{BA}\rho_B^e}{k}\right)\mathsf{A}_{BA} + \left(\frac{\kappa_{CA}\rho_C^e}{k}\right)\mathsf{A}_{CA} \\ \frac{dx_B}{dt} &= \left(\frac{\kappa_{CB}\rho_C^e}{k}\right)\mathsf{A}_{CB} + \left(\frac{\kappa_{AB}\rho_A^e}{k}\right)\mathsf{A}_{AB}. \end{aligned} \tag{7.124}$$

The third equation is omitted, since it is not independent.

For maximum symmetry, let us choose A_{CA} and A_{CB} as the two independent affinities. Then

$$\mathsf{A}_{AB} = -\mathsf{A}_{BA} = \mathsf{A}_{CB} - \mathsf{A}_{CA}.$$

Consequently,

$$\begin{aligned} J_A &= \frac{dx_A}{dt} = \left(\frac{\kappa_{CA}\rho_C^e + \kappa_{BA}\rho_B^e}{k}\right)\mathsf{A}_{CA} - \left(\frac{\kappa_{BA}\rho_B^e}{k}\right)\mathsf{A}_{CB} \\ J_B &= \frac{dx_B}{dt} = -\left(\frac{\kappa_{AB}\rho_A^e}{k}\right)\mathsf{A}_{CA} + \left(\frac{\kappa_{CB}\rho_C^e + \kappa_{AB}\rho_A^e}{k}\right)\mathsf{A}_{CB}. \end{aligned} \tag{7.125}$$

Molecules of species A are produced directly through the affinity A_{CA} and indirectly through the affinity A_{CB}, etc. In view of detailed balance, Eqs. (7.119), there is again a reciprocal relation.

This example is of considerable historic importance. Onsager investigated this problem in his first paper* on nonequilibrium thermodynamics and concluded that the concept of detailed balance at equilibrium must form the molecular basis for macroscopically observed reciprocal relations. He then used fluctuation theory to provide a general proof of this connection, not limited to any particular mechanism or type of mechanism.

7.7 MODEL FOR HEAT AND MOLECULAR TRANSPORT

A simple model for steady-state molecular transport is analyzed in Section 7.2 (see also Fig. 7.3). Our object here is to alter this model, in as elementary a way as possible, to provide an illustration of simultaneous molecular *and* heat transport. The essential complications required are the introduction of a temperature gradient, of individual energy levels for the adsorbed (solute) molecules, and of separate transition probabilities between these levels. In contrast to this is the treatment in Section 7.2 where we group all the energy levels together and use the partition function $q(T)$, whether or not the system is at equilibrium. This assumes internal equilibrium among the energy levels—even in nonequilibrium states.

The present section also serves to illustrate, at the molecular level, some aspects of the thermodynamically oriented Sections 7.1 and 7.4.

In Fig. 7.3, the baths will now have different temperatures as well as chemical potentials. Bath A is characterized by T_A and μ_A; bath B by T_B and μ_B. As before, the membrane separating the baths contains M independent and equivalent sites for binding solute molecules. The relevant energy levels and transitions for solute molecules are shown in Fig. 7.15.

---

* L. Onsager, *Phys. Rev.* **37,** 405 (1931).

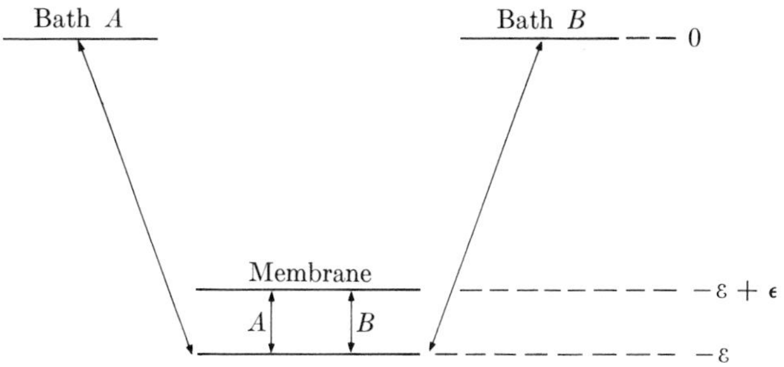

Fig. 7.15. Energy levels and allowed transitions of solute for model with heat and molecular transport.

Only the ground state in the baths and the two lowest levels in the membrane (all nondegenerate) are considered. The bath ground state is chosen as a convenient zero of energy for solute molecules. Higher levels than those shown in Fig. 7.15 are assumed to be high enough that they are essentially unpopulated. Adsorption and desorption occur only to and from the membrane ground state. The solvent, in both baths, is assumed to have a practically continuous set of energy levels of its own, or at the least, it has transitions with $\Delta E = \pm\epsilon$ and* $\Delta E = \pm\mathcal{E}$, so as to be able to couple† with the solute transitions shown. Coupling between solute and solvent transitions is necessary for conservation of energy. Whenever a solute molecule is adsorbed, the solvent in the appropriate bath absorbs energy in amount $\mathcal{E}$. On desorption of a solute molecule, the bath (solvent) concerned loses energy $\mathcal{E}$. The double arrows in Fig. 7.15, labeled A and B, indicate that bound molecules may be excited or deexcited through coupling with a solvent transition ($\Delta E = \pm\epsilon$) in either bath A or bath B.

Figure 7.16 shows the three possible states for each of the M units or sites: (0) empty, (1) ground state occupied, and (2) excited state occupied. The corresponding basic diagram and the assumed transition probabilities are also given in this figure. The notation is as follows:

$$\lambda_A = e^{\mu_A/kT_A}, \qquad \lambda_B = e^{\mu_B/kT_B}, \qquad \tau_A = e^{-\mathcal{E}/kT_A},$$
$$\tau_B = e^{-\mathcal{E}/kT_B}, \qquad \eta_A = e^{-\epsilon/kT_A}, \qquad \text{and} \qquad \eta_B = e^{-\epsilon/kT_B}.$$

The quantities $\mathcal{E}$, ϵ, β and γ are all constants which, in principle, are provided by quantum mechanics. The τ's and η's are simple "activation

* This $\mathcal{E}$, of course, has nothing to do with the $\mathcal{E}$ in Chapter 5 or in Chapter 6.
† In this context, "couple" has a quite different meaning, of course, than in irreversible thermodynamics.

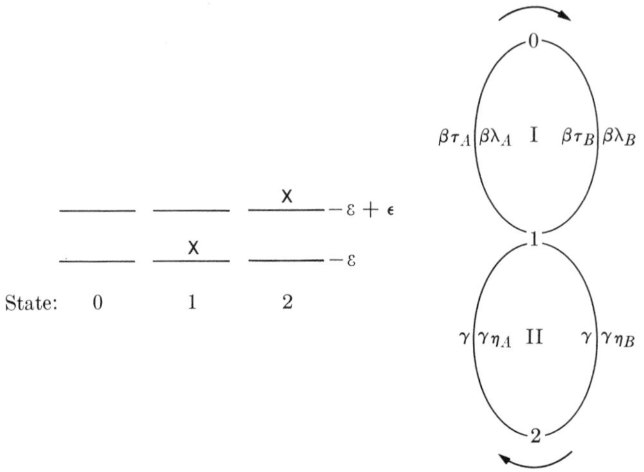

Fig. 7.16. States and basic diagram for model in Fig. 7.15.

energy" factors; they include the temperature of whichever bath is coupled to the solute transition.

The model described in Figs. 7.15 and 7.16 is quite arbitrary and has been chosen for its extreme simplicity, not for its resemblance to any real system. Also, it has the required feature of being consistent with thermodynamic equilibrium when $\mu_A = \mu_B$ and $T_A = T_B$, and $t = \infty$.

The slightly more complicated model with three available levels for a bound molecule has been treated elsewhere.*

The kinetic equations are

$$\frac{dN_0}{dt} = (\beta\tau_A N_1 - \beta\lambda_A N_0) + (\beta\tau_B N_1 - \beta\lambda_B N_0),$$
$$\frac{dN_2}{dt} = (\gamma\eta_A N_1 - \gamma N_2) + (\gamma\eta_B N_1 - \gamma N_2), \tag{7.126}$$

$$N_0 + N_1 + N_2 = M. \tag{7.127}$$

The equation in dN_1/dt is not independent and is therefore omitted.

Let us first check the equilibrium properties of our model. We have, from Eqs. (7.126) and (7.127),

$$\frac{N_1^e}{N_0^e} = \frac{\lambda}{\tau} = e^{\varepsilon/kT}\lambda, \qquad \frac{N_2^e}{N_0^e} = \frac{\eta\lambda}{\tau} = e^{(\varepsilon-\epsilon)/kT}\lambda$$

and

$$\frac{N^e}{M} = \frac{N_1^e + N_2^e}{M} = \frac{q\lambda}{1+q\lambda}, \tag{7.128}$$

* T. L. Hill, *Proc. Nat. Acad. Sci.* **56,** 45 (1966). Also, see Problem 7.15.

where

$$q(T) = \sum_i e^{-\epsilon_i/kT} = e^{\mathcal{E}/kT} + e^{(\mathcal{E}-\epsilon)/kT}.$$

This is a special case of Eq. (2.37).

At steady state, we find easily that

$$\frac{N_0^\infty}{M} = \frac{2(\tau_A + \tau_B)}{[\;]}, \quad \frac{N_1^\infty}{M} = \frac{2(\lambda_A + \lambda_B)}{[\;]}, \quad \frac{N_2^\infty}{M} = \frac{(\lambda_A + \lambda_B)(\eta_A + \eta_B)}{[\;]}, \tag{7.129}$$

where

$$[\;] = 2(\tau_A + \tau_B) + (\lambda_A + \lambda_B)(2 + \eta_A + \eta_B).$$

Note that β and γ do not appear in Eqs. (7.129). If we define T^∞ by means of the steady-state "Boltzmann distribution" between levels $-\mathcal{E}$ and $-\mathcal{E} + \epsilon$, we have

$$\frac{N_2^\infty}{N_1^\infty} = e^{-\epsilon/kT^\infty} = \frac{e^{-\epsilon/kT_A} + e^{-\epsilon/kT_B}}{2}. \tag{7.130}$$

Of course, with three or more levels, in general, there would not be a single T^∞ of this sort.

Let us define the fluxes J_N and J_E as the rate of arrival of molecules and energy in bath B. Then

$$\begin{aligned} J_N &= \beta\tau_B N_1 - \beta\lambda_B N_0, \\ J_E &= -\mathcal{E}(\beta\tau_B N_1 - \beta\lambda_B N_0) + \epsilon(\gamma N_2 - \gamma\eta_B N_1). \end{aligned} \tag{7.131}$$

The latter equation follows because each desorption of a solute molecule into bath B must be accompanied by a loss of an amount of energy $\mathcal{E}$ by bath B, and each deexcitation from level $-\mathcal{E} + \epsilon$ to $-\mathcal{E}$, when coupled to bath B, must involve a transfer of energy ϵ to bath B.

At steady state, Eqs. (7.129) and (7.131) yield

$$\begin{aligned} J_N^\infty &= \frac{2\beta M(\lambda_A\tau_B - \lambda_B\tau_A)}{[\;]}, \\ J_E^\infty &= -\mathcal{E}J_N^\infty + \frac{\epsilon\gamma(\lambda_A + \lambda_B)M(\eta_A - \eta_B)}{[\;]}. \end{aligned} \tag{7.132}$$

Although the constants β and γ do not affect the steady-state distribution among states [Eqs. (7.129)], they do influence the fluxes.

We see from the basic diagram in Fig. 7.16 that the "forces" associated with the two cycles (labeled I and II) are $\lambda_A\tau_B - \lambda_B\tau_A$ and $\eta_A - \eta_B$, respectively. These expressions appear in Eqs. (7.132). Cycle I is concerned with molecular transport, and cycle II with pure heat transport (no molecular flux), but both cycles are involved in energy transport because adsorption and desorption (cycle I) have to be coupled with the baths to maintain conservation of energy.

Near equilibrium,

$$\eta_A - \eta_B = \eta_B[e^{-(\epsilon/kT_A)+(\epsilon/kT_B)} - 1]$$
$$\rightarrow \eta\left(\frac{\epsilon}{kT_B} - \frac{\epsilon}{kT_A}\right) = \frac{\eta\epsilon X_E}{k} \qquad \text{(cycle II)}$$

and

$$\lambda_A\tau_B - \lambda_B\tau_A = \lambda_B\tau_B\left[\left(\frac{\lambda_A - \lambda_B}{\lambda_B}\right) - \left(\frac{\tau_A - \tau_B}{\tau_B}\right)\right]$$
$$\rightarrow \lambda\tau\left[\left(\frac{\mu_A}{kT_A} - \frac{\mu_B}{kT_B}\right) - \left(\frac{\mathcal{E}}{kT_B} - \frac{\mathcal{E}}{kT_A}\right)\right]$$
$$= \lambda\tau\left(\frac{X_N}{k} - \frac{\mathcal{E}X_E}{k}\right) \qquad \text{(cycle I)}.$$

Because two forces are operative in cycle I, there will be coupling in the flux-force equations.

Equations (7.132) become, near equilibrium,

$$J_N^\infty = \left(\frac{\beta\tau N_1^e}{2k}\right)X_N - \left(\frac{\beta\tau N_1^e\mathcal{E}}{2k}\right)X_E,$$
$$J_E^\infty = -\left(\frac{\beta\tau N_1^e\mathcal{E}}{2k}\right)X_N + \left(\frac{\beta\tau N_1^e\mathcal{E}^2}{2k} + \frac{\gamma\eta N_1^e\epsilon^2}{2k}\right)X_E. \tag{7.133}$$

There is a reciprocal relation, as expected.

The form of Eqs. (7.133) suggests a simplifying redefinition of the forces and fluxes: define $X' = X_N - \mathcal{E}X_E$ and use J_N^∞, X' and X_E. Then, from [see Eq. (7.8)]

$$\dot{S} = J_E^\infty X_E + J_N^\infty X_N$$
$$= J_E^\infty X_E + J_N^\infty(X' + \mathcal{E}X_E)$$
$$= (J_E^\infty + \mathcal{E}J_N^\infty)X_E + J_N^\infty X',$$

we see that the second flux should be defined as $J^\infty = J_E^\infty + \mathcal{E}J_N^\infty$. Equations (7.133) are then modified to read

$$J_N^\infty = \left(\frac{\beta\tau N_1^e}{2k}\right)X', \tag{7.134}$$

$$J^\infty = \left(\frac{\gamma\eta N_1^e\epsilon^2}{2k}\right)X_E. \tag{7.135}$$

There are no coupling terms here. Equation (7.134) relates to cycle I only (molecular transport); Eq. (7.135) is concerned with cycle II only (pure heat transport).

Some rather similar models of steady-state systems* can be set up to illustrate optical pumping, lasers, photochemical experiments, etc.

7.8 MODELS ILLUSTRATING ACTIVE TRANSPORT

Our primary object here is to present two examples showing how models of the type introduced in Section 7.5 may be extended to include coupling between membrane transport and a source of chemical free energy such as ATP $\rightarrow$ ADP + P. This is known as "active transport" if the force (affinity) of the chemical reaction contributes, by means of coupling, to the transport of a component across the membrane.

As a preliminary, we shall first consider briefly two models which illustrate the fact that the chemical reaction does *not* couple with membrane transport if the reaction is not accompanied by an oriented or directional change of state in the membrane.

In all the models of this section we shall use a prototype chemical reaction $T \rightarrow D$ to represent a chemical free energy source such as

$$\text{ATP} \rightarrow \text{ADP} + \text{P}.$$

It is assumed that the species participating in the reaction besides the main reactant and product (denoted T and D) have invariant activities, so that the affinity is completely determined by the absolute activities of T and D. The species T and D are bound on other molecules or carriers in the membrane. The binding rate constants are designated α_T and α_D. As usual, these are proportional to the concentrations or absolute activities of T and D in the appropriate reservoir. There is a reservoir for T and a reservoir for D. Either of these might be bath A or bath B, or both. Because T and D may be in the same bath, the reaction flux itself is not directional (it is a scalar). The reaction $T \rightleftarrows D$ takes place (enzymatically) on the membrane only—not in the reservoir. But for a given value of α_D, we let α_T represent that value of α_T which would correspond to chemical equilibrium in the reservoir. At equilibrium,

$$\mu_T^e = \mu_D + \text{constant (other species)}.$$

The affinity is defined as $\mathsf{A} = (\mu_T - \mu_T^e)/T$. Thus $(\alpha_T/\alpha_T^e) - 1$ corresponds to the driving "force" of a transported species i, $(\alpha_{Ai}/\alpha_{Bi}) - 1$. At ordinary biological concentrations, $\alpha_T - \alpha_T^e$ is positive so the reaction

---

* See, for example, C. Kittel, *Elementary Statistical Physics*. New York: Wiley, 1958.

$T \rightarrow D$ proceeds spontaneously (on the membrane) with a decrease in free energy.

The concentrations of T and D in the reservoirs are assumed to remain constant in any given steady state. This, of course, implies further coupling, presumably at a location other than the membrane, with another chemical free energy source (metabolism) to convert the D produced back into T. This latter coupling does not appear explicitly in the models discussed here.

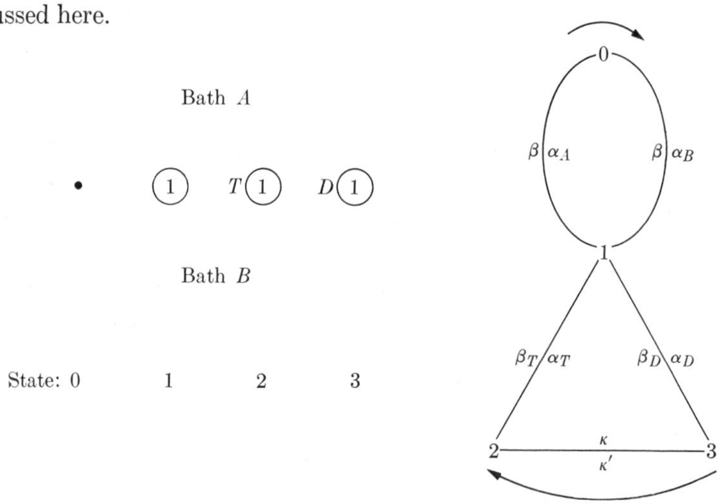

Fig. 7.17. Model with transport and chemical reaction but no coupling.

Model (a). The membrane has one layer of M sites for binding component 1 (the species being transported between baths A and B). Each bound molecule of component 1 can bind a T or a D on a catalytic site for the reaction $T \rightleftarrows D$. The states and basic diagram are shown in Fig. 7.17. There is a detailed balance condition (triangular cycle): $\alpha_T^e \kappa \beta_D = \alpha_D \kappa' \beta_T$. At equilibrium, $\alpha_A = \alpha_B$ and $\alpha_T = \alpha_T^e$. Each of the two cycles contains only one "force" ($\alpha_A - \alpha_B$ or $\alpha_T - \alpha_T^e$). Therefore there can be no coupling between the flux J_1^∞ (component 1, $A \rightarrow B$) and the reaction flux J_r^∞ ($T \rightarrow D$). Hence, active transport does not occur here. This is consistent with the fact that the chemical reaction in this model has no directional aspect and therefore cannot, by itself, cause a flux in component 1, one way or the other (compare the model in Fig. 7.14).

Model (b). This model generalizes the previous one somewhat. There are two layers of sites* and the membrane is asymmetrical (Fig. 7.18). Both

---

* The two "sides" of the membrane, as in states 1 and 2, for example, may represent two different macromolecular configurations. See p. 143.

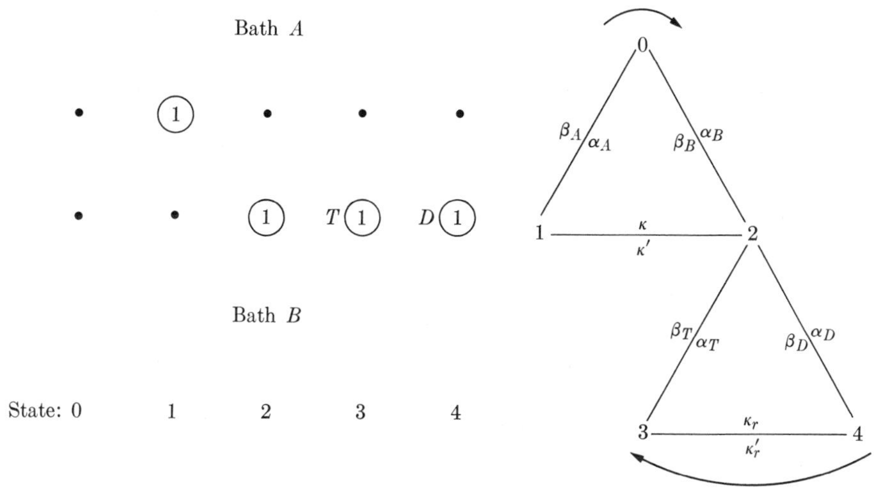

Fig. 7.18. Model, with similar properties, related to that in Fig. 7.17.

T and D can be bound on component 1 only on the B "side" of the membrane, and the reaction takes place on this side. The change of state $3 \rightleftarrows 4$ (reaction) is not oriented perpendicular to the membrane. The two detailed balance relations are $\kappa\beta_B = \kappa'\beta_A$ and $\alpha_T^e\kappa_r\beta_D = \alpha_D\kappa_r'\beta_T$. Despite the generalization over the previous model, each cycle still has only one "force." Hence, again, there is no coupling or active transport.

Model (c). This model (Fig. 7.19) alters model (b) in such a way that the change of state ($3 \rightleftarrows 4$) which occurs with the reaction now has a direction:

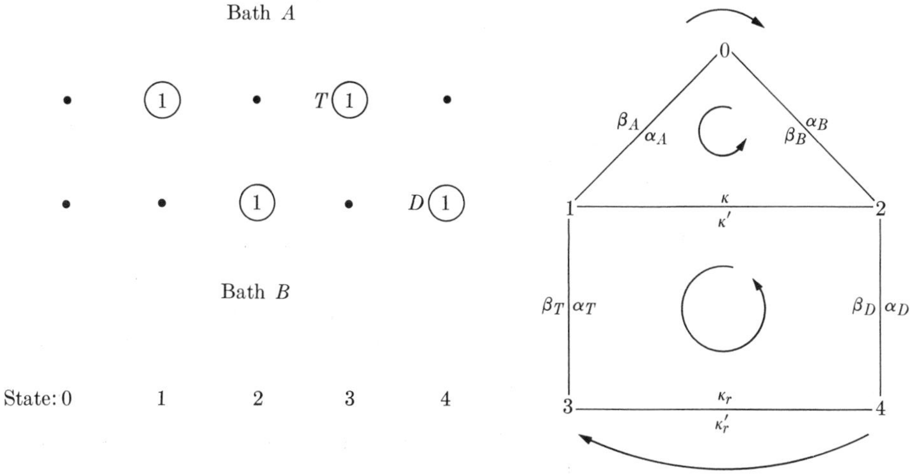

Fig. 7.19. Simple model illustrating active transport.

while T is transformed to D, component 1 is transferred from side A to side B. Note how the diagram in Fig. 7.18 is converted into the diagram in Fig. 7.19. The transport and reaction parts of the diagram are no longer connected by a single point. Therefore the cycle 013420, which involves two forces and hence coupling, becomes possible. The other two cycles are 0120 and 13421 (no coupling).

Next, we notice that Fig. 7.19 is formally the same as Figs. 7.7 and 7.8 so that the two mathematical problems are equivalent. A comparison of the basic diagrams establishes the connection between the two notations.

From a molecular point of view, T and D in Fig. 7.19 represent different substates of the same substance in basically the same way that, in Fig. 7.7, component 2 on side A and component 2 on side B represent different substates of component 2. The deviation from equilibrium $\alpha_T - \alpha_T^e$ corresponds to the concentration gradient $\alpha_{2A} - \alpha_{2B}$. However, $\alpha_T - \alpha_T^e$ is a scalar, and the directional character of the process $T \rightleftarrows D$ stems from the concomitant oriented change in state of component 1 in the membrane. This and the next model show that, given an appropriate type of anisotropy in the membrane, a scalar reaction can be coupled to a vector flow.*

If $\alpha_T - \alpha_T^e$ (or $\mu_T - \mu_T^e$) is large enough, component 1 will be transported from bath A to bath B against its own chemical-potential gradient ($\alpha_A - \alpha_B$ and $\mu_A - \mu_B$ are negative). The essential feature which makes this possible is that the reaction $T \rightarrow D$ (state 3 $\rightarrow$ state 4) is accompanied by a transition or transport of component 1 from "side" A to "side" B of the membrane. Thus the chemical reaction drives the transport of component 1 along a "path" (state 3 $\rightarrow$ state 4; 013420) different from component 1's own independent "path" (state 1 $\rightarrow$ state 2; 0120).

Near equilibrium, Eqs. (7.98) apply here:

$$\begin{aligned} J_1^\infty &= \left[\frac{M(a^e + b^e)}{\sum^e k}\right] X_1 + \left[\frac{Ma^e}{\sum^e k}\right] \mathsf{A} \\ J_r^\infty &= \left[\frac{Ma^e}{\sum^e k}\right] X_1 + \left[\frac{M(a^e + 2c'^e)}{\sum^e k}\right] \mathsf{A}. \end{aligned} \tag{7.136}$$

We shall not bother to write out a^e, etc., in the new notation. The ratio between transport and chemical reaction is J_1^∞/J_r^∞. If $\kappa = \kappa' = 0$ [that is, if $\kappa_1 = \kappa_1' = 0$ in Eqs. (7.98)], $b^e = c'^e = 0$ and $J_1^\infty/J_r^\infty = 1$. In this case, no independent path is available for the transport and the two processes are completely coupled.

---

* Coupling of this type is not possible in an *isotropic* system (this is a special case of what is known as "Curie's law").

Net transport against a gradient of chemical potential will take place if the affinity is large enough, that is, if

$$\mathsf{A} > \frac{(a^e + b^e)}{a^e}(-X_1). \tag{7.137}$$

The steady-state entropy production is

$$\dot{S}^\infty = J_1^\infty X_1 + J_r^\infty \mathsf{A} \geq 0. \tag{7.138}$$

With active transport, we have:

$$J_1^\infty > 0, \quad X_1 < 0, \quad J_1^\infty X_1 < 0,$$
$$J_r^\infty > 0, \quad \mathsf{A} > 0, \quad \text{and} \quad \dot{S}^\infty > 0.$$

Because of the last inequality, we can be certain that $J_r^\infty \mathsf{A} > J_1^\infty(-X_1)$, except at equilibrium.

Free energy is stored at steady state as a thermodynamic potential gradient at the rate $TJ_1^\infty(-X_1)$, and the rate of chemical free energy expenditure is $TJ_r^\infty \mathsf{A}$. The efficiency, ϵ, of the active transport may be defined as

$$\epsilon = J_1^\infty(-X_1)/J_r^\infty \mathsf{A}. \tag{7.139}$$

Then ϵ goes to unity only for $\kappa = \kappa' = 0$ and $\mathsf{A} \to -X_1$. Under these conditions, J_1^∞ and J_r^∞ vanish simultaneously and the system approaches ideal efficiency at infinitely slow rates. For finite values of κ and κ', $\epsilon = 0$ at $J_1^\infty = 0$: chemical free energy is expended for the maintenance of the concentration gradient, without net transport. This occurs when

$$\mathsf{A} = (a^e + b^e)(-X_1)/a^e. \tag{7.140}$$

Model (d). As a final example, we discuss a somewhat more complicated case. This is a possible model for Na^+ and K^+ transport across cell membranes (though it is not the most likely model). It is generally believed that K^+ transport often occurs at approximately zero force ($X_{K^+} \cong 0$) but that Na^+ is transported ("actively") against a very considerable electrochemical potential gradient,* with the help of ATP $\to$ ADP + P, from cell interior to cell exterior.

Also, the present model has been selected, to some extent, to illustrate further the relation between cycles and reciprocal relations.

The eight states for each of the M units are shown in Fig. 7.20. Note that

$$\text{bath } A = \text{cell interior}$$

and

$$\text{bath } B = \text{cell exterior}.$$

* See, for example, A. L. Lehninger, *Bioenergetics*. New York: Benjamin, 1965.

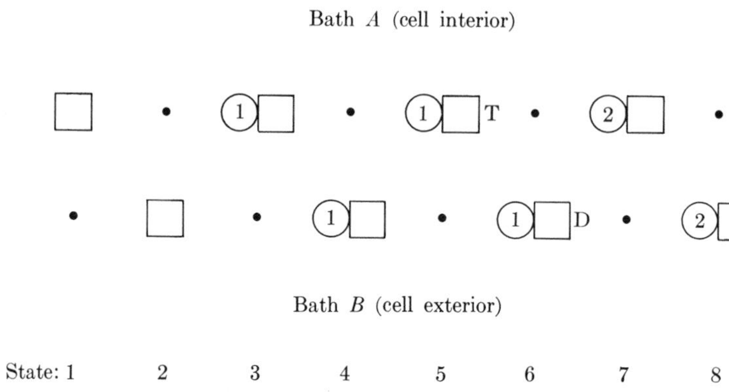

Fig. 7.20. Eight states for model of Na^+, K^+ transport.*

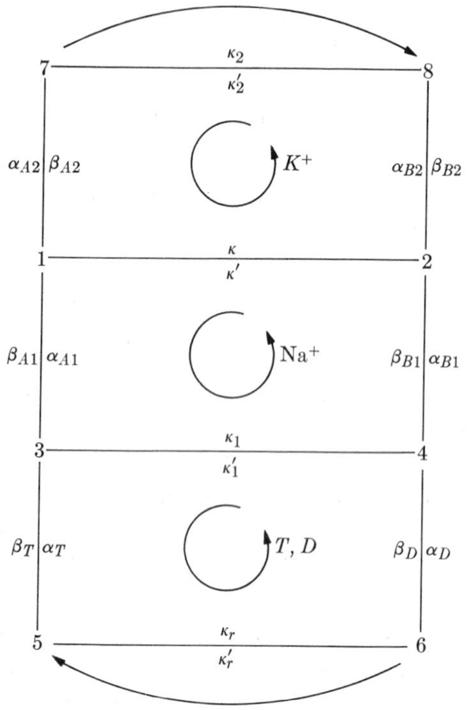

Fig. 7.21. Basic diagram for model in Fig. 7.20.*

*Adapted from T. L. Hill, "Diagram Methods for Unimolecular Systems," *J. Theoret. Biol.* **10,** 442 (1966), pp. 455 and 456.

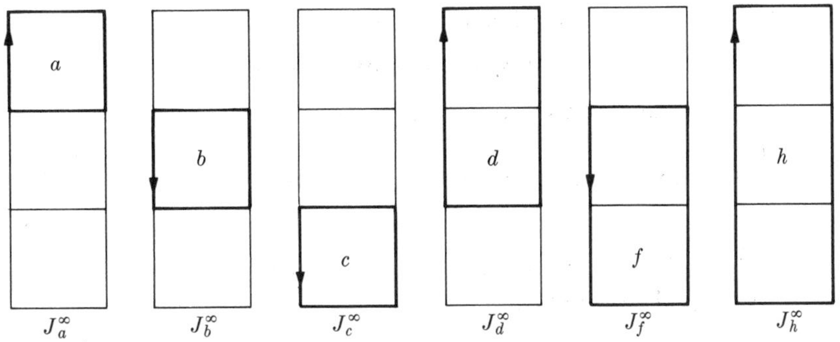

Fig. 7.22. Cycles for the model in Fig. 7.20.*

The allowed transitions and the rate constants are given in Fig. 7.21. Component 1 = Na^+, component 2 = K^+, and the "squares" represent a macromolecule which can exist in two different states (a "carrier"). Binding of T and D on the macromolecule is possible only after "activation" by Na^+ binding. The Na^+ transport is directly aided by the chemical reaction $T \to D$ in the transition: state 5 $\to$ state 6. But T and D are not similarly involved in the K^+ transport (in this model).

At equilibrium: $\alpha_{A1} = \alpha_{B1}$, $\alpha_{A2} = \alpha_{B2}$, and $\alpha_T = \alpha_T^e$.

For this model, the six possible cycles are shown in Fig. 7.22; J_a^∞ in this figure is the flux associated with cycle a (with the choice of direction indicated by the arrow),

$$J_a^\infty = \frac{M \times \text{cycle } a}{\text{sum of directional diagrams}} = \frac{M \times \text{sum of cycle } a \text{ flux diagrams}}{\text{sum of directional diagrams}}, \tag{7.141}$$

etc. There are eleven flux diagrams based on cycle a, nine based on cycle b, etc. (see Fig. 7.22). We leave it to the reader to draw the flux diagrams.

If we separate out the α differences as in Eqs. (7.87) and (7.89), we can write

$$\begin{aligned}
J_a^\infty &= M(\alpha_{A2} - \alpha_{B2})a'/\Sigma, \\
J_b^\infty &= M(\alpha_{A1} - \alpha_{B1})b'/\Sigma, \\
J_c^\infty &= M(\alpha_T - \alpha_T^e)c'/\Sigma, \\
J_d^\infty &= M(\alpha_{A2}\alpha_{B1} - \alpha_{B2}\alpha_{A1})d'/\Sigma, \\
J_f^\infty &= M(\alpha_{A1}\alpha_T - \alpha_{B1}\alpha_T^e)f'/\Sigma, \\
J_h^\infty &= M(\alpha_{A2}\alpha_{B1}\alpha_T^e - \alpha_{B2}\alpha_{A1}\alpha_T)h'/\Sigma,
\end{aligned} \tag{7.142}$$

---

* *Ibid.*, p. 457.

where $\sum$ is the sum of directional diagrams,

$$a' = \kappa\kappa_2'\beta_{A2} \times \text{sum of 11 terms},$$

etc. As an example, let us write out J_f^∞ in more detail:

$$J_f^\infty = \frac{M}{\sum}(\alpha_{A1}\alpha_T\kappa_r\beta_D\beta_{B1}\kappa' - \alpha_{B1}\alpha_D\kappa_r'\beta_T\beta_{A1}\kappa)(\kappa_2'\beta_{A2} + \kappa_2\beta_{B2} + \beta_{A2}\beta_{B2}). \tag{7.143}$$

The detailed balance condition for cycle f is $\alpha_T^e\kappa_r\beta_D\beta_{B1}\kappa' = \alpha_D\kappa_r'\beta_T\beta_{A1}\kappa$. Using this, Eq. (7.143) reduces to J_f^∞ in (7.142) if we define

$$f' = \frac{\alpha_D\kappa_r'\beta_T\beta_{A1}\kappa}{\alpha_T^e}(\kappa_2'\beta_{A2} + \kappa_2\beta_{B2} + \beta_{A2}\beta_{B2}).$$

We define the steady-state thermodynamic fluxes for this model by

$$\begin{aligned} J_1^\infty &= \text{net flux of 1 out of bath } A \text{ or into bath } B,\\ J_2^\infty &= \text{net flux of 2 out of bath } A \text{ or into bath } B,\\ J_r^\infty &= \text{net flux } T \to D. \end{aligned}$$

Then

$$\begin{aligned} J_1^\infty &= J_{1\to3}^\infty = J_{4\to2}^\infty = J_b^\infty - J_d^\infty + J_f^\infty - J_h^\infty,\\ J_2^\infty &= J_{1\to7}^\infty = J_{8\to2}^\infty = J_a^\infty + J_d^\infty + J_h^\infty,\\ J_r^\infty &= J_{5\to6}^\infty = J_c^\infty + J_f^\infty - J_h^\infty. \end{aligned} \tag{7.144}$$

Let us arbitrarily consider bath B as the reference bath and, in the last three of Eqs. (7.142), substitute

$$\alpha_{A1} = (\alpha_{A1} - \alpha_{B1}) + \alpha_{B1}, \qquad \alpha_{A2} = (\alpha_{A2} - \alpha_{B2}) + \alpha_{B2},$$
$$\alpha_T = (\alpha_T - \alpha_T^e) + \alpha_T^e.$$

On combining Eqs. (7.142) and (7.144), we then find that

$$\begin{aligned} J_1^\infty = \frac{M}{\sum}\Bigg[&(b+d+f+h)\left(\frac{\alpha_{A1}}{\alpha_{B1}} - 1\right) - (d+h)\left(\frac{\alpha_{A2}}{\alpha_{B2}} - 1\right)\\ &+ (f+h)\left(\frac{\alpha_T}{\alpha_T^e} - 1\right) + (f+h)\left(\frac{\alpha_{A1}}{\alpha_{B1}} - 1\right)\left(\frac{\alpha_T}{\alpha_T^e} - 1\right)\Bigg],\\ J_2^\infty = \frac{M}{\sum}\Bigg[&-(d+h)\left(\frac{\alpha_{A1}}{\alpha_{B1}} - 1\right) + (a+d+h)\left(\frac{\alpha_{A2}}{\alpha_{B2}} - 1\right)\\ &- h\left(\frac{\alpha_T}{\alpha_T^e} - 1\right) - h\left(\frac{\alpha_{A1}}{\alpha_{B1}} - 1\right)\left(\frac{\alpha_T}{\alpha_T^e} - 1\right)\Bigg],\\ J_r^\infty = \frac{M}{\sum}\Bigg[&(f+h)\left(\frac{\alpha_{A1}}{\alpha_{B1}} - 1\right) - h\left(\frac{\alpha_{A2}}{\alpha_{B2}} - 1\right) + (c+f+h)\left(\frac{\alpha_T}{\alpha_T^e} - 1\right)\\ &+ (f+h)\left(\frac{\alpha_{A1}}{\alpha_{B1}} - 1\right)\left(\frac{\alpha_T}{\alpha_T^e} - 1\right)\Bigg], \end{aligned} \tag{7.145}$$

where

$$a = a'\alpha_{B2}, \qquad b = b'\alpha_{B1}, \qquad c = c'\alpha_T^e,$$
$$d = d'\alpha_{B1}\alpha_{B2}, \qquad f = f'\alpha_{B1}\alpha_T^e, \qquad h = h'\alpha_{B1}\alpha_{B2}\alpha_T^e.$$

These are "flux-force" equations, but they are not restricted to near-equilibrium steady states. Note that nonlinear terms are present, and that the coefficients of linear terms obey reciprocal relations. These coefficients are properties of the steady state, not of the equilibrium state.

In the near-equilibrium special case,

$$\begin{aligned} J_1^\infty &= (M/\Sigma^e k)[(b^e + d^e + f^e + h^e)X_1 - (d^e + h^e)X_2 + (f^e + h^e)\mathsf{A}], \\ J_2^\infty &= (M/\Sigma^e k)[-(d^e + h^e)X_1 + (a^e + d^e + h^e)X_2 - h^e\mathsf{A}], \\ J_r^\infty &= (M/\Sigma^e k)[(f^e + h^e)X_1 - h^e X_2 + (c^e + f^e + h^e)\mathsf{A}], \end{aligned} \tag{7.146}$$

where the thermodynamic forces are, as usual,

$$X_1 = (\mu_{A1} - \mu_{B1})/T, \qquad X_2 = (\mu_{A2} - \mu_{B2})/T,$$
$$\mathsf{A} = \text{affinity} = (\mu_T - \mu_T^e)/T.$$

These are conventional flux-force equations in which reciprocal relations hold. The coefficients of the forces are properties of the equilibrium state.

A typical biological active transport case is

$$\begin{aligned} (\alpha_{A1}/\alpha_{B1}) - 1 < 0, \quad (\alpha_{A2}/\alpha_{B2}) - 1 \cong 0, \quad (\alpha_T/\alpha_T^e) - 1 > 0, \\ J_1^\infty > 0, \quad J_2^\infty, < 0, \quad J_r^\infty > 0. \end{aligned} \tag{7.147}$$

The near-equilibrium equations, (7.146), are of little interest in this connection because the typical biological membrane steady state is very far from equilibrium (e.g., we might have $\alpha_{B1}/\alpha_{A1} \cong 10$).

The reciprocal relations in Eqs. (7.145) and (7.146) are seen to follow* from separate and more basic sets of reciprocal relations: one set for each cycle that involves two or more forces and fluxes (cycles d, f, and h, but not a, b, and c). Unless the basic diagram for a model permits such cycles, force-flux coupling is not possible. For example, for cycle d only,

$$\begin{aligned} J_1^\infty &= \frac{M}{\Sigma}\left[d\left(\frac{\alpha_{A1}}{\alpha_{B1}} - 1\right) - d\left(\frac{\alpha_{A2}}{\alpha_{B2}} - 1\right)\right], \\ J_2^\infty &= \frac{M}{\Sigma}\left[-d\left(\frac{\alpha_{A1}}{\alpha_{B1}} - 1\right) + d\left(\frac{\alpha_{A2}}{\alpha_{B2}} - 1\right)\right]. \end{aligned} \tag{7.148}$$

---

* The coefficients in Eqs. (7.145) and (7.146) form matrices. Each of these matrices is a sum of submatrices, one submatrix for each cycle. The submatrices (linear part) are symmetrical so the sums (linear part) are also symmetrical.

There is a cycle reciprocal relation here which is a consequence of the more general property that *all four* of the coefficients in Eq. (7.148) have the same magnitude. This property, in turn, is a conseqence of the following: (i) a cycle makes the same contribution to the net flux (in the same direction) along all lines of the cycle, hence $J_1^\infty = -J_d^\infty$ and $J_2^\infty = +J_d^\infty$; (ii) the "combined force" $(\alpha_{A2}\alpha_{B1} - \alpha_{B2}\alpha_{A1})/\alpha_{B1}\alpha_{B2}$ operative in cycle d can be factored out of the other rate constants in Eq. (7.142) by virtue of detailed balance; and (iii) the two separate forces involved make contributions of equal magnitude to the combined force:

$$\frac{\alpha_{A2}\alpha_{B1} - \alpha_{B2}\alpha_{A1}}{\alpha_{B1}\alpha_{B2}} = -\left(\frac{\alpha_{A1}}{\alpha_{B1}} - 1\right) + \left(\frac{\alpha_{A2}}{\alpha_{B2}} - 1\right) \cdot$$

It is easy to see from (i) and (iii) why pairs of cross-coefficients will always have the same sign.

Essentially equivalent remarks can be made about the flux-force relations (linear terms only) for any cycle that involves two or more flux-force components.

7.9 STEADY STATE IN A CONTINUOUS SYSTEM WITH LOCAL EQUILIBRIUM

We investigated the entropy production at steady state, under certain special circumstances, in Section 7.4. In this section we shall see that there are severe limitations on the utility of the entropy production in providing a criterion for a general steady state.

To begin with, let us consider a continuous system, such as the one shown in Fig. 7.2 (there may be any number of components). Now we assume (throughout this section) that there is local thermodynamic equilibrium in each element of volume of the continuous system, though the complete system may be arbitrarily far from equilibrium (baths A and B may have very different properties). Then we can imagine the continuous system sliced up into a very large number (infinite, in the limit) of thin parallel slabs, within each of which would be found constant values of all thermodynamic intensive properties. Thus a continuous system with local equilibrium may be regarded as a composite of pairs of discontinuous subsystems of the type shown in Fig. 7.1.

In order to avoid introduction of a general (integral) notation, let us turn our attention to the special case in Fig. 7.23, with the assurance that the system described in the preceding paragraph may be handled in exactly the same way as the system in Fig. 7.23.

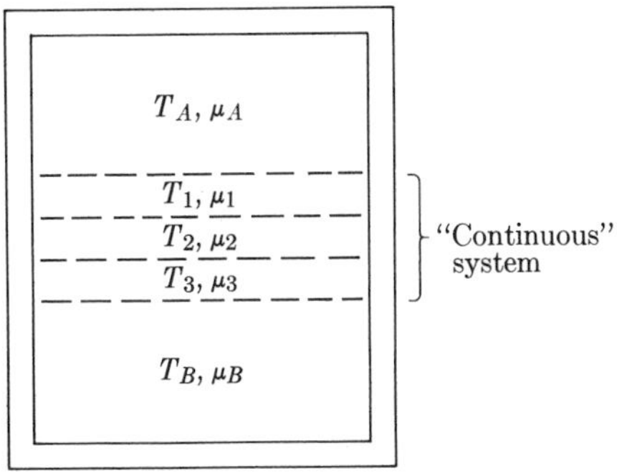

Fig. 7.23. Special case of a "continuous" system.

We apply the methods of Section 7.1 to successive pairs of subsystems in Fig. 7.23 and we find for the total entropy production (in $A + 1 + 2 + 3 + B$)

$$\begin{aligned}\dot{S} = \frac{d_iS}{dt} &= J_E^{A1}X_E^{A1} + J_N^{A1}X_N^{A1} + J_E^{12}X_E^{12} + J_N^{12}X_N^{12} \\ &\quad + J_E^{23}X_E^{23} + J_N^{23}X_N^{23} + J_E^{3B}X_E^{3B} + J_N^{3B}X_N^{3B} \\ &\equiv \sum_i J_iX_i, \end{aligned} \tag{7.149}$$

where J_E^{A1} is the energy flux $A \to 1$,

$$X_E^{A1} \equiv \frac{1}{T_1} - \frac{1}{T_A}, \qquad X_N^{A1} \equiv \frac{\mu_A}{T_A} - \frac{\mu_1}{T_1}, \quad \text{etc.} \tag{7.150}$$

The baths are assumed to be very large and to have time-independent properties ($T_A =$ const, etc.). But, in general, $\dot{S}$ and all the J's and X's vary with time as the system evolves toward an ultimate steady state (the final state would be an equilibrium state only if $T_A = T_B$ and $\mu_A = \mu_B$). At steady state, $\dot{S}$ and all the J's and X's have constant values which, in general, are nonvanishing. In view of some of the results in Section 7.4 for a different type of steady state (see also Problem 7.18), the question naturally arises whether in the present system $\dot{S}$ decreases monotonically, as time passes, to a minimum value at steady state. Intuitively, one might expect this. An equivalent question is: Do we have $d\dot{S}/dt \leq 0$ for all t (with the equality holding at steady state)? The answer is "no," as we shall demonstrate with a counter-example below. The actual situation is, in fact, that in the expression [see Eq. (7.149)]

$$\frac{d\dot{S}}{dt} = \sum_i J_i \frac{dX_i}{dt} + \sum_i X_i \frac{dJ_i}{dt} \tag{7.151}$$

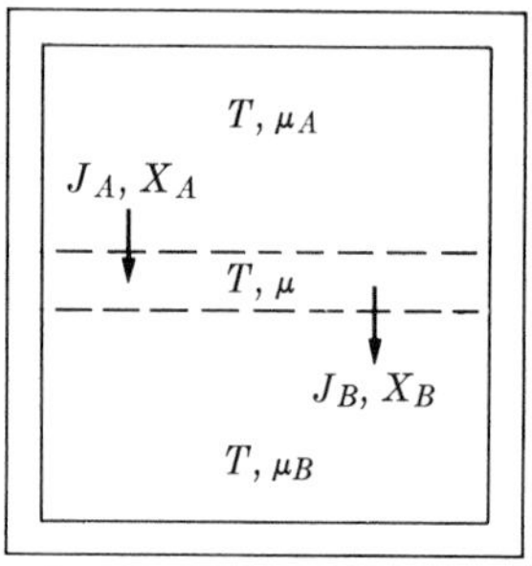

Fig. 7.24. Notation for the simple membrane model in Fig. 7.3.

we do *not* have $d\dot{S}/dt \leq 0$, but rather

$$\sum_i J_i \frac{dX_i}{dt} \leq 0. \tag{7.152}$$

We shall return to the relation (7.152) later.

Counterexample on $d\dot{S}/dt \leq 0$. Consider the simple membrane model in Fig. 7.3 and Sections 7.2 and 7.3, with the membrane assumed to be in internal equilibrium ("internal" = "local" in this case because there is only one layer of sites). The notation we use for present purposes is shown in Fig. 7.24. We have

$$\dot{S}(t) = J_A(t)X_A(t) + J_B(t)X_B(t) \tag{7.153}$$

with

$$J_A(t) = \alpha_A[M - N(t)] - \beta N(t), \tag{7.154}$$

$$J_B(t) = \beta N(t) - \alpha_B[M - N(t)], \tag{7.155}$$

$$X_A(t) = \frac{\mu_A}{T} - \frac{\mu(t)}{T}, \qquad X_B(t) = \frac{\mu(t)}{T} - \frac{\mu_B}{T}, \tag{7.156}$$

where $\mu(t)/T$ is related to $N(t)$ by Eq. (7.33). Thus $\dot{S}$ is a function of N, and N is a function of t. Therefore the question of interest here is whether the minimum in $\dot{S}(N)$ occurs at $N = N^\infty$ (steady state), where N^∞ is given by Eq. (7.22). To test this, we deduce from the above equations (using $q\lambda_A = \alpha_A/\beta$ and $q\lambda_B = \alpha_B/\beta$) that

$$\begin{aligned}\frac{d(\dot{S}/k)}{dN} = 0 = {} & [2\beta N - (\alpha_A + \alpha_B)(M - N)] \cdot \frac{M}{N(M - N)} \\ & + (\alpha_A + \alpha_B + 2\beta) \ln \frac{N}{M - N} \\ & - (\alpha_A + \beta) \ln \frac{\alpha_A}{\beta} - (\alpha_B + \beta) \ln \frac{\alpha_B}{\beta}.\end{aligned} \tag{7.157}$$

We then note that Eq. (7.21) for N^∞ does *not* satisfy* Eq. (7.157). That is, in general $N_{\min} \neq N^\infty$, where $N_{\min}$ is the root of Eq. (7.157).

This single example suffices to disprove the conjecture that $d\dot{S}/dt \leq 0$.

Steady-State Criterion. We now want to prove the steady-state criterion, (7.152) (due originally to Glansdorff and Prigogine). But, for simplicity, we shall do this only for a special case that is even more restricted than that shown in Fig. 7.23. Namely, we consider (in this figure) heat transport only. The generalization to any number of components, to transport of both heat and molecules, and to an infinite number of slabs (i.e., to a truly continuous system with local equilibrium) may be formulated in a straightforward way by combining the argument used below with that in a paper by Li.† This is left to the interested reader.

In Fig. 7.23, we have for slab 1, with heat transport only,

$$J_E^{A1} - J_E^{12} = \frac{dE_1}{dt} = \left(\frac{\partial E_1}{\partial 1/T_1}\right)_{N_1, V_1} \frac{d1/T_1}{dt} = -T_1^2 C_{V1} \frac{d1/T_1}{dt}. \quad (7.158)$$

There are similar expressions for slabs 2 and 3.

Now we also have

$$\begin{aligned}\sum_i J_i \frac{dX_i}{dt} &= J_E^{A1} \frac{dX_E^{A1}}{dt} + J_E^{12} \frac{dX_E^{12}}{dt} + J_E^{23} \frac{dX_E^{23}}{dt} + J_E^{3B} \frac{dX_E^{3B}}{dt} \\ &= J_E^{A1} \frac{d1/T_1}{dt} + J_E^{12} \left(\frac{d1/T_2}{dt} - \frac{d1/T_1}{dt}\right) + \cdots \\ &= (J_E^{A1} - J_E^{12}) \frac{d1/T_1}{dt} + \cdots \\ &= -T_1^2 C_{V1} \left(\frac{d1/T_1}{dt}\right)^2 - \cdots \leq 0, \end{aligned} \quad (7.159)$$

since C_V is positive for any system (a thermodynamic stability condition).

The corresponding result, as the reader may easily verify, for isothermal molecular flow only (in Fig. 7.23), is

$$\sum_i J_i \frac{dX_i}{dt} = -\frac{1}{T}\left(\frac{\partial N_1}{\partial \mu_1}\right)_{V_1, T} \left(\frac{d\mu_1}{dt}\right)^2 - \cdots \leq 0, \quad (7.160)$$

since $(\partial N/\partial \mu)_{V,T}$ is also always positive.

---

* It is left to the reader to show that N^∞ does satisfy Eq. (7.157) if the steady state is near equilibrium.

† J. C. M. Li, *J. Phys. Chem.* **66,** 1414 (1962), Eqs. (5) through (12). See also I. Prigogine, *Thermodynamics of Irreversible Processes.* New York: Interscience, 1961.

In summary, we state again that the basic result (7.152) holds for a continuous system in local equilibrium which is approaching a steady state that may be arbitrarily far from equilibrium. Of course, if there is *not* local equilibrium, then the μ's, T's, and X's are not even defined locally.

PROBLEMS

7.1 Define $X = (\mu_A - \mu_B)/T$ and $\mu = (\mu_A + \mu_B)/2$. Find the terms in X and X^3 when J^∞ in Eq. (7.23) is expanded in powers of X about the average state μ.

7.2 Define $X = (\mu^e - \mu)/T$ and expand J in Eq. (7.31) in powers of X, about the equilibrium state, to find the terms in X and X^2.

7.3 Take into account the complications at $N = 0$ and $N = M$ mentioned in connection with the derivation of the mean value rate equation, (7.51).

7.4 Find the explicit solution $\sigma^2(t)$ for the differential equation (7.55).

7.5 Use Eq. (7.42) to prove that $\sigma_e^2 = \lambda\, \partial \overline{N}^e/\partial\lambda$, for an open one-component system, as in Eq. (7.57).

7.6 Prove that for any normal distribution, (7.44), $\sigma^2 = \overline{N}(M - \overline{N})/M$.

7.7 (a) Prove the inequality (7.62).

(b) Express $\dot{S}$ as a quadratic form in the X_i's when there are n fluxes and forces [see Eqs. (7.15), (7.16), and (7.61)]. What is the generalization of Eq. (7.62)?

7.8 Minimize $\dot{S}(X_1, \ldots, X_n)$ with respect to $X_{r+1}, \ldots, X_n$ holding $X_1, \ldots, X_r$ constant. Show that, at the minimum, $J_{r+1} = 0, \ldots, J_n = 0$.

7.9 Derive the steady state N_i^∞ and fluxes for the model in Fig. 7.14 using (a) the kinetic equations directly and (b) the diagram method. Verify that the results are the same, and that $L_{12} = L_{21} = 0$.

7.10 Prove the theorem on flux diagrams, (7.81), from the theorem on directional diagrams, (7.78).

7.11 Verify, by direct substitution, that the solution for P_N^e in Eq. (7.38) satisfies the recursion formula (7.37).

7.12 Make a schematic drawing of the surface $\dot{S}(X_N, X_E)$ in Eq. (7.61) [take $\dot{S}$ as the z-axis (vertical) and X_N and X_E as the x, y-axes (horizontal)]. Show the location of the absolute minimum (equilibrium) and the conditional minimum (when $X_E =$ const).

7.13 Find the next higher term in the expansion of J in powers of **A** in Eq. (7.112).

7.14 Suppose that, in the model of Section 7.7, the ground state energy of solute molecules in the bath is reckoned as ϵ_0 instead of zero. Make the necessary modifications in the equations of this section.

7.15 Extend the model in Section 7.7 to include a third energy level for a bound solute molecule, $-\mathcal{E} + \epsilon + \epsilon'$. The only transitions involving the third level are those to and from the second level (coupled to either bath). Use the constant γ again for these new transitions.

7.16 In model 7.8(d), Fig. 7.21, how many partial diagrams are there? How many terms in $\sum$ [Eq. (7.142)]?

7.17 Draw all the flux diagrams for Fig. 7.22.

7.18 In the steady-state case discussed in Eqs. (7.63) through (7.67), prove that $d\dot{S}/dt \leq 0$ for all t.

SUPPLEMENTARY READING

De Groot, S. R., and P. Mazur, *Nonequilibrium Thermodynamics.* New York: Interscience, 1962.

De Groot, S. R., *Thermodynamics of Irreversible Processes.* New York: Interscience, 1952.

Fitts, D. D., *Nonequilibrium Thermodynamics.* New York: McGraw-Hill, 1962.

Hill, T. L., *J. Theoret. Biol.* **10,** 442 (1966).

Hill, T. L., and O. Kedem, *J. Theoret. Biol.* **10,** 399 (1966).

Katchalsky, A., and P. F. Curran, *Nonequilibrium Thermodynamics in Biophysics.* Cambridge, Mass.: Harvard University Press, 1965.

Kittel, C., *Elementary Statistical Physics.* New York: Wiley, 1958.

Onsager, L., *Phys. Rev.* **37,** 405 (1931).

Prigogine, I., *Thermodynamics of Irreversible Processes.* New York: Interscience, 1961.

Van Rysselberghe, P., *Thermodynamics of Irreversible Processes.* New York: Blaisdell, 1963.

INDEX

ABCDE698